The Amphibians and Reptiles
of El Salvador

The Amphibians and Reptiles of El Salvador

Gunther Köhler
Forschungsinstitut und Naturmuseum Senckenberg,
Senckenberganlage 25, D-60325
Frankfurt am Main, Germany

Milan Veselý
Department of Zoology, Faculty of Natural Sciences,
Palacky University, Svobody 26, 77146
Olomouc, Czech Republic

Eli Greenbaum
Natural History Museum & Biodiversity Research Center,
and Department of Ecology & Evolutionary Biology,
The University of Kansas, Lawrence, KS 66045-7561 USA

KRIEGER PUBLISHING COMPANY
Malabar, Florida
2006

Cover Photos:
Background—Cloud forest at Volcán de San Vicente (2000 m), Depto. San Vicente, El Salvador. (Photo by M. Vesely)
Top Center—*Bufo marinus* (KU 289750) at Parque National El Imposible (720 m), Depto. Ahuachapán, El Salvador. (Photo by E. Greenbaum)
Bottom Center—*Ninia sebae* (KU 289803) at Colegio Bautista, San Salvador, Depto. San Salvador, El Salvador. Gravid female. (Photo by E. Greenbaum)

Original Edition 2006

Printed and Published by
KRIEGER PUBLISHING COMPANY
KRIEGER DRIVE
MALABAR, FLORIDA 32950

Library of Congress Cataloging-in Publication Data

Köhler, Gunther.
The amphibians and reptiles of El Salvador / Gunther Köhler, Milan Vesely, Eli Greenbaum.
p. cm.
Includes bibliographical references (p.) and index.
ISBN 1-57524-252-4 (alk. paper)
1. Reptiles—El Salvador. 2. Amphibians—El Salvador. I. Köhler, Gunther. II. Vesely, Milan.
III. Greenbaum, Eli. IV. Title.

QL656.S2K64 2006
597.9!097284—dc22

2005045137

10 9 8 7 6 5 4 3 2

Contents

Acknowledgments

This book would not have been possible without the support of numerous organizations and people. We appreciate the support we received from Minister Ana María Majano, Patricia Quintana vda. de López, Carmen Celina Dueñas, and Andrés Sánchez (Ministerio de Agricultura y Ganadería, Dirección General de Recursos Naturales Renovables, Servicio de Parques Nacionales y Vida Silvestre), San Salvador, El Salvador. We are especially grateful to Mr. Sánchez for granting collecting and export permits.

We thank Francisco Serrano, San Salvador, for his generous logistic support and valued cooperation; Serrano also provided logistical support for E. Greenbaum´s trip to Isla San Sebastián. Gunther Köhler is grateful to Monika Laudahn for technical help. Eli Greenbaum thanks the following from The University of Kansas: William E. Duellman and Linda Trueb, the Panorama Society, Department of Ecology and Evolutionary Biology, College of Liberal Arts and Sciences, the Natural History Museum and Biodiversity Research Center, and especially Oliver Komar for logistic support. Eli Greenbaum also acknowledges Leslie Greenbaum and travel grants from The Explorers Club, the Museum of Vertebrate Zoology, and Field Museum of Natural History. Eli Greenbaum thanks owners of many fincas for permission to collect on their land in 2000. For field assistance, we thank Elke Köhler, Jörg Kreutz, Julio Pérez, Emilio Sánchez, and Jorge Porras. We are especially grateful to John L. Carr, William E. Duellman, Carlos Roberto Hasbún, Oliver Komar, James R. McCranie, Joeseph R. Mendelson III, Francisco Serrano, Eric N. Smith, Peter Stafford, and Linda Trueb for reviewing portions of the manuscript; all provided valuable comments that significantly improved the text. We thank Juan Manuel Guayasamin and Omar Torres-Carvajal for translating the identification keys into Spanish. David Wake kindly shared unpublished data on *Bolitoglossa*. Carlos Roberto Hasbún provided data from specimens in the MUHNES collection and from his studies on *Ctenosaura flavidorsalis*. We are grateful to numerous colleagues for photos of Salvadoran species—these photographers are acknowledged in the captions of their respective photos.

For the loan of specimens or access to the collections under their care we thank Linda Ford and Darrel R. Frost, American Museum of Natural History (AMNH), New York; Colin J. McCarthy, The Natural History Museum (BMNH), London; Bob Drewes and Jens Vindum, California Academy of Sciences (CAS), San Francisco; Alan Resetar and Harold Voris, Field Museum of Natural History (FMNH), Chicago; John E. Simmons, Linda Trueb, and William E. Duellman, University of Kansas Natural History Museum (KU), Lawrence; David Kizirian and Kent Beaman, Natural History Museum of Los Angeles County (LACM), Los Angeles; Jimmy McGuire and Adam Leache, Museum of Natural Science (LSUMZ), Baton Rouge; José Rosado and James Hanken, Museum of Comparative Zoology (MCZ), Cambridge; Eunice E. Echeverría, Museo de Historia Natural de El Salvador (MUHNES), San Salvador; David B. Wake and Carla Cicero, Museum of Vertebrate Zoology (MVZ), Berkeley; Franco Andreone, Museo Regionale di Scienze Naturali (MZUT), Torino; James R. Dixon and Katherine Vaughan, Texas Cooperative Wildlife Collection (TCWC), College Station; F. Wayne King and Kenneth Krysko, Florida Museum of Natural History (UF), Gainesville; Ronald Nussbaum, Arnold Kluge, and Greg Schneider, University of Michigan Museum of Zoology (UMMZ), Ann Arbor; Eric Rickart, Utah Museum of Natural History (UMNH), Salt Lake City; W. Ronald Heyer and Robert Wilson, Smithsonian Institution, National Museum of Natural History (USNM), Washington, DC; Jonathan Campbell and Rhonda L. Ackley, University of Texas at Arlington (UTA), Arlington; Victor J. Hellebuyck (VH), San Salvador; Jacques Gauthier, Twan Leenders, and Gregory Watkins-Colwell, Yale Peabody Museum (YPM), New Haven; Wolfgang Böhme, Zoologisches Forschungsinstitut und Museum Alexander Koenig (ZFMK), Bonn; and Rainer Günther, Museum für Naturkunde der Humboldt-Universität zu Berlin (ZMB), Berlin. The above museum abbreviations are consistent with those used in the species accounts.

Abstract

As presently understood, the herpetofauna of El Salvador consists of 130 species representing 88 genera and 30 families. For each of these species the following information is provided: (1) a partial synonymy, including reference, the current name, and references to the species in El Salvador; (2) the total geographic distribution; (3) ecological distribution in El Salvador; (4) a short description of the morphology; (5) natural history and taxonomic comments; (6) conservation status of evaluated species; and (7) a list of Salvadoran specimens examined and their locality data. Distribution maps and color photographs are provided for each species. Dichotomous keys for the identification of the orders, genera, and species of Salvadoran amphibians (including tadpoles) and reptiles are provided in English and Spanish.

Resumen

Actualmente, se considera que la herpetofauna de El Salvador consta de 130 especies, incluídas en 88 géneros y 30 familias. Para cada una de esas especies se proporciona la siguiente información: (1) sinonimia parcial, incluyendo el nombre común, referencias de las especies en El Salvador y citas bibliográficas; (2) la distribución geográfica total; (3) distribución ecológica en El Salvador; (4) una breve descripción morfológica; (5) comentarios taxónomicos y sobre historia natural; (6) estado de conservación de las especies evaluadas y (7) una lista de los ejemplares examinados con su respectiva localidad de colección en El Salvador. Además, el libro contiene fotografías a color y mapas de distribucion para cada especie y claves dicotómicas en inglés y español para la identificación de géneros y especies de anfibios (renacuajos y adultos) y reptiles.

Chapter 1
Introduction

At the time Karl Schmidt published a small report about the reptiles of El Salvador only 17 species of reptiles were known from the country (K. Schmidt 1928). The well-known herpetologist Robert Mertens (Senckenberg Museum) published several species and subspecies descriptions and the first comprehensive treatment of the herpetofauna of El Salvador (Mertens 1952a–d); subsequently, several papers have addressed the amphibians and reptiles of this small Central American country. Brongersma (1954a, b) presented locality information and morphological data on 10 species of lizards and 4 species of snakes. Rand (1957) reported on 43 species of amphibians and reptiles he collected in El Salvador in 1951. Uzzell & Starrett (1958) provided detailed data on scalation of 10 species of snakes obtained in 1957. K. Williams (1978) described a new subspecies of snake. Hidalgo (1979, 1980a, b, 1981a, b, 1982a, b, c, 1983) provided several new taxonomic records for the country, natural history information for a turtle, and descriptions of two new species of *Abronia* (one of which is now confined to the current boundary of Honduras). Greding & Hellebuyck (1980) provided information on stomach contents of 5 species of frogs from El Salvador. New taxa of lizards were described by Köhler & Klemmer (1994) and Köhler (1999). Köhler (1996) discussed lizards and snakes collected by German scientists in the 1950s that had not

been included by Mertens (1952 a–d). Hasbún & Vásquez (1991, 1999) discussed the sea turtle fauna of El Salvador; Hasbún (2001) and Hasbún et al. (2001) discussed Salvadoran populations of *Ctenosaura flavidorsalis*. Veselý & Köhler (2001) discussed an anguid species in El Salvador. An updated list of the herpetofauna of El Salvador was presented by Dueñas et al. (2001). A new species of salamander and four new country records were reported by Greenbaum (2002, 2004), Greenbaum et al. (2002a, b), and Köhler (2003a). Leenders (2003) discussed the herpetofauna of Parque Nacional El Imposible, Depto. Ahuachapán. Leenders & Watkins-Colwell (2003a–c, 2004) discussed the geographic distribution and natural history of several species of Salvadoran amphibians and reptiles.

The herpetofauna of El Salvador is still considered "one of the most poorly known in the area, inasmuch as it has not been subjected to a modern, systematic survey" (Dueñas et al. 2001: 93). The present work is intended to summarize the morphological variation and distributions of the amphibians and reptiles in El Salvador. We attempted to include data on specimens in all major collections in the United States, Europe, and El Salvador, and hope that our endeavors will be useful to future herpetological research in El Salvador and other areas of Central America.

Chapter 2
Materials and Methods

Species accounts, keys, and descriptions are based on the literature and examination of preserved specimens from the museum collections listed in the acknowledgments (and Forschungsinstitut und Naturmuseum Senckenberg, SMF), and refer exclusively to Salvadoran material unless otherwise indicated. If few or no specimens of Salvadoran origin were available, the species accounts were either abbreviated or included specimens from nearby countries; in some cases, species accounts are based solely on information from the literature. Some vernacular names (in Spanish) of amphibians and reptiles follow Köhler (2000, 2001a, b); others were kindly suggested by E. N. Smith (pers. comm.). Partial synonymies are in chronological order (by first date) and include the following checklists: Peters & Donoso-Barros (1970), Peters & Orejas-Miranda (1970), Villa et al. (1988), Dueñas et al. (2001), Köhler (2000, 2001a, 2003b), species accounts in the *Catalogue of American Amphibians and Reptiles,* and scientific papers that cite Salvadoran specimens. Within species accounts, subspecies are considered for synonymies only.

Sources for geographic distribution of each species were derived from the literature and in the case of El Salvador, from specimen records, photographs, and citations included herein. Some sight records of the authors are included in the "Natural history" section of the species accounts, but are not included in the distribution maps because these identifications cannot be independently verified. Information on the ecological distribution (including vertical distribution of species) refers only to Salvadoran populations and is based on data associated with the specimens examined, reports in the literature, and unpublished observations of the authors. Ecological distributions are based on the vegetation categories discussed in Chapter 3 (e.g., mangrove, sandy beach, dry savanna, dry forest, pine-oak forest, and cloud forest), and are restricted to data from Salvadoran specimens. Data regarding anuran calls and larvae are based on the literature, field notes, and specimens. Data regarding global conservation status of threatened species were obtained from the Global Amphibian Assessment

(GAA; IUCN et al. 2004), and websites for the Convention on International Trade of Endangered Species (CITES 2003) and World Conservation Union (IUCN 2003); abbreviations of global IUCN criteria are those of IUCN (2001). The national threatened status and conservation prioritization of El Salvador's herpetofauna is discussed in a separate publication (Greenbaum & Komar in press). We drew distribution maps for species with precise locality data in El Salvador; circles denote specimens examined, whereas squares represent literature records. Light shading on these maps indicates 600–1200 m elevation, dark shading indicates elevations ≥ 1200 m, and large bodies of freshwater are outlined in bold, black lines. Thirty-eight localities that could not be located precisely were not mapped; these are indicated by a bold asterisk in parentheses in the "Specimens examined" section of the species accounts. Three localities were considered to be questionable and not mapped because the habitat and elevation did not match the known requirements for the species. Most illustrations and photographs were made from specimens originating from El Salvador, but when Salvadoran material was not available, we relied upon specimens from Mexico, Central America, and rarely, northern South America.

Preserved specimens of three species of Salvadoran sea turtles (*Chelonia mydas, Dermochelys coriacea,* and *Lepidochelys olivacea*) were not available for examination. However, preserved hatchling specimens are reported from the Museo de Historia Natural de El Salvador, San Salvador (Hasbún & Vásquez 1999). Also, C. R. Hasbún (pers. comm.) has preserved specimens of all four species of sea turtle (including *Eretmochelys imbricata*) in his private collection. The inclusion of these species in the Salvadoran herpetofauna also is supported by Cornelius (1995), Ernst & Barbour (1989), Iverson (1992), and Hasbún & Vásquez (1999). Benitez (1985) reported the occurrence and nesting of *Caretta caretta* in El Salvador; however, neither data nor evidence to support this contention were provided, and Marquez (1990) and Hasbún & Vásquez (1999) agree that this identification was not clear and most likely corresponded to *Lepidochelys olivacea*. Moreover, both *Caretta caretta* and *Lepidochelys olivacea* have been misidentified in the East Pacific (Frazier 1985); therefore, we omit *Caretta caretta*. One freshwater turtle species, *Trachemys venusta,* is reported from El Salvador by several citations and observations (Mittermeier 1970, Legler 1990, F. Serrano, pers. comm.) and one museum specimen.

Abbreviations for museum collections follow Leviton et al. (1985) except for the addition of MUHNES (Museo de Historia Natural de El Salvador, San Salvador) and VH (private collection of Victor Hellebuyck). The following abbreviations are used in the keys and text: HL: head length (snout to anterior margin of ear opening); HW: head width; SVL (LRC, Spanish): snout–vent length; h: hours; mya: million years ago; m: meters elevation; Depto: Departamento. In the snake species key, dorsal scale rows refer to the number of scale rows around the midbody. In some species accounts with few Salvadoran specimens, morphometric data from specimens in other Central American counties (locality data noted in accounts) were included to provide a better understanding of intraspecific morphological variation. Description of coloration refers to color in life if not otherwise specified. Cited specimens in the collections of SMF, MUHNES, VH, ZFMK, and ZMB were identified by G. Köhler; those from the remaining collections were identified by E. Greenbaum.

Chapter 3
The Environment

Physiography

El Salvador comprises an area of about 21,140 square kilometers between 13° and 14° north latitude and 87° and 90° west longitude (Ziehr 1974). El Salvador is limited to the Pacific versant and has about 321 km of Pacific Ocean coastline (Gierloff-Emden 1976). To the west, El Salvador borders Guatemala and to the north and east it borders Honduras (Map 1). The Río Goascorán forms the eastern border between El Salvador and Honduras and flows into the Gulf of Fonseca, the largest bay on the Pacific side of Central America. There are four physiographic regions in El Salvador: (1) the Pacific lowlands; (2) the southern volcanic highlands; (3) the interior valley between the northern mountains and the southern volcanic highlands; and (4) the northern mountains (Campbell & Lamar 1989).

The Pacific lowlands include the coastal plain and foothills, extending up to 25 km inland. To the north, the region is bordered by the southern volcanic highlands. El Salvador is called the "land of volcanoes" (Mertens 1952e) because of the prominent chain of about 15 major volcanic cones and several dozen small cones that extend from west to east across the country. Some of these volcanoes reach more than 2000 m above sea level (e.g., Volcán de Santa Ana, 2365 m; Volcán de San Vicente, 2182 m; Volcán de San Miguel, 2130 m), and some, such as Volcán de Izalco, have been active recently. The broad dry interior valley lies between elevations of 300–600 m. The largest river in El Salvador, the Río Lempa (about 290 km in length), passes through the interior valley. The northern mountains include El Salvador's highest peak, Cerro El Pital, about 2730 m above sea level.

Climate

In the lowlands of El Salvador, a tropical climate prevails with temperatures varying from 23–29°C; this decreases to 16–22°C above elevations of 1500 m. The mean annual temperature in the capital, San Salvador (about 700 m above sea level), is about 23°C; the difference between the average values of the hottest month (April: 24.2°C) and the coldest month (January: 21.8°C) is less than 3°C (Ziehr 1974, Guzmán López 1995). Situated completely on the Pacific versant, El Salvador lies in

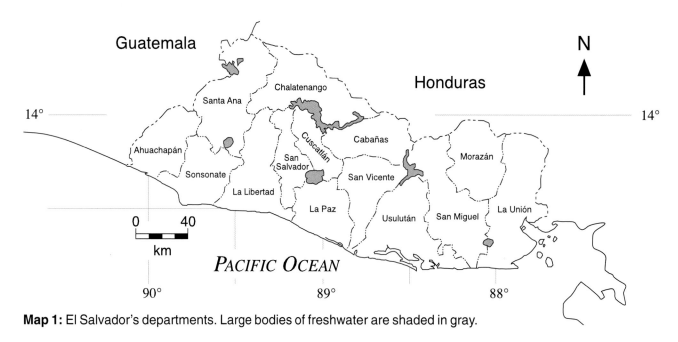

Map 1: El Salvador's departments. Large bodies of freshwater are shaded in gray.

the rainshadow of the high mountains of nuclear Central America. Average rainfall ranges from 1000–2000 mm per year in most of the country; the higher windward elevations of the highlands can receive up to 2500 mm annual precipitation (Guzmán López 1995). The average monthly precipitation varies from a maximum of nearly 400 mm during the rainy season (mid-May to mid-October) to a minimum of 2 mm during the dry season (mid-November to mid-April). The rainy season is characterized by persistently overcast days and intermittent, but heavy downpours; the latter occur most frequently in June and September (Guzmán López 1995).

Plate 1: Sandy beach EL SALVADOR: Usulután: Isla San Sebastián (~1 m). Photo: E. Greenbaum.

Vegetation

The various vegetation types of El Salvador reflect climatic, geologic (soil type) and hydrologic factors (Map 2). Sandy beaches extend intermit-

tently along much of the Pacific coast, and are protected by offshore reefs (Plate 1). Most original beach vegetation has been replaced by plantations

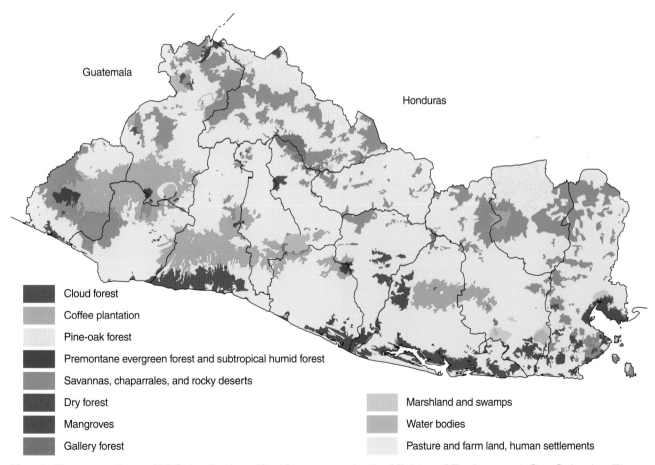

Cloud forest

Coffee plantation

Pine-oak forest

Premontane evergreen forest and subtropical humid forest

Savannas, chaparrales, and rocky deserts

Dry forest

Mangroves

Gallery forest

Marshland and swamps

Water bodies

Pasture and farm land, human settlements

Map 2: The ecoregions of El Salvador (modified from a map by the Ministry of Environment, San Salvador, El Salvador).

Plate 2: Mangrove swamp EL SALVADOR: Ahuachapán: Barra de Santiago (0 m). Photo: O. Komar.

Plate 4: Dry forest in January EL SALVADOR: Cuscatlán: Bosque Colima (300 m). Photo: O. Komar.

Plate 3: Dry forest with waterfall in August EL SALVADOR: Cabañas: Bosque Cinquera (400 m). Photo: E. Greenbaum.

of coconut palms. In some places, exposed sand bars support the growth of scrubby xerophytic vegetation such as low shrubs, grasses, and matted cacti (*Rhipsalis*). Exposed sandy habitats are important nesting sites for sea turtles (*Lepidochelys*) and spinytail iguanas (*Ctenosaura*) (Köhler 2000).

Mangroves are found along the Pacific coast, mostly in estuaries of the large rivers (Serrano 1995). Red mangroves (*Rhizophora mangle*) are the most tolerant of salt water and occur along the edges of every lagoon and bay. These mangroves commonly form dense, swampy forests characterized by tangles of aerial and adventitious roots (Plate 2). Further inland, the red mangrove is replaced by other species of mangroves: *Avicennia germinans*, *Laguncularia racemosa*, and *Conocarpus erecta*.

Most of the lowlands, including the coastal plain and the interior valleys, formerly supported dry forests (semideciduous and deciduous forests) and dry savanna (sabanas and chaparrales). However, in Central America, most of these habitats have been converted into pasture and farm land, as well as human settlements. Dry forests consist of a thick understory of drought-resistant shrubs. Trees usually do not exceed 20 m in height, and many are armed with thorns (Plate 3). During the dry season when precipitation is negligible, most trees shed their leaves, thereby permitting sunlight and wind to desiccate the ground surface (Plate 4). Only the large rivers have water year round; smaller streams dry out during the dry season (Ventura Montenegro 1995). A typical example of dry forest is

Plate 5: Pine forest with burned understory EL SALVA-DOR: Chalatenango: Bosque La Montañona (1300 m). Photo: O. Komar.

Plate 6: Mix of coffee plantation (finca) and semi-deciduous forest EL SALVADOR: La Libertad: Finca La Giralda (1080 m). Photo: O. Komar.

Plate 7: Humid broad-leaf evergreen forest EL SALVA-DOR: Ahuachapán: Parque Nacional El Imposible (700 m). Photo: O. Komar.

the San Diego Forest in Metapán (Depto. Santa Ana) in northwestern El Salvador. This area receives less than 1200 mm average precipitation per year and has extensive drainage from young porous volcanic soils (F. Serrano pers. comm. 2002).

The highlands of El Salvador used to be extensively covered by pine-oak forests (Plate 5). Today, much of this vegetation type has been converted to coffee plantations (i.e., fincas), especially on the rich soils of the volcanic chain (Plate 6). Both oak and pine trees subsist on relatively poor soils, but oaks are more common in humid areas, such as in valleys and canyons.

Premontane evergreen forest and subtropical humid forest are found at mid-elevations (600–1000 m above sea level) at a few places in El Salvador. The largest area covered by this kind of vegetation is located at Parque Nacional El Imposible in the western portion of the country (Plate 7). This forest type is characterized by a deciduousness of less than 50% of the trees during the dry season. Marshlands and swamps are present from low to mid-elevations throughout El Salvador (Plate 8).

Cloud forest is the natural vegetation on several mountains and volcano peaks including Cerro El Pital and Cerro Montecristo, in the north, as well as Volcán de Santa Ana and Volcán de San Vicente in the southern volcanic highlands (O. Komar pers. comm., Serrano 1995). Because of low temperatures (5–15°C) and high humidity, water condenses and drips on the vegetation year-round,

Plate 8: Freshwater marsh EL SALVADOR: Ahuachapán: Laguna de Las Ninfas (1630 m). Photo: M. Veselý.

Plate 10: Paramo EL SALVADOR: Santa Ana: Volcán de Santa Ana (2350 m). Photo: O. Komar.

even when there is no actual rain. The trees in the cloud forest are densely covered with epiphytes, such as bromeliads, orchids, ferns, and mosses. Tree ferns reach several meters in height (Plate 9). Paramo (high-altitude grassland) exists on the tops of just two volcanoes in El Salvador (O. Komar pers. comm.), Santa Ana volcano and the San Miguel volcano (Plate 10), and has a distribution too small to appear on the vegetation map.

Plate 9: Cloud forest with epiphytes EL SALVADOR: Santa Ana: Volcán de Santa Ana (1900 m). Photo: O. Komar.

Chapter 4
Composition of the Herpetofauna

As presently understood, the herpetofauna of El Salvador consists of 130 species (32 amphibians and 98 reptiles) representing 88 genera and 30 families (Table 4.1). Several questionable records of species that might occur in this country are excluded from this count. Our list differs from that of Dueñas et al. (2001), which also listed 32 amphibian and 98 reptilian species. However, in their addendum, they deleted 4 species (*Abronia salvadorensis, Hyla catracha, Ninia espinali,* and *Rhadinaea pinicola*) from their main list and changed names of an additional 4 species, thereby reducing their list to 31 amphibians and 95 reptiles. Therefore, compared to Dueñas et al. (2001), we list 1 additional amphibian and 3 additional reptilian species that were documented to occur in El Salvador during examination of museum specimens and field work by E. Greenbaum and O. Komar (*Hemidactylus frenatus, Mesoscincus managuae,* and *Ninia espinali*) and G. Köhler (*Bufo valliceps*), respectively.

Table 4.1: Taxonomic composition of the herpetofauna of El Salvador.

Group	Families	Genera	Species
Caecilians	1	1	1
Salamanders	1	2	4
Anurans	7	16	27
Crocodilians	2	2	2
Turtles	4	8	8
Lizards	8	20	30
Snakes	7	39	58
Total	**30**	**88**	**130**

Amphibian and Reptilian Taxa with a Type Locality in El Salvador

Twenty-four nominal taxa have their type localities in El Salvador (Table 4.2).

Table 4.2: Taxa with type localities in El Salvador.

Taxon	Type locality	Current Nomenclature
Amphibia		
Bolitoglossa heiroreias Greenbaum 2004	Camel Cigarettes Field Station, Cerro Montecristo, 14°24'04"N, 89°21'02"W, 1880 m, Depto. Santa Ana, El Salvador	*Bolitoglossa heiroreias*

Taxon	Type locality	Current Nomenclature
Hyla euthysanota Kellogg 1923	Los Esesmiles [= Cerro El Pital], 1951 m, Depto. Chalatenango, El Salvador	*Ptychohyla euthysanota*
Hyla salvadorensis Mertens 1952c	Hacienda San José, 800 m, Cordillera de Metapán, Depto. Santa Ana, El Salvador	*Ptychohyla salvadorensis*
Oedipina salvadorensis Rand 1952	Vicinity of San Salvador, Depto. San Salvador, El Salvador	*Oedipina taylori*
Reptilia		
Abronia montecristoi Hidalgo 1983	Hacienda Montecristo, 2250 m, Cordillera de Metapán, Depto. Santa Ana, El Salvador	*Abronia montecristoi*
Anolis heteropholidotus Mertens 1952a	Hacienda Los Planes, Cerro Miramundo, 2000 m, Depto. Santa Ana, El Salvador	*Norops heteropholidotus*
Anolis ustus wellbornae Ahl 1940	El Salvador	*Norops sericeus*
Ctenosaura completa Bocourt 1874	Guatemala and La Unión, El Salvador	*Ctenosaura similis*
Emys incisa Bocourt 1868	Volcán Conchagua, Depto. La Unión, El Salvador	*Rhinoclemmys pulcherrima*
Geophis fulvoguttatus Mertens 1952b	Hacienda Montecristo, 2200 m, Cordillera de Metapán, Depto. Santa Ana, El Salvador	*Geophis fulvoguttatus*
Gerrhonotus salvadorensis K. Schmidt 1928	Los Esesmiles, 1829–2438 m, Depto. Chalatenango, El Salvador	*Mesaspis moreletii*
Himantodes gemmistratus Cope 1861	Near Izalco, El Salvador	*Imantodes gemmistratus*
Lampropeltis triangulum stuarti K. Williams 1978	Finca Los Cedros, ca. 1000 m, Santa Tecla [=Nuevo San Salvador], Depto. La Libertad, El Salvador	*Lampropeltis triangulum stuarti*
Lampropholis assatus Cope 1864	Volcán Izalco, Depto. Sonsonate, El Salvador	*Sphenomorphus assatus*
Loxocemus bicolor Cope 1861	Type locality unknown; restricted to La Unión, El Salvador, by Smith & Taylor (1950b)	*Loxocemus bicolor*

Taxon	Type locality	Current Nomenclature
Norops serranoi Köhler 1999	Mariposario, El Refugio of Francisco Serrano, 13°49.46′N, 89°59.98′W, 225 m, near San Francisco Menéndez, Depto. Ahuachapán, El Salvador	*Norops serranoi*
Phyllodactylus eduardofischeri Mertens 1952a	Rio Chilama, Depto. La Libertad, El Salvador	*Phyllodactylus tuberculosus*
Pliocercus elapoides salvadorensis Mertens 1952a	Hacienda San José, Santa Tecla [=Nuevo San Salvador], 1150 m, Depto. La Libertad, El Salvador	*Pliocercus elapoides*
Rhadinaea montecristi Mertens 1952b	Hacienda Montecristo, 2200 m, Cordillera de Metapán, Depto. Santa Ana, El Salvador	*Rhadinaea montecristi*
Rhadinaea pinicola Mertens 1952b	above Hacienda San José, 1500 m, Cordillera de Metapán, Depto. Santa Ana, El Salvador	*Rhadinaea kinkelini*
Rhadinaea zilchi Mertens 1952a	Laguna de Las Ninfas, 1630 m, Depto. Ahuachapán, El Salvador	*Rhadinaea godmani*
Sceloporus fulvus Bocourt 1874	La Unión, El Salvador	*Sceloporus squamosus*
Stenorrhina lactea Cope 1861	La Unión, El Salvador	*Stenorrhina freminvillii*
Tantilla brevicauda Mertens 1952b	El Grito, Los Angeles, 1510 m, Depto. La Libertad, El Salvador	*Tantilla brevicauda*

Erroneous and Questionable Records

Several species of amphibians and reptiles were listed by Villa et al. (1988) for El Salvador but are not supported by the literature cited in that paper (Mertens 1952d, Savage & D. Wake 1972). These include *Bolitoglossa engelhardti, Gymnopis multiplicata, Hypopachus variolosus* (a species that does occur in El Salvador; see species accounts), *Clelia clelia, Imantodes cenchoa, Bothrops asper* (as *B. atrox*), and *Sphenomorphus cherriei*. *Chironius grandisquamis* was also listed by Villa et al. (1988) but is unlikely to occur in El Salvador (Dixon et al. 1993). *Clelia clelia* and *Bothriechis schlegelii* are listed by CITES (2003), but we are not

aware of confirmed records of these taxa in El Salvador.

Previous Salvadoran records for *Bufo valliceps* (Mertens 1952d, Porter 1970, Villa et al. 1988, Campbell 1999) are based on specimens of *B. luetkenii* (Mendelson 1998; Dueñas et al. 2001, D. Frost 2002). The former species was confirmed in El Salvador by Köhler (2003a). The sea snake *Laticauda colubrina*, otherwise known from the Bay of Bengal to Australia, New Zealand and Oceania, was listed by Villa et al. (1988) for El Salvador. However, its occurrence along the Pacific coast of Central America is doubtful because reports are based purely on dubious sight records and no specimens have entered scientific collections. Campbell (1989, 1999) reported the remote possibility or "probable occurrence" of several amphibians and reptiles in El Salvador, including: *Bolitoglossa celaque, B. conanti, Bothriechis bicolor, Bothrops asper, Heloderma horridum, Micrurus latifasciatus, Oedipina ignea, Oedipina stuarti,* and *Rana vaillanti;* none of these species have been confirmed by us from museum specimens. Because

of a 1992 binding decision of the International Court of Justice, some localities for species that have been reported from El Salvador north of Perquín (e.g., *Abronia salvadorensis, Hyla catracha*) are now a part of Honduran territory (Dueñas et al. 2001). It is possible these two species occur in El Salvador, but we have not included these taxa in the species accounts.

Chapter 5
Class Amphibia

Amphibians are tetrapods with glandular skin, which is not covered with scales as it is in reptiles. Although each of the three orders of Lissamphibia (Gymnophiona [caecilians], Caudata [salamanders], and Anura [frogs and toads]) is ancient (up to 350 mya), the phylogenetic relationships of each group to the others remains contentious (Duellman 2003a, D. Wake 2003a). Amphibians lack embryonic membranes and must reproduce in moist or aquatic habitats; these vertebrates can give live birth, lay eggs that hatch into free-swimming larvae, or lay eggs that contain direct-developing young. This group is distributed throughout the world except for the Arctic and Antarctic regions (Duellman 2003a). Adults range in size from tiny frogs (10.2 mm) to giant salamanders (150 cm). Many new species of amphibians are still being described, but the most recent count lists approximately 5800 species of caecilians, frogs, and salamanders in 44 families (Biju & Bossuyt 2003, Duellman 2003b, D. Wake 2003a, M. Wake 2003a, AmphibiaWeb 2005).

Key to Adults of the Orders of Amphibians

1 a. Limbs absent .... **Gymnophiona**
  b. Limbs present **2**
2 a. Tail absent .... **Anura**
  b. Tail present .... **Caudata**

Clave para Determinar el Orden de Anfibios Adultos

1 a. Extremidades ausentes .... **Gymnophiona**
  b. Extremidades presentes **2**
2 a. Cola ausente .... **Anura**
  b. Cola presente .... **Caudata**

Order Gymnophiona (Caecilians)

The five families of caecilians (ca. 165 species in 33 genera) are distributed in the tropics throughout the world except for Madagascar and the Australo-Papuan region (M. Wake 2003a). Resembling earthworms, these fossorial and aquatic creatures use a tentacle between the eye and nostril to assist in locating invertebrate and small vertebrate prey (Zug et al. 2001). Adult caecilians range in size from 115 mm to 160 cm long. Although most structures of the eye have been lost, most caecilians can distinguish between light and dark. This group can exude a toxic substance through their skin to discourage predators. Depending on the family, caecilians can lay eggs or give live birth (M. Wake 2003a). One family is represented in El Salvador.

Family Caeciliidae

According to M. Wake (2003b) this family includes 26 genera in 107 species, but the family Typhlonectidae (*sensu* Wilkinson 1996), is not recognized as a separate group. Distributed from Mexico to Argentina in the New World, islands off the coast of West and East Africa, India, Sri Lanka, Bangladesh, southern China through the Malay Peninsula, and East Indies to the southern Philippines (McCranie & Wilson 2002, M. Wake 2003b). These caecilians are egg layers with free-swimming larvae that have small gills and tail fins (M. Wake 2003a). Only one genus occurs in El Salvador.

13

Genus *Dermophis*

Commonly called Mexican Caecilians, this genus currently includes seven species distributed from southern Mexico to northwestern Colombia (D. Frost 2002, 2004). All species are viviparous (Savage 2002). Only one species occurs in El Salvador.

Dermophis mexicanus (Duméril & Bibron 1841)
(Tepelcua del Pacífico)
Plate 11, Map 3

1841 *Siphonops mexicanus* Duméril & Bibron, Erp. Gén. 8: 284; type locality: Mexico.
Gymnopis mexicana mexicana: Dunn 1942, Mertens 1952d.
Dermophis mexicana mexicana: Taylor 1968.
Dermophis mexicanus: Savage & M. Wake 1972, Villa et al. 1988, Campbell 1999, Dueñas et al. 2001, Savage & M. Wake 2001, Leenders 2003.
Geographic distribution: Along the Atlantic versant from south-central Veracruz, Mexico, to northeastern Honduras, and along the Pacific versant from eastern Oaxaca, Mexico, to western Nicaragua; also in the lower Motagua Valley of Guatemala (Frost 2004).
Ecological distribution: Dry forest and savanna between sea level and 900 m.
Description: Largest Salvadoran specimen examined is 430 mm in total length; head triangular, bluntly pointed anteriorly, snout projecting beyond mouth; eye visible externally; distance from eye to tentacular opening shorter than distance from tentacular opening to nostril; two distinct nuchal collars; 102–105 primary folds, 70–81 secondary grooves, 6–11 complete grooves anterior to cloaca. Dorsum grayish olive-brown, venter dirty white to yellowish ivory; grooves bordered by black; a yellowish to whitish spot at cloaca.
Natural history: O. Komar (field notes) collected an individual under a rotting wooden plank near a coffee plantation at Volcán de San Miguel, Depto. San Miguel in May. According to Mertens (1952d), this species can be found in loose dirt and under rotten plant material in El Salvador. M. Wake (1980) described several aspects of the natural history of this species in Guatemala. She noted that adults are not sexually dimorphic. Males reach sexual maturity at 1–2 years; females at 1 year. Females give birth from May–June to young that are 108–155 mm total length. Campbell (1998a) remarked

Plate 11: *Dermophis mexicanus* EL SALVADOR: Ahuachapán: El Refugio (225 m). Photo: G. Köhler.

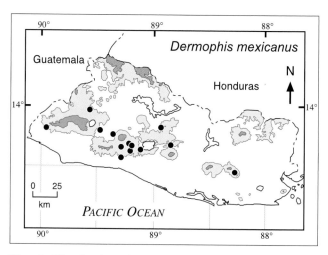

Map 3: Distribution of *Dermophis mexicanus* in El Salvador.
Closed circles represent examined-specimen locality records; open squares are published locality records. Light shading indicates 600–1200 m elevation; dark shading indicates elevations ≥ 1200 m; large bodies of freshwater are outlined in bold, black lines.

that this species is very common in coffee plantations and primarily feeds upon earthworms, but termites and beetle larvae are also eaten. McCranie & Wilson (2002) collected this species in swampy pastures in Honduras in April and June.
Conservation status: GAA: Least concern (LC).
Specimens examined: <u>Ahuachapán</u>: Finca San Benito, Parque Nacional El Imposible, 660 m: MUHNES 1146. <u>Cuscatlán</u>: 2.5 km E Tenancingo, ca. Río Quezalapa. <u>La Libertad</u>: Finca El Paraíso near Nuevo San Salvador [= Santa Tecla], 900 m: SMF 42253, 42302, 42400, 42666–67; Hacienda Zapotitán, Municipio Ciudad Arce, 457 m: MVZ 39732; 17.4 km E Ciudad Arce, Municipio de San Juan Opico: UMMZ 118332. <u>San Miguel</u>: Volcán de San Miguel, 740 m: KU 291384, MUHNES C–30–

1484. <u>San Salvador</u>: Instituto Tropical de Investigaciones Científicas: KU 61859–62, SMF 81364, 81367; San Salvador: MUHNES 621, 664, SMF 81355, ZMB 718, 35719–20, AMNH 52804, KU 184386, 291288; Planes de Renderos: UU 4860; San Salvador, Parque Saburo-Hirao: AMNH 125853. <u>Santa Ana</u>: 10 km S Santa Ana, 500 m: USNM 166375–76. <u>San Vicente</u>: km 60 on the road from San Salvador to San Miguel: SMF 52094. <u>Depto. unknown</u>: no specific locality: SMF 52095 (*).

Order Caudata (Salamanders)

This diverse group of amphibians includes approximately 500 species (61 genera) in 10 families; they have a Holarctic distribution from southern Canada to central Bolivia in the New World, northern and Central Asia, Europe, and North Africa. Adult salamanders range in size from 4–150 cm. This group includes aquatic, terrestrial, fossorial, and arboreal species that can have external (cryptobranchids) or internal (Salamandroidea) fertilization; salamanders can have live birth, lay eggs that hatch into aquatic larvae, or have direct-developing young in eggs. Salamanders typically feed upon arthropods and worms, although small vertebrates are taken by some species (Zug et al. 2001, D. Wake 2003a, b).

Key to the Salamanders of El Salvador

1 a. Body extremely slender and elongate; limbs very short; tail much longer than SVL; costal grooves 20 or more; more than 10 costal folds exposed when limbs adpressed to sides of body .... ***Oedipina taylori***

   b. Body robust; limbs well developed; tail length about equal to SVL; costal grooves 14 or less; less than 6 costal folds exposed when limbs adpressed to sides of body **2**

2 a. Hands and feet nearly completely webbed; dorsum mostly pale tan with contrasting dark brown markings; maximum SVL more than 65 mm .... ***Bolitoglossa salvinii***

   b. Hands and feet with reduced webbing, 1–2 phalanges free of webbing; dorsum mostly dark brown or blackish; maximum SVL less than 60 mm **3**

3 a. Usually at least 2 phalanges free of webbing; head relatively narrow, head width/SVL ratio of 0.15–0.18 .... ***Bolitoglossa synoria***

   b. Usually only 1.5–2.0 phalanges free of webbing; head relatively broad, head width/SVL ratio of 0.16–0.21 .... ***Bolitoglossa heiroreias***

Clave para las Salamandras de El Salvador

1 a. Cuerpo extremadamente angosto y alargado; extremidades muy cortas; cola mucho más larga que longitud rostro–cloacal (LRC); 20 ó más surcos costales; más de 10 pliegues costales expuestos cuando las extremidades son presionadas a lo lados del cuerpo .... ***Oedipina taylori***

   b. Cuerpo robusto; extremidades bien desarrolladas; longitud de la cola similar a LRC; 14 ó menos surcos costales; menos de 6 pliegues costales expuestos cuando las extremidades son presionadas a los lados del cuerpo **2**

2 a. Manos y pies con extensas membranas entre los dedos; dorso claro con machas oscuras (café); LRC máxima > 65 mm .... ***Bolitoglossa salvinii***

   b. Manos y pies con membranas reducidas entre los dedos, 1–2 falanges distales sin membranas; mayor parte del dorso oscuro (café o negro); LRC máxima < 60 mm **3**

3 a. Normalmente, al menos 2 falanges distales sin membranas; cabeza relativamente angosta, ancho de la cabeza representa entre 15–18% de LRC .... ***Bolitoglossa synoria***

   b. Normalmente, 1.5–2.0 falanges distales sin membranas; cabeza relativamente ancha, ancho de la cabeza representa entre 16–21% de LRC .... ***Bolitoglossa heiroreias***

Family Plethodontidae

Distributed from southern Canada to northern Bolivia and northeastern Brazil in the New World and Central Mediterranean Europe, this family includes approximately 350 species in 28 genera, but the number of described species is expected to increase in the near future. Commonly known as lungless salamanders, most undergo direct development in eggs with no larval stage (D. Wake 2003b). Four species in two genera occur in El Salvador.

Genus *Bolitoglossa*

Commonly called Tropical Lungless Salamanders, this genus encompasses approximately 90 species from Mexico to northern Bolivia and northeastern Brazil; it is the largest genus of salamanders (D. Frost 2002, 2004, Savage 2002, Greenbaum, 2004, Parra-Olea et al. 2004). The phylogenetic relationships within this genus and the number of species associated with it are currently under revision (Parra-Olea et al. 2004). Three species are known from El Salvador.

Bolitoglossa heiroreias Greenbaum 2004
(Salamandra de Montecristo)
Plate 12, Map 4, Figure 1ab

2004 *Bolitoglossa heiroreias* Greenbaum, J. Herpetol. 37(3): 412; type locality: Camel Cigarettes Field Station, Cerro Montecristo (14°24"04"N, 89°21"02"W), 1880 m, Depto. Santa Ana, El Salvador.
Magnadigita engelhardti: Mertens 1952d, Rand 1957.
Bolitoglossa dunni: D. Wake & Lynch 1976, Villa et al. 1988.
Bolitoglossa engelhardti: Villa et al. 1988.
Bolitoglossa conanti: Campbell 1999, Dueñas et al. 2001, McCranie & Wilson 1993, 2002.
Bolitoglossa cf. *conanti*: Leenders & Watkins-Colwell 2004.
Geographic distribution: Cerro Montecristo and Cerro Miramundo at the convergence of El Salvador, Guatemala, and Honduras (Greenbaum 2004).
Ecological distribution: Pine-oak and cloud forests at elevations of 1840–2300 m.
Description: Largest Salvadoran specimen examined is 63.1 mm SVL; tail length/SVL 0.58–0.84; HL/SVL 0.25–0.26; HW/SVL 0.16–0.21; HW/HL 0.74–0.75; reduced webbing on digits, about 1.5–2.0 phalanges of longest toes on both forelimbs and

Plate 12: *Bolitoglossa heiroreias* EL SALVADOR: Santa Ana: Cerro Montecristo (2200 m). Photo: M. Veselý.

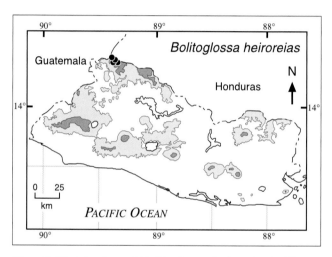

Map 4: Distribution of *Bolitoglossa heiroreias* in El Salvador.
Closed circles represent examined-specimen locality records; open squares are published locality records. Light shading indicates 600–1200 m elevation; dark shading indicates elevations ≥ 1200 m; large bodies of freshwater are outlined in bold, black lines.

hind limbs free of webbing; 28–67 maxillary teeth, 2–7 premaxillary teeth, 18–33 vomerine teeth.

Mertens (1952d) reported the color in life of SMF 43042 and SMF 43249 as dark gray with many white and red spots on the belly. Greenbaum (2004) described the color in life of this species as dark gray, dull brown, or black with gray lichenous blotches or black blotches. Throat and subcaudal coloration is orange to rusty brown; iris is grayish tan or reddish brown. Leenders & Watkins-Colwell (2004) noted daytime and nighttime colors change in this species; nocturnal coloration is similar to the banded phase of *B. conanti*.

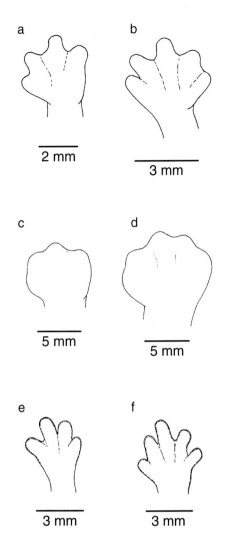

Figure 1: Ventral views of right forefoot and right hindfoot of: a,b. *Bolitoglossa heiroreias* (SMF 81052); c,d. *B. salvinii* (SMF 79386); e,f. *B. synoria* (SMF 78083).

Natural history: One of the UMMZ specimens was regurgitated by a *Rhadinaea montecristi* (Serpentes: Colubridae). El Salvador specimens of this species have been collected in bromeliads, on vegetation at ground level, and under debris and logs at Cerro Montecristo, Depto. Santa Ana during the dry and rainy seasons (W. E. Duellman, E. Greenbaum, T. Leenders & M. Veselý field notes, Leenders & Watkins-Colwell 2004). Mertens (1952d) found a specimen under a rotten log and reported a second specimen that was collected in *Tillandsia* by a colleague in El Salvador. Rand (1957) reported specimens from leaf axils in bromeliads in trees in Salvadoran cloud forest.

Conservation status: S. Stuart (pers. comm.): Not evaluated because taxon was formerly considered a population of *B. conanti*. Greenbaum (2004) noted the small geographic distribution of *B. heiroreias* satisfies the "Endangered" criterion of the IUCN Red List.

Specimens examined: Santa Ana: Camel Cigarettes Field Station at Parque Nacional Montecristo, 1880 m: KU 289800; Hacienda Los Planes, Metapán, 2000 m: SMF 43042; Hacienda Montecristo, Metapán, 2200 m: SMF 43249; same locality at 2250 m: MVZ 200535, UMMZ 118338, MCZ 106389–90, KU 61864–66, 66204–06, LACM 137082; Cerro Miramundo, 2000 m: FMNH 65025–26; same locality at 2200 m: FMNH 65027; same locality at 2300 m: SMF 52093; Parque Nacional Montecristo: MUHNES 67–68, 70–71, 86–89, 144, 148–153, 849, 854, 864; same locality at 1850 m: YPM 7240–43.

***Bolitoglossa salvinii* (Gray 1868)**
(Salamandra Pintada)
Plate 13, Map 5, Figure 1cd

1868 *Oedipus salvinii* Gray, Ann. Mag. Nat. Hist., 2(4): 297; type locality: Pacific coast of Guatemala.
Oedipus salvinii: Dunn 1926.
Bolitoglossa salvinii: D. Wake & Lynch 1976, Villa et al. 1988, Campbell 1999, Dueñas et al. 2001, D. Frost 2002, 2004.
Geographic distribution: Upper coastal plain and moderate elevations of the Pacific slopes of southern Guatemala and El Salvador (D. Wake & Lynch 1976).
Ecological distribution: Dry forest around 700 m.
Description: Maximum SVL 97.0 mm (a female);

Plate 13: *Bolitoglossa salvinii* GUATEMALA: Finca El Salto. Photo: KU color transparency collection (KU CT 2432).

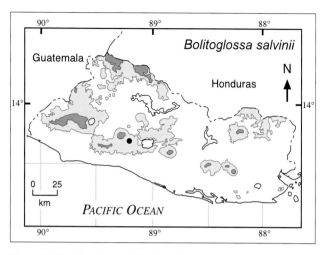

Map 5: Distribution of *Bolitoglossa salvinii* in El Salvador.
Closed circles represent examined-specimen locality records; open squares are published locality records. Light shading indicates 600–1200 m elevation; dark shading indicates elevations ≥ 1200 m; large bodies of freshwater are outlined in bold, black lines.

the only two available specimens from El Salvador (with precise locality data) are adult females, only one (KU 61863) has an original tail (tail length/SVL 1.03); HL/SVL 0.13–0.15; HW/SVL 0.13–0.14; HW/HL 0.95–1.06; digits completely webbed; 41–56 maxillary teeth; 6–8 premaxillary teeth; 32–36 vomerine teeth. In preservative, dorsum mostly pale tan with contrasting rusty orange or brownish markings.
Natural history: D. Wake & Lynch (1976) reported this species in lowland wet forests (< 1600 m) of Guatemala. A prehensile tail of a specimen from Escuintla, Guatemala was illustrated. This species was classified as terrestrial and arboreal.
Conservation status: GAA: Endangered (EN B1ab[iii]).
Specimens examined: <u>San Salvador</u>: San Salvador, Instituto Tropical de Investigaciones Científicas: KU 61863, SMF 79386.

Bolitoglossa synoria McCranie & Köhler 1999
(Salamandra de Bromelias de El Pital)
Plate 14, Map 6, Figures 1ef, 2a

1999 *Bolitoglossa synoria* McCranie & Köhler, Senckenberg. biol. 78(1/2): 226; type locality: Quebrada La Quebradona (14°23.96´N, 89°07.38´W), north slope of Cerro El Pital, 2150 m elevation,

Plate 14: *Bolitoglossa synoria* HONDURAS: Ocotepeque: Cerro El Pital, Quebrada La Quebradona (2150 m). Photo: G. Köhler.

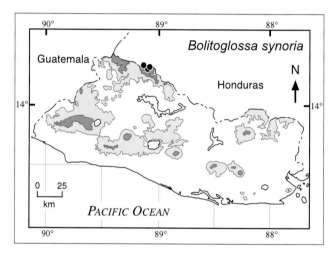

Map 6: Distribution of *Bolitoglossa synoria* in El Salvador. Closed circles represent examined-specimen locality records; open squares are published locality records. Light shading indicates 600–1200 m elevation; dark shading indicates elevations ≥ 1200 m; large bodies of freshwater are outlined in bold, black lines.

Depto. Ocotepeque, Honduras.
Bolitoglossa celaque: McCranie & Wilson 1993a, Dueñas et al. 2001.
Bolitoglossa synoria: D. Frost 2002, 2004, McCranie & Wilson 2002.
Geographic distribution: A few kilometers on either side of the Honduran-Salvadoran border on Cerro El Pital (McCranie & Wilson 2002).
Ecological distribution: Cloud forests at elevations of 2200–2713 m.
Description: Maximum SVL 52.0 mm in males and 59.8 mm in females; tail length/SVL 0.70–0.90; HL/SVL 0.23–0.29; HW/SVL 0.15–0.19; HW/HL 0.57–0.70; reduced webbing on digits, usually slightly over two phalanges on both sides of digit III

a   b

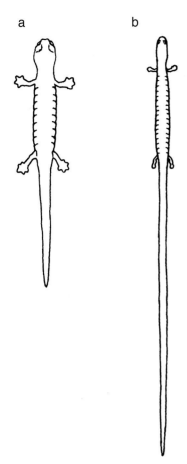

Figure 2: A comparison of body shape between a. *Bolitoglossa synoria* (SMF 78083; SVL 43.0 mm); and b. *Oedipina taylori* (SMF 44392; SVL 49.0 mm).

on forelimbs and between digits III–IV on hind limbs free of webbing; 31–64 maxillary teeth; 2–9 premaxillary teeth; 16–32 vomerine teeth (McCranie & Köhler 1999). Head and body uniformly dark grayish brown, tail dark grayish brown with clay-colored mottling and flecking (McCranie & Köhler 1999).

Natural history: O. Komar (field notes) recorded a juvenile from a bromeliad in cloud forest during the day at Cerro El Pital, Depto. Chalatenango in June. Another individual was collected under leaf litter during the day at this same locality. McCranie & Köhler (1999) reported this species from a tree trunk and tree fern 1–2 m above the ground, and commented it was absent from bromeliads in Honduras. Field notes from the MVZ series documented specimens from under orchid roots near a small stream, and another on a rock near a small stream.

Conservation status: GAA: Critically endangered (CR B1ab[iii]).

Specimens examined: <u>Chalatenango</u>: NW slope Los Esesmiles, Cerro El Pital, 2438 m: MVZ 39734; same locality at 2713 m: MVZ 39733, 39735–40; E slope Los Esesmiles, Cerro El Pital, 2438 m: MVZ 39773; same locality at 2469 m: MVZ 39741–44, 39745–57; same locality at 2652 m: MVZ 39758–72; Cerro El Pital: KU 184397–401, 291379.

Genus *Oedipina*

This genus includes 23 species of Tropical Worm Salamanders distributed from Chiapas, Mexico to western Colombia and south-central Ecuador (D. Frost 2002, 2004). Savage (2002) noted this genus is elongate with very long tails compared to the more robust salamanders in the genus *Bolitoglossa* (Figure 2). Only one species occurs in El Salvador.

Oedipina taylori Stuart 1952
(Salamandra-lombriz de Taylor)
Plate 15, Map 7, Figures 2b, 3

1952 *Oedipina taylori* Stuart, Proc. Biol. Soc. Washington, 65: 2; type locality: 4 kilometers east of Hacienda La Trinidad (23 airline kilometers southeast of Chiquimulilla), 100 m elevation, Depto. Jutiapa, Guatemala.
Oedipina salvadorensis: Rand 1952, 1957, Mertens 1952d.
Oedipina taylori: Brame 1968, Villa et al. 1988, Dueñas et al. 2001, D. Frost 2002, 2004, Leenders 2003.

Geographic distribution: From southeastern Guatemala (including Río Motagua Valley) to eastern El Salvador and southern Honduras (McCranie & Wilson 2002).

Ecological distribution: Dry forest, premontane evergreen forest, and subtropical humid forest at elevations of 220–1140 m.

Description: Largest Salvadoran specimen examined is 69.3 mm SVL; tail length/SVL 2.01–2.06; HL/SVL 0.13–0.15; HW/SVL 0.067–0.074; HW/HL 0.51–0.55; total number of maxillary teeth 0–13.

In preservative dark blue above and below; in life this species varies from dark gray to black. Rand (1957:509) gave the following color description (in life) for specimens collected in San Salvador: "Black above, venter strongly pigmented but lighter back; a whitish spot behind insertion of hind leg;

Plate 15: *Oedipina taylori* (SMF 81349) EL SALVA-
DOR: San Salvador: San Salvador; Parque Zoológico
Nacional (700 m). Photo: M. Veselý.

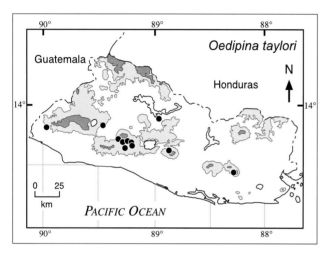

Map 7: Distribution of *Oedipina taylori* in El Salvador.
Closed circles represent examined-specimen locality records;
open squares are published locality records. Light shading
indicates 600–1200 m elevation; dark shading indicates elevations ≥ 1200 m; large bodies of freshwater are outlined in bold,
black lines.

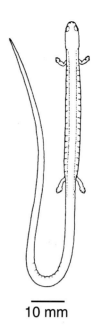

Figure 3: *Oedipina taylori* (SMF 44392) in dorsal view.

limbs above lighter than back, above and below
with brownish tinge; mental area also with a
brownish tinge."

Natural history: This species seems to do well in
disturbed areas, as evidenced by its presence in the
San Salvador Zoo, Depto. San Salvador and residen-
tial areas of the capital city. Residents near Bosque
Cinquera, Depto. Cabañas informed E. Greenbaum
(field notes) that this species will enter human
habitations after heavy rains. The specimen collected at Bosque Cinquera was collected from the
inside of a rotten log in dry forest in July. O.
Komar (field notes) collected an individual from
under a wood pile in a coffee plantation at Volcán de
San Miguel, Depto. San Miguel in May. Mertens
(1952d) found specimens of this species under rocks
and reported a specimen that was collected in a
bamboo internode by a colleague in El Salvador.
Rand (1957) found three specimens under half-
buried rocks in damp earth at the bottom of a
brush-grown gully running through scrub pasture
during the dry season. McCranie & Wilson (2002)
noted their single Honduran specimen was taken
from under a rock along a stream in November
near premontane dry forest.

Conservation status: GAA: Data deficient (DD).

Specimens examined: <u>Ahuachapán</u>: El Refugio,
vicinity of Mariposario of Francisco Serrano,
13°49.46´N, 89°59.98´W, 225 m: SMF 79053; Parque
Nacional El Imposible, Finca San Benito: MUHNES
895, 1148. <u>Cabañas</u>: Bosque Cinquera, 13°53.13´N,
88°57.36´W, 400 m: KU 289997. <u>La Libertad</u>: La
Joya, Ciudad Arce, 400 m: SMF 44392; Finca El
Paraíso near Nuevo San Salvador [= Santa Tecla],
900 m: SMF 42843, 43054, MVZ 40472; El
Boqueron, Finca Buenos Aires, 1045 m: SMF 44393;
Nuevo San Salvador [= Santa Tecla]: SMF 52096,
MVZ 40473. <u>San Miguel</u>: Volcán de San Miguel,
1140 m: KU 291281. <u>San Salvador</u>: San Salvador,
Parque Zoológico Nacional, 13°58.8´N, 89°11.9´W,
700 m: SMF 81349; San Salvador, San Salvador: KU
61869, 289994; San Salvador, 670 m: FMNH 65029–
30; San Salvador, Los Planes de Renderos: KU
61870; Colónia San Carlos, Calle Los Naranjos,
pasaje San Gerardo, San Salvador: MUHNES C–30–
1342. <u>San Vicente</u>: Finca El Carmen: SMF 81351.

Order Anura (Frogs)

There are approximately 4850 species (ca. 355 genera; 29 families) of frogs currently known, including the recently described family Nasikabatrachidae from the Western Ghats of India (Channing & Stanley 2002, Biju & Bossuyt 2003, Duellman 2003b). There are two major groups of frogs: archaeobatrachians (basal frogs) and neobatrachians (advanced frogs). Frogs have a distinct and unique morphology, including a broad head, large mouth, large protuberant eyes, short body, and in most cases, no tail. Adult size ranges from just 10.2 mm to 32 cm. The aquatic larvae (tadpoles) of frogs undergo dramatic morphological changes during the process of metamorphosis into the adult form. However, some frogs (e.g., *Eleutherodactylus*) undergo direct development in eggs. Frogs are nearly ubiquitous— they are absent from Greenland, Antarctica, Arctic regions of North America and Europe, and some oceanic islands, but present in a wide array of habitats elsewhere. Because of the thin, porous skin of most anurans, activity is limited to moist or aquatic habitats; even toads that have relatively thick skin must return to water to reproduce (Duellman 2003b). There are seven families of frogs and toads in El Salvador.

Key to the Frogs and Toads of El Salvador

1 a. Cranial crests and distinctly enlarged parotoid glands present **2**

   b. No cranial crests; no distinctly enlarged parotoid glands although scattered warts and tubercles may be present on dorsum **6**

2 a. Parotoid gland large, several times area of upper eyelid; adult size 150 mm or more .... ***Bufo marinus***

   b. Parotoid gland moderate to small, less than twice area of upper eyelid; adult size less than 100 mm **3**

3 a. Parotoid gland much smaller than area of upper eyelid .... ***Bufo luetkenii***

   b. Parotoid gland moderate, 1.0 to 1.5 times the area of upper eyelid **4**

4 a. Parotoid gland elongate .... ***Bufo canaliferus***

   b. Parotoid gland ovoid **5**

5 a. No definite linear series of dorsolateral tubercles clearly demarcated from other tubercles on dorsolateral surfaces; usually a broad pale (yellow) interorbital bar present .... ***Bufo coccifer***

   b. A definite linear series of dorsolateral tubercles clearly demarcated from other tubercles on dorsolateral surfaces; usually a narrow dark brown interorbital bar present .... ***Bufo valliceps***

6 a. Four toes; two elongate spade-like inner metatarsal tubercles, with a free edge .... ***Rhinophrynus dorsalis***

   b. Five toes; never two elongate spade-like inner metatarsal tubercles, with a free edge **7**

7 a. A transverse fold of skin across head usually present posterior to eyes; an ocellated blotch in upper inguinal region present **8**

   b. No transverse fold of skin across head posterior to eyes; no ocellated blotch in upper inguinal region **10**

8 a. No large black or dark brown blotches on venter; SVL of adult < 25 mm .... ***Gastrophryne usta***

   b. Usually prominent black or dark brown blotches on venter; SVL of adults > 25 mm **9**

9 a. Outer metatarsal tubercle large, narrowly separated from the inner metatarsal tubercle (inner and outer metatarsal tubercles separated from each other by 0.3–0.6 times width of outer metatarsal tubercle) .... ***Hypopachus variolosus***

   b. Outer metatarsal tubercle small, widely separated from the inner metatarsal tubercle (inner and outer metatarsal tubercles separated from each other by 0.9–1.7 times width of outer metatarsal tubercle).. ***Hypopachus barberi***

10 a. Appearance toad-like; dorsum with many scattered warts; tympanum indistinct
or invisible externally .... ***Physalaemus pustulosus***

b. Appearance not toad-like; dorsum smooth or with ridges and small tubercles;
tympanum distinct **11**

11 a. A ventral disk present; toes only webbed basally, or lacking webbing **12**

b. No ventral disk; toes usually extensively webbed **15**

12 a. Tips of digits not expanded; toes without webbing **13**

b. Tips of digits slightly or distinctly expanded; toes webbed basally, or
lacking webbing **14**

13 a. Toes with lateral fringes; no distinct creamish horizontal stripe on posterior surface
of thigh; males with two horny spines on thumb .... ***Leptodactylus melanonotus***

b. Toes lacking lateral fringes; a distinct creamish horizontal stripe on posterior
surface of thigh; males without horny spines on thumb .... ***Leptodactylus fragilis***

14 a. A distinct dark brown stripe from nostril to beyond tympanum; tips of fingers
with swollen, but not expanded discs .... ***Eleutherodactylus rhodopis***

b. No dark brown stripe from nostril to beyond tympanum; tips of fingers with
distinctly expanded discs .... ***Eleutherodactylus rupinius***

15 a. Neither finger nor toe discs present **16**

b. Finger and toe discs present **17**

16 a. Skin with distinct denticulations (small white tubercles, scattered
throughout the dorsum, easily seen with the aid of a dissecting microscope);
dorsal blotches, if present, indistinct; tips of toes slightly expanded; a distinct
dark brown or blackish face mask usually present .... ***Rana maculata***

b. Skin smooth or rugose, but without denticulations; distinct dorsal
blotches present; tips of toes pointed; distinct dark (brown or black)
face mask absent .... ***Rana forreri***

17 a. Venter transparent, internal organs visible .... ***Hyalinobatrachium fleischmanni***

b. Venter not transparent, internal organs not visible **18**

18 a. Color in life green; pupil of eye vertical in bright light (in life) or in
preservative .... ***Agalychnis moreletii***

b. Color in life brown or gray; pupil of eye horizontal or round in bright light (in life)
or in preservative **19**

19 a. Skin of dorsum usually distinctly glandular (indicated by thickened skin, most
conspicuous in occipital and frontal regions) .... ***Phrynohyas venulosa***

b. Skin of dorsum smooth or with scattered small tubercles **20**

20 a. Upper lips with dark brown bars; a series of white swellings or a dermal ridge
along posteroventral margin of lower arm .... ***Smilisca baudinii***

b. Upper lips immaculate; no series of white swellings or dermal ridges along
posteroventral margin of lower arm **21**

21 a. Prepollex enlarged with projecting distal end **22**

b. No projecting prepollex **24**

22 a. Prepollical process bifid .... ***Plectrohyla guatemalensis***

b. Prepollical process pointed, or flat **23**

23 a. Prepollical process flat, not protruding; vocal slits absent .... ***Plectrohyla psiloderma***

b. Prepollical spine pointed, protruding; vocal slits present................................... ***Plectrohyla sagorum***

24 a. Thumbs in males with enlarged spines or with tiny nuptial excrescences;
males with or without ventrolateral glands **25**

b. Nuptial tuberosities on thumbs of males not composed of horny spines;
males without ventrolateral glands **26**

25 a. Thumbs in males with enlarged spines; ventrolateral glands present
in males .... ***Ptychohyla euthysanota***

    b. Thumbs in males with tiny nuptial excrescences, not spines; ventrolateral glands
absent in males .... ***Ptychohyla salvadorensis***

26 a. Head narrow; dorsum with scattered minute tubercles; snout projecting
(shelf-like) beyond lower jaw .... ***Scinax staufferi***

    b. Head broad; dorsum smooth; snout not projecting (shelf-like)
beyond lower jaw ....***Hyla robertmertensi***

Clave para las Ranas y Sapos de El Salvador

1 a. Crestas craneales y glándulas parotoideas distintivamente agrandadas presentes ....,................ **2**

    b. Crestas craneales ausentes; glándulas parotoideas ausentes, pero el dorso
puede tener verrugas y/o tubérculos **6**

2 a. Glándula parotoidea grande, su superficie es de al menos el doble de la superficie
inmediatamente por encima del globo ocular; longitud rostro–cloacal (LRC)
en adultos > 150 mm .... ***Bufo marinus***

    b. Glándula parotoidea pequeña o mediana, su superficie es menor al doble de la
superficie inmediantamente por encima del globo ocular; longitud rostro–cloacal
(LRC) en adultos < 100 mm **3**

3 a. Superficie de glándula parotoidea mucho más pequeña que la superficie
inmediatamente por encima del globo ocular .... ***Bufo luetkenii***

    b. Glándula parotoidea mediana, su superficie es de 1.0 a 1.5 veces la superficie que
está inmediatamente por encima del globo ocular **4**

4 a. Glándula parotoidea alargada .... ***Bufo canaliferus***

    b. Glándula parotoidea ovoide **5**

5 a. Tubérculos dorsales no alineados dorsolateralmente; normalmente hay una
banda interorbital ancha y clara (amarilla) .... ***Bufo coccifer***

    b. Tubérculos alineados dorsolateralmente; normalmente hay una banda
interorbital angosta y oscura (café oscura) ....***Bufo valliceps***

6 a. Pies con cuatro dedos; dos tubérculos metatarsales alargados, con forma de
espada y borde libre .... ***Rhinophrynus dorsalis***

    b. Pies con cinco dedos; tubérculos metatarsales nunca tienen forma de espada,
con borde libre **7**

7 a. Normalmente pliegue dermal transversal ubicado en la cabeza, posterior al
nivel de los ojos; mancha ocelada en la región por sobre la ingle **8**

    b. Pliegue transversal posterior al nivel de los ojos ausente; mancha ocelada por
sobre la ingle ausente **10**

8 a. Sin manchas color negro o café oscuro en el vientre; longitud rostro–cloacal (LRC)
en adultos < 25 mm .... ***Gastrophryne usta***

    b. Normalmente con evidentes manchas color negro o café oscuro en el vientre; LRC
en adultos > 25 mm **9**

9 a. Tubérculo metatarsal externo grande, apenas separado del tubérculo metatarsal
interno (distancia entre ambos tubérculos es de 0.3–0.6 veces el ancho del tubérculo
metatarsal externo) ....***Hypopachus variolosus***

    b. Tubérculo metatarsal externo pequeño, separado del tubérculo metatarsal
interno por una distancia equivalente a 0.9–1.7 veces el ancho del tubérculo
metatarsal externo .... ***Hypopachus barberi***

10 a. Especie con apariencia de sapo bufónido; dorso con verrugas; tímpano no visible
externamente .... ***Physalaemus pustulosus***

    b. Sin apariencia de sapo bufónido; dorso liso o con crestas o tubérculos pequeños;
tímpano evidente **11**

11 a. Disco ventral presente; dedos de los pies con membranas interdigitales basales o
sin membranas **12**

    b. Disco ventral ausente; dedos de los pies con extensas
membranas interdigitales **15**

12 a. Dedos no expandidos distalmente; dedos de los pies sin
membrana interdigital **13**

    b. Dedos expandidos o ligeramente expandidos distalmente; dedos de los pies con
membrana interdigital basal o sin membrana **14**

13 a. Dedos de los pies con pliegues laterales; superficie posterior del
muslo sin línea horizontal clara; machos con dos espinas nupciales en el
dedo I .... ***Leptodactylus melanonotus***

    b. Dedos de los pies sin pliegues laterales; superficie posterior del
muslo con línea horizontal clara; machos sin espinas nupciales en el
dedo I .... ***Leptodactylus fragilis***

14 a. Línea café oscura evidente desde el nostrilo hasta región posterior al
tímpano; punta de los dedos de las manos distalmente adultados, pero sin
discos expandidos .... ***Eleutherodactylus rhodopis***

    b. Sin línea café oscura desde el nostrilo hasta región posterior al tímpano;
discos de los dedos de la mano claramente expandidos
distalmente .... ***Eleutherodactylus rupinius***

15 a. Dedos de las manos y de los pies sin discos digitales **16**

    b. Dedos de las manos y de los pies con discos digitales **17**

16 a. Dorso con espínulas (tubérculos blancos pequeños, facilmente visibles a través del
microscopio de disección); manchas dorsales ausentes o difíciles de ver; dedos de
los pies ligeramente expandidos distalmente; máscara facial oscura (café o negro)
normalmente presente .... ***Rana maculata***

    b. Piel dorsal lisa o rugosa, sin espínulas; manchas dorsales evidentes;
dedos de los pies distalmente punteagudos; sin máscara facial oscura
(café o negro) .... ***Rana forreri***

17 a. Vientre transparente, órganos internos visibles a través de
la piel .... ***Hyalinobatrachium fleischmanni***

    b. Vientre no transparente, órganos internos no visibles a través de la piel **18**

18 a. Color en vida verde; pupila del ojo vertical en vida o en
alcohol ....***Agalychnis moreletii***

    b. Color en vida café o gris; pupila del ojo horizontal o redonda en
vida o en alcohol **19**

19 a. Piel dorsal glandular (evidente por engrosamiento de la piel, sobretodo
en las regiones occipital y frontal) .... ***Phrynohyas venulosa***

    b. Piel dorsal lisa o con pequeños tubérculos esparcidos **20**

20 a. Labio superior con barras café oscuras; con serie de tubérculos o pliegues
ulnares a lo largo del margen posteroventral del antebrazo .... ***Smilisca baudinii***

    b. Labio superior sin barras; antebrazo sin tubérculos ni pliegues ulnares **21**

21 a. Prepollex agrandado, con extremo distal distinguible externamente **22**

    b. Prepollex no distinguible externamente **24**

22 a. Proceso distal del prepollex bífido .... ***Plectrohyla guatemalensis***

    b. Proceso distal del prepollex plano o punteagudo **23**

23 a. Proceso distal del prepollex plano, no visible externamente; hendiduras
vocales ausentes .... ***Plectrohyla psiloderma***

    b. Proceso distal del prepollex punteagudo, visible externamente;
hendiduras vocales presentes .... ***Plectrohyla sagorum***

24 a. En machos, dedo I con espinas o con pequeñas excrecencias nupciales;
machos con o sin glándulas ventrolaterales **25**

    b. En machos, las excrecencias nupciales no forman espinas; machos sin glándulas
ventrolaterales **26**

25 a. En machos, dedo I con espinas agrandadas; machos con glándulas
  ventrolaterales ....*Ptychohyla euthysanota*
  b. En machos, dedo I con muy pequeñas excrecencias nupciales, espinas nupciales
  ausentes; machos sin glándulas ventrolaterales ....*Ptychohyla salvadorensis*
26 a. Cabeza angosta; minúsculos tubérculos (espinulas) esparcidos en el dorso
  hocico sobrepasa el nivel de la mandíbula anteriormente ....*Scinax staufferi*
  b. Cabeza ancha; dorso liso; anteriormente, el hocico no sobrepasa el nivel de la
  mandíbula ....*Hyla robertmertensi*

Family Bufonidae

This nearly cosmopolitan family of toads is
distributed in all temperate and tropical regions of
the world with the exception of the Australo-
Papuan region, Madagascar, and the Sahara of
Africa. *Bufo marinus* has been introduced to
Australia and many tropical regions worldwide.
The family is represented by approximately 430
species in 35 genera (Channing & Stanley 2002,
McCranie & Wilson 2002). One genus is known
from El Salvador.

Genus *Bufo*

Bufo is the most widespread genus in the
family Bufonidae; its distribution is equivalent to
that of the entire family. There are approximately
255 species known from this genus, but this
number is expected to increase in the near future
(D. Frost 2004). Parotoid glands containing
toxins are present in all species of this genus
(Cannatella 2003). Five species are known from El
Salvador.

Bufo canaliferus Cope 1877
(Sapo Rojo)
Plate 16, Map 8, Figure 4a

1877 *Bufo canaliferus* Cope, Proc. Am. Philos. Soc.,
17: 85; type locality: "West Tehuantepec," Oaxaca,
Mexico.
Bufo canaliferus: Mertens 1952d, Rand 1957, Porter
1964a, Nelson 1966a, Villa et al. 1988, Dueñas et al.
2001, D. Frost 2002, 2004, Leenders 2003.
Geographic distribution: From the Pacific slopes
of Oaxaca and Chiapas, Mexico, to Guatemala and
El Salvador (D. Frost 2002, 2004).
Ecological distribution: Dry forest, premontane
evergreen forest, and subtropical humid forest at
elevations of 200–800 m; also in wet pastures with

Plate 16: *Bufo canaliferus* (SMF 81275–77) EL
SALVADOR: Ahuachapán: El Refugio (225 m). Photo:
G. Köhler.

small ponds and streams (Mertens 1952d).
Description: Largest Salvadoran specimen examined is 52.0 mm SVL; HW/SVL 0.34–0.38; HL/SVL
0.28–0.33; shank length/SVL 0.39–0.45; foot length/
SVL 0.38–0.47; tympanum diameter/SVL 0.05–0.06;
parotoid gland length/SVL 0.17–0.24; parotoid gland
width/SVL 0.06–0.10; interparietal crest width/SVL
0.11–0.15; supratympanic crest length/SVL 0.03–
0.07. Snout blunt or slightly pointed in dorsal view,
truncate in profile; supraorbital, postorbital,
supratympanic crests narrow; pretympanic and
preorbital crest barely evident. Nostrils directed
dorsally; canthus rostralis indistinct; loreal region
slightly concave; supralabial crest narrow, extending from point below nostril to corner of jaw.
Forelimbs slender, short, relative length of fingers
II < I < IV < III; finger webbing absent; finger tips
not enlarged; palmar tubercle rounded to ovoid,
low, about twice as large as thenar tubercle, latter
tubercle ovoid and low; subarticular tubercles
distinct, elevated, triangular in profile, bifid or
divided; supernumerary tubercles rounded,
subconical, distinct. Hind limbs short, slender;
inner tarsal fold absent, replaced by a row of

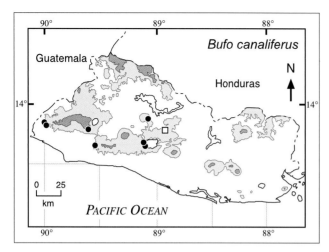

Map 8: Distribution of *Bufo canaliferus* in El Salvador. Closed circles represent examined-specimen locality records; open squares are published locality records. Light shading indicates 600–1200 m elevation; dark shading indicates elevations ≥ 1200 m; large bodies of freshwater are outlined in bold, black lines.

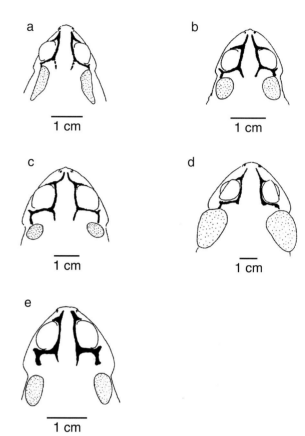

Figure 4: Shape of cranial crests and parotoid glands in the Salvadoran species of *Bufo*. a. *B. canaliferus* (SMF 81373); b. *B. coccifer* (SMF 81461); c. *B. luetkenii* (SMF 78069); d. *B. marinus* (SMF 81278); e. *B. valliceps* (SMF 81319).

distinctly enlarged, sharply conical tubercles; outer metatarsal tubercle small, low, ovoid; inner metatarsal tubercle about same size as, or slightly larger than outer metatarsal tubercle, ovoid, raised, protruding distally in profile; relative length of toes I < II < V < III < IV; toes basally webbed; subarticular tubercles distinct, rounded and raised; supernumerary tubercles equal in size, raised. Dorsum smooth with many small conical tubercles. Parotoid glands distinct, larger than upper eyelids, prolonged posteriorly; dorsolateral row of enlarged tubercles with 1–4 apices extending from posterior corner of parotoids to about 2/3 length of flanks; venter and gular area covered with small granular tubercles; no vomerine teeth or processes. Males with unilateral vocal slits.

Dorsum orange brown, yellowish brown or tan with two dorsal longitudinal, darker orange bands; creamish middorsal line extending from snout to vent, darker transverse bands on tarsi, lower part of tarsi also darker; occasionally two dark brown irregular blotches in frontoparietal region; venter pale to dirty yellow.

Call: Porter (1964b) described the call of *Bufo canaliferus* as "a pulse rate of 8–17 notes per second ... emitted in erratic bursts, several calls being produced in a short interval followed by a pause and then several more closely spaced calls. The length of the individual call (0.8 to 8.4 sec) appeared to depend largely upon the interval between calls. ...

always called from moving water." He also noted that the call of this species tends to increase in length with an increase in temperature and that this species has a variation in pulse rate throughout the length of its call.

Natural history: M. Veselý (field notes) collected an individual during the day (following rainfall) on a dirt road at El Refugio, Depto. Ahuachapán in May. Mertens (1952d) found this toad in wet grassland with numerous ponds in El Salvador. He recorded breeding activity and calling males during the second half of August. Rand (1957) collected a single specimen under a rock at the bottom of a wooded gully at Laguna Ilopango, Depto. San Salvador in May. Duellman (1960) reported *B. canaliferus* calling from a flooded field in Mexico.

Conservation status: GAA: Least concern (LC).

Specimens examined: Ahuachapán: Parque Nacional El Imposible, Finca San Benito: MUHNES

549–550; Parque Nacional El Imposible, La Fincona: MUHNES 1102–03, VH 92; El Refugio, vicinity of Mariposario of Francisco Serrano, 13°49.46′N, 89°59.98′W, 225 m: SMF 81275–77. Cuscatlán: 7 km SSW Suchitoto: KU 184570. San Salvador: 2.4 km SE Ilopango, Cantón Asino: KU 184571; Lago de Ilopango, 400 m: FMNH 65042. Sonsonate: Hacienda Cuyan-Cuya near Izalco: SMF 42548–51; Hacienda Chilata, 610 m: MVZ 39776–79. **Published locality records:** Cuscatlán: 5 km WNW of Cojutepeque (Nelson 1966a).

Bufo coccifer Cope 1866
(Sapo Gris)
Plate 17, Map 9, Figures 4b, 15a

1866 *Bufo coccifer* Cope, Proc. Acad. Nat. Sci. Philad. 18: 130; type locality: "Arriba" ["this name apparently was applied loosely to the Meseta Central," according to Savage 1974:77], Costa Rica. *Bufo coccifer*: Mertens 1952d, Rand 1957, Nelson & Hoyt 1961, Porter 1964a, 1965, Greding & Hellebuyck 1980, Villa et al. 1988, Dueñas et al. 2001, D. Frost 2002, 2004, McCranie & Wilson 2002, Leenders 2003, Leenders & Watkins-Colwell 2004, Mendelson et al. 2005.
Geographic distribution: From the Guatemala-Mexico border along the Pacific versant to the Guanacaste region of Costa Rica; additional records from the Atlantic versant of Honduras, Atlantic coastal region of Honduras and Nicaragua, and Oaxaca, Mexico (Mendelson et al., 2005).
Ecological distribution: Dry forest, premontane evergreen forest, subtropical humid forest, savanna, and pine-oak forest from sea level to 2080 m.
Description: Largest Salvadoran specimen examined is 74.6 mm SVL; HW/SVL 0.36–0.45; HL/SVL 0.29–0.37; shank length/SVL 0.31–0.40; foot length/SVL 0.31–0.41; tympanum diameter/SVL 0.04–0.06; parotoid gland length/SVL 0.11–0.15; parotoid gland width/SVL 0.07–0.11; interparietal crest width/SVL 0.13–0.16; supratympanic crest length/SVL 0.04–0.07. Snout rounded to pointed in dorsal aspect, sloping to almost truncate in profile. Rostral keel distinct in some specimens. Canthal, preorbital, supraorbital, postorbital, parietal, supratympanic and pretympanic crests present. Nostrils directed dorsoposteriorly, canthus rostralis distinct; loreal region slightly concave; distinct supralabial crest, not extending length of upper jaw; tympanum distinct, ovoid, about 1/2 diameter of eye. Forelimbs slender, fingers short, relative length of

Plate 17: *Bufo coccifer* (KU 290030) EL SALVADOR: Morazán: Perquín (1150 m). Photo: E. Greenbaum.

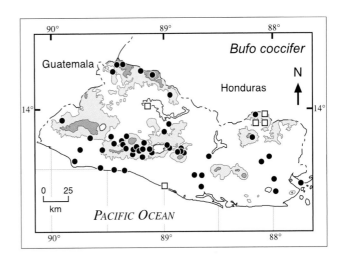

Map 9: Distribution of *Bufo coccifer* in El Salvador. Closed circles represent examined-specimen locality records; open squares are published locality records. Light shading indicates 600–1200 m elevation; dark shading indicates elevations ≥ 1200 m; large bodies of freshwater are outlined in bold, black lines.

fingers I < II < IV < III; finger webbing absent; finger tips not enlarged; palmar tubercle distinct, relatively flat, thenar tubercle smaller, ovoid, flattened; subarticular tubercles bifid to divided (fingers III, IV); supernumerary tubercles distinct, round. Hind limbs short, slender, tarsal fold absent; relative length of toes I < II < V < III < IV; outer metatarsal tubercle ovoid, flat, equal in size to inner metatarsal tubercle which is ovoid, raised; subarticular tubercles rounded, divided on toe IV; toes about 1/3 webbed; supernumerary tubercles equal in size, numerous, rounded; skin on dorsum smooth with many rounded tubercles turning sharply conical laterally in some specimens, otherwise rounded in profile; ventral surface and throat rugose with small conical tubercles; parotoid glands smaller or equal in size to eyelids, distinctly raised, ovoid; vomerine teeth and processes absent. Males with unilateral vocal slits.

Dorsum yellowish orange in life (only in calling males), yellowish, gray or olive in preserved specimens; dull brown blotches irregularly scattered on dorsal body and limb surfaces; parotoid glands orange, head usually with creamish interorbital bar, continuing onto upper eyelids; a dorsal thin cream longitudinal stripe from the tip of snout to the vent; venter cream, pale yellow or dirty yellowish orange, sometimes with irregular darker blotches.

Call: Porter (1965) and Mendelson et al. (2005) provided data for 14 toads from El Salvador with the following summarized data: duration of 3.0–16.3 seconds, frequency of 2200–2700 Hz, pulse rate of 80–101 per second.

Taxonomic comments: As this book went to press, Mendelson et al. (2005) split Central American populations of *Bufo coccifer* into six species based on calls, morphology, and molecular data. One of these newly recognized taxa, *B. ibarrai*, likely occurs in moderate elevations (1360–2020 m) of northwestern El Salvador. Some Salvadoran specimens of *B. coccifer* from Depto. Ahuachapán and Depto. Chalatenango were not available for reexamination by us following the publication of Mendelson et al. (2005), and thus our identifications must now be considered tentative.

Natural history: E. Greenbaum (field notes) collected a pair in amplexus as they crossed a road at night at Bosque Cinquera, Depto. Cabañas in August. O. Komar (field notes) recorded an individual during the day near pine-oak forest at Perquín, Depto. Morazán in June; M. Veselý (field notes) collected an individual from this same locality at night in late May. Mertens (1952d) observed numerous specimens of this toad in the vicinity of San Salvador, especially during the rainy season. The first calling males were recorded by him on 12 July. Rand (1957) described the mating calls and behavior of Salvadoran specimens collected between April and June. Nelson & Hoyt (1961) reported calling males at night during heavy rains in rain-filled temporary pools at San Salvador, Depto. San Salvador in June. Greding & Hellebuyck (1980) noted large amounts of Hymenoptera in the diet of three frogs collected at night at a pond in Depto. San Salvador in June. Savage (2002) noted 2000–4000 eggs are laid in two strings in single files.

Conservation status: Prior to the proposed taxonomic changes of Mendelson et al. (2005), the Global Amphibian Assessment classified this species as Least Concern (LC). Given the extensive distribution and tolerance for human disturbance of *Bufo coccifer* (sensu Mendelson et al. 2005), we do not see any justification for reclassifying this species as threatened.

Specimens examined: Ahuachapán: 1.6 km S Ahuachapán, Laguna El Espino [=Laguna El Llano]: TCWC 37787–96. Cabañas: Bosque Cinquera, 13°53.13′N, 88°57.36′W, 400 m: MUHNES C–30–1429, KU 289995. Chalatenango: Los Esesmiles, Cerro El Pital: SMF 44557 (1755 m elevation), 44558 (2080 m elevation); 16.5 km WNW Chalatenango: KU 184659–62; 10 km NE La Palma, Cantón Las Pilas: KU 184663–69. Cuscatlán: 7 km W Cojutepeque, 884 m: KU 97495; 6.5 km E El Carmen (17.5 km E Cojutepeque), 823 m: KU 97498; 2 km E Cojutepeque, 991 m: KU 97496; 8 km W Cojutupeque, 869 m: KU 97499–504; Cojutepeque, 982 m: KU 97505–09; 0.8 km SE Cojutepeque, 768 m: KU 97510–11; Tenancingo, Río Quezalapa: KU 184572–73. La Libertad: Finca El Paraíso near Nuevo San Salvador [= Santa Tecla]: SMF 4222; road San Salvador–Sonsonate, turnoff to Talnique, 520 m: SMF 52102–03; La Libertad: MUHNES 253, UF 48508; road San Salvador–Sonsonate, turnoff to Santa Ana: SMF 52104–06; Club Atami (near Playa El Palmarcito, Municipio Tamanique), 13°30.2′N, 89°25.0′W, 40 m: MUHNES C–30–1194; Laguna de Chanmico: UMMZ 118357; 16.1 km NW Nuevo San Salvador [= Santa Tecla]: KU 41411–29; 12.9 km WNW Nuevo San Salvador [= Santa Tecla]: KU 42623; 8.1 km W Colón: KU 97473–86; 8.7 km W La Libertad, 207 m: KU 97487–92; 10 km E La Libertad: KU 184612–13; Guadalupe, 640 m: KU 291372. La Unión: Laguna de Olomega: KU 184574; Puente Goascoran: TCWC 55703. Morazán: Montecristo Mine, 213 m: MVZ 39782–83, 39799; km 164 on the road San Miguel–San Francisco Gotera: SMF 42495; Cerro Cacahuatique: MUHNES 771, KU 291306–07; Perquín, 13°57.17′N, 88°10.01′W, 1150 m: KU 290021, 290030, 291321–22, 291335, MUHNES C–30–1233, C–30–1421–24. San Miguel: km 155 road San Miguel–La Unión: SMF 44559. San Salvador: 3.2 km S Río Lempa Bridge and intersection of Guazapa Hwy: UTA A-50497–98, 50501; San Bartolo, 11 km E San Salvador, 791 m: KU 97493; Finca Tino Castro near San Salvador: SMF 42201 (*); San Salvador, Instituto Tropical de

Investigaciones Científicas: SMF 43062–64, 44552–56, 48020–21, 51634, 52113–25, KU 61871–74; San Salvador, 65 Avenida Sur: SMF 42223–29, 42411–15, 42428–29; San Salvador: MUHNES 211–13, 244–50, 252, 254, USNM 167197; San Salvador, Parque Saburo-Hirao: MUHNES 214; San Salvador city limits: UTA A-50492–96, UMMZ 117585, 118358; San Salvador, Ciudad Universitaria, 700 m: KU 184610–11, 184614–58, 184715–16, UTA A-50504; 1.6 km NW San Salvador: KU 42613–20, 42624; 1.6 km S Los Planes de Renderos: KU 42621–22; 16 km E San Salvador, 878 m: KU 97494; 3 km SE Ilopango, Cantón Asino: KU 184575–77, 184670–74. Santa Ana: Metapán, Hacienda Los Planes de Montecristo: AMNH 125854; Hacienda San José, 800 m: KU 65372; Metapán: MUHNES 256. San Vicente: Cantón San Nicolás Lempa: UTA A-50505, 50507; 16 km E Cojutupeque, 610 m: KU 97734; 11.3 km E San Vicente on Pan American Hwy: MVZ 76087–90; Lempa bridge: SMF 52126–75; road San Salvador–San Miguel, turnoff to San Vicente: SMF 52176–77; Cantón San Judas: MUHNES 257; 1 km E El Carmen (12 km E Cojutepeque), 799 m: KU 97497. Sonsonate: Morrotal on the road to Los Cobanos, 1 km S of road Sonsonate–Acajutla: SMF 44551; Acajutla: UF 104622; Hacienda Cuyan-Cuya near Izalco: SMF 42554–60; Hacienda San Antonio near Sonsonate: SMF 48044; Hacienda Chilata 5 km S San Julián, 500 m: SMF 52097–101. Usulután: San Marcos Lempa, Nancuchiname: MUHNES 241–42, UF 48510.

Published locality records: Porter (1965) illustrated five localities for this species in El Salvador, but precise localities were not provided, which precluded their inclusion for distribution maps. La Paz: 6 km N Los Blancos (Rand 1957). Morazán: Município Arambala, Cantón Cumaro, Bailadero del Diablo (13.931°N, 88.102°W), 696 m: YPM 7230 (Leenders & Watkins-Colwell 2004); Município Arambala, Cantón Cumaro, Nahuaterique, near border crossing with Honduras (13.995°N, 88.093°W), 1389 m: YPM 7227–29 (Leenders & Watkins-Colwell 2004); Município Arambala, Cantón Cumaro, Río Sapo (13.959°N, 88.132°W), 1118 m: YPM 7231 (Leenders & Watkins-Colwell 2004). San Salvador: 3.2 km SW of a bridge over the Río Lempa on the highway between San Salvador and La Palma, 270 m (Greding & Hellebuyck 1980).

Bufo luetkenii Boulenger 1891
(Sapo Amarillo)
Plate 18, Map 10, Figures 4c, 15b

Plate 18: *Bufo luetkenii* (KU 289749) EL SALVADOR: Ahuachapán: Parque Nacional El Imposible, La Fincona (720 m). Photo: E. Greenbaum.

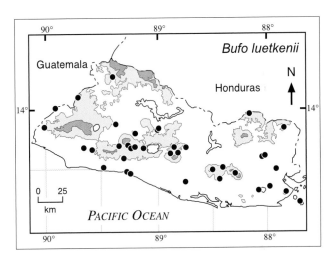

Map 10: Distribution of *Bufo luetkenii* in El Salvador. Closed circles represent examined-specimen locality records; open squares are published locality records. Light shading indicates 600–1200 m elevation; dark shading indicates elevations ≥ 1200 m; large bodies of freshwater are outlined in bold, black lines.

1891 *Bufo luetkenii* Boulenger, Ann. Mag. Nat. Hist. 8(6): 455; type locality: Cartago, Costa Rica.
Bufo valliceps: Mertens 1952d, Rand 1957, Porter 1970 (in part), Köhler 2003a.
Bufo luetkenii: Villa et al. 1988, Haas & Köhler 1997, Köhler et al. 2000, Dueñas et al. 2001, D. Frost 2002, 2004, Leenders 2003.

Geographic distribution: From southeastern Guatemala along the Pacific versant to northwestern Costa Rica; dry interior valleys on the Atlantic versant of Guatemala and Honduras (McCranie & Wilson 2002).

Ecological distribution: Dry forest, premontane evergreen forest, subtropical humid forest, and savanna from sea level to 1300 m.

Description: Largest Salvadoran specimen examined is 98.5 mm SVL; HW/SVL 0.33–0.38; HL/SVL 0.27–0.34; shank length/SVL 0.32–0.39; foot length/SVL 0.33–0.37; tympanum diameter/SVL 0.05–0.07; parotoid gland length/SVL 0.07–0.11; parotoid gland width/SVL 0.04–0.07; interparietal crest width/SVL 0.12–0.14; supratympanic crest length/SVL 0.04–0.07. Snout pointed in dorsal view, truncate in profile; canthal, preorbital, supraorbital, postorbital, parietal, supratympanic and pretympanic crests distinct; supralabial crest distinct, extending from point under the anterior border of orbit to the corner of the jaw; nostrils directed dorsally, canthus rostralis distinct; loreal region slightly concave; tympanum distinct, ovoid, about 2/3 diameter of eye. Forelimbs relatively robust; fingers short and stout, relative length of fingers IV < II < I < III; finger webbing absent; tips of fingers not enlarged; palmar tubercle distinct, large, ovoid and flat; thenar tubercle ovoid, low, about half size of palmar tubercle; subarticular tubercles distinct only on first two fingers, enlarged, raised. Numerous supernumerary tubercles, differing in size, rounded, subconical; in sexually active males nuptial thumb pad with dark brown excrescences. Hind limbs short, stout, inner tarsal fold absent, replaced by row of keeled, subconical tubercles; outer metatarsal tubercle small, rounded, flat, smaller than inner metatarsal tubercle which is almost spade-shaped; toes short, stout, relative length of toes: I < II < V < III < IV; only basal webbing present, subarticular tubercles small, single, spinelike; supernumerary tubercles subconical, small, equal in size. Dorsum smooth with numerous small conical tubercles, most lateral ones and those on limbs bearing single, keratinized apices; parotoid glands very small, less than 1/2 area of upper eyelid; barely distinct lateral rows of slightly enlarged tubercles; skin on throat and venter covered with minute conical tubercles. Males with unilateral vocal slits.

Coloration variable; in most females, dorsum reddish brown, orange to olive green, mostly with two darker, violet brown or reddish brown triangular marks on dorsum, separated from each other by a creamish middorsal stripe. Males usually olive green or dark green, but in breeding season with bright yellow dorsal color and black cranial crests. Venter in both sexes uniformly white or cream.

Call: Porter (1966) described the call of *Bufo luetkenii* as a trill of 19–22 notes per second with a frequency of 1650–1950 Hz and a call length of 3.2–5.2 seconds.

Natural history: E. Greenbaum (field notes) found this species (along with *B. marinus*) around human habitations at Parque Nacional El Imposible, Depto. Ahuachapán and in great numbers at Cerro del Tigre, Depto. Usulután in July. Males in breeding color were recorded from Cerro del Tigre in July. M. Veselý (field notes) observed bright-yellow calling males and mating pairs in natural ponds of a small stream and a swimming pool at Club Atami, Depto. La Libertad during the first rains in late May. Rand (1957) reported calling males at Instituto Tropical, Depto. San Salvador in May and June. McCranie & Wilson (2002) described breeding adults in temporary ponds and river overflows in June and October in Honduras; a tadpole lot was noted in April.

Conservation status: GAA: Least concern (LC).

Specimens examined: Ahuachapán: El Refugio, vicinity of Mariposario of Francisco Serrano, 13°49.46′N, 89°59.98′W, 225 m: SMF 79240; Parque Nacional El Imposible, La Fincona, 13°50.8′N, 89°58.8′W, 720 m: SMF 78069, SMF 81436–40, 81443, MUHNES 1095, KU 289749; Las Chimanas: UTA A-49362. Cuscatlán: 20.3 km E Cojutepeque, 701 m: KU 97735; Tenancingo, El Sitio de los Sánchez: KU 184675–79; 3.2 km NE Tenancingo: KU 184690–91. La Libertad: Río Amayo: UTA A-50420; Hacienda La Argentina near San Juan Opico: UTA A-50423; La Libertad, Club Atami (near Playa El Palmarcito, Municipio Tamanique): AMNH 125854, CAS 188353; 10 km E La Libertad: KU 184689; Los Chorros, 4.8 km W Nuevo San Salvador [= Santa Tecla]: UF 20422–25; Guadalupe, 640 m: MUHNES C–30–1425. La Unión: road from La Unión to Conchagua: SMF 44562; Bosque del Monte at Maculis, 10 km SE Turnoff Carretera Litoral, 8.5 km from El Tamarindo: MVZ 143987; 28 km NNW Sirama, 190 m: KU 65512; El Carmen, 300 m: KU 65513–14; Isla Meanguera: MUHNES 269–70. Morazán: Montecristo Mine, 213 m: MVZ 39798; Divisadero, 244 m: USNM 73283; Perquín, 13°57.17′N, 88°10.01′W, 1150 m: KU 290031, 291356. San Miguel: Laguna de Olomega, 61 m: MVZ 39797; Volcán de San Miguel, 740 m: KU 291265–68, MUHNES C–30–1427–28. San Salvador: Río Acelhuate near Apopa: SMF 42433, 42474; San Salvador, Instituto Tropical de Investigaciones Científicas: SMF 44560–61; San Salvador, Parque Zoológico Nacional: MUHNES 1160; San Salvador: UMMZ 118348; San Salvador, 670 m: FMNH 65046; San Salvador, 700 m: FMNH 65044–45, 65047; 3 km SE Ilopango, Cantón Asino: KU 184680–88. Santa

Ana: San Juan Mine, 12.1 km SE Metapán, 488 m: MVZ 39796; Candelaria de la Frontera: UMMZ 118347. San Vicente: Finca El Carmen, 13°36.8´N, 88°50.3´W, 1240 m: SMF 81441; 6 km E El Carmen, 918 m: KU 97736; 7 km E El Carmen, 823 m: KU 97737; Barranca del Sisimico, near San Vicente, 350 m: FMNH 65043. Sonsonate: Hacienda La Puerta near Sonsonate: UTA A-50421; Hacienda Chilata, 610 m: MVZ 39781. Usulután: Jucuapa, Beneficio San José, 650 m: SMF 42927; Laguna Alegría, 13°29.3´N, 88°29.9´W, 1300 m: SMF 81442; Cerro del Tigre, 13°28.37´N, 88°26.21´W, 1100 m: KU 289850, 289852–55, MUHNES C–30–1234–37.

Bufo marinus (Linnaeus 1758)

(Sapo Lechero)

Plate 19, Map 11, Figures 4d, 15c

1758 *Rana marina* Linnaeus, Systema Naturae, ed. 10: 214; type locality: America; restricted to Surinam by Müller & Hellmich (1936: Wiss. Ergebn. Deutsch. Gran Chaco-Exped., Amph. Rept.: 4).

Bufo marinus: Mertens 1952d, Rand 1957, Nelson & Hoyt 1961, Greding & Hellebuyck 1980, Easteal 1986, Villa et al. 1988, Dueñas et al. 2001, Leenders 2003, Leenders & Watkins-Colwell 2004.

Geographic distribution: From extreme southern Texas (USA) through Mexico and Central America to Bolivia, Peru, and Brazil. Introduced to many localities in the tropics worldwide (D. Frost 2002, 2004, Meshaka et al. 2004).

Ecological distribution: This species is virtually ubiquitous in the lowlands of El Salvador; it occurs from sea level to about 1250 m.

Description: Largest Salvadoran specimen examined is 165.0 mm SVL; HW/SVL 0.34–0.40; HL/SVL 0.26–0.32; shank length/SVL 0.33–0.41; foot length/SVL 0.28–0.40; tympanum diameter/SVL 0.04–0.06; parotoid gland length/SVL 0.23–0.34; parotoid gland width/SVL 0.17–0.25; interparietal crest width/SVL 0.12–0.17; supratympanic crest length/SVL 0.03–0.06. Snout rounded or slightly pointed in dorsal view, bluntly rounded in profile; canthal, preorbital, supraorbital, postorbital, and supratympanic crests present, pretympanic crest short, temporal crest absent, rostral keel barely visible; nostrils directed dorsolaterally; canthus rostralis distinct; loreal region concave; supralabial crest indistinct, about 2/3 of eye diameter. Limbs short and robust, relative length of fingers II ~ IV < I < III; tips of fingers not enlarged; finger webbing absent; palmar tubercle

Plate 19: *Bufo marinus* EL SALVADOR: Ahuachapán: El Refugio (225 m). Photo: G. Köhler.

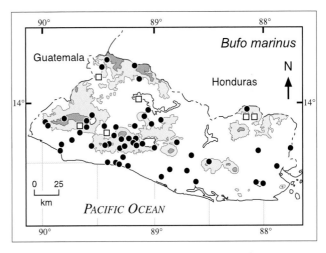

Map 11: Distribution of *Bufo marinus* in El Salvador. Closed circles represent examined-specimen locality records; open squares are published locality records. Light shading indicates 600–1200 m elevation; dark shading indicates elevations ≥ 1200 m; large bodies of freshwater are outlined in bold, black lines.

large, irregular, flat, about twice as large as pollical tubercle which is ovoid and flat; subarticular tubercles distinct, bifid, elevated, triangular in profile, that on first finger largest; supernumerary tubercles differing in size. Toes with basal webbing; relative length of toes I < II < V < III < IV; distinct inner tarsal fold present; outer metatarsal tubercle large, ovoid, equal in size to inner one which is spade-shaped; subarticular tubercles single, rounded, supernumerary tubercles rounded, differing in size. Dorsum with numerous, irregularly scattered warts and tubercles; parotoid glands large, ovoid, extending posteriorly onto shoulder; venter granular, posteriorly with enlarged tu-

bercles, longitudinally wrinkled in larger specimens. Males with bilateral vocal slits.

Males usually tan above and laterally, with
scattered pale tan spots; females with mottled pattern on dorsum and flanks. Venter dirty yellow.
Call: Campbell (1998a) described the call of this
species as a "loud, rolling trill." Described as "a
protracted, low-pitched trill with a dominant
frequency of 650–800 Hz and a pulse rate of about
15–20 pulses per second" by Lee (1996). According
to Savage (2002), the call of *B. marinus* is "usually
long, 10 to 20 seconds, with ten or so trills."
Natural history: E. Greenbaum (field notes)
recorded this species at numerous lowland localities
near human habitations throughout El Salvador
from July–August. Mertens (1952d) recorded
breeding activity (including calling males) from
early July through late October in El Salvador.
Rand (1957) described dry-season breeding activity
in Salvadoran animals. Nelson & Hoyt (1961)
reported calling males at night during heavy rains
in rain-filled temporary pools at San Salvador,
Depto. San Salvador in June. Campbell (1998a)
noted that this species will eat "almost anything
that moves and can be swallowed" including
arthropods and small vertebrates. Breeding may
occur throughout the year, but eggs (5000–25,000
per clutch) and tadpoles have been observed from
March–July. McCranie & Wilson (2002) reported
breeding activity in this species in temporary pools,
along rivers, and inundated areas from May–
November in Honduras; tadpoles were noted from
this same general time. Leenders & Watkins-
Colwell (2004) noted calling males in January in El
Salvador.
Conservation status: GAA: Least concern (LC).
Specimens examined: Ahuachapán: Laguna
Verde: SMF 47940–42; Finca Concepción Miramar,
13°48.46´N, 89°48.03´W, 920 m: KU 289934; Parque
Nacional El Imposible: MUHNES 1104; Parque
Nacional El Imposible, La Fincona, 13°50.8´N,
89°58.8´W, 720 m: KU 289750, 289757; El Refugio,
vicinity of Mariposario of Francisco Serrano,
13°49.46´N, 89°59.98´W, 225 m: SMF 81278.
Cabañas: Bosque Cinquera, 13°53.13´N, 88°57.36´W,
400 m: KU 289991–92, MUHNES C–30–1238.
Chalatenango: La Palma, 1000 m: SMF 52182–83;
1.6 km N Tejutla: UTA A-50499. Cuscatlán: Finca
on the eastern slopes of Cerro de Guazapa, 800 m:
SMF 44540; 2.4 km E Tenancingo, Río Quezalapa:
KU 184692; 2.9 km N Suchitoto: UU 7943. La
Libertad: Laguna de Chanmico,480 m: SMF 42633–

65, 47927–35; around Jayaque, 800 m: SMF 42261;
Finca San José, 1200 m, near Nuevo San Salvador
[= Santa Tecla]: SMF 42879–80; Finca El Paraíso
near Nuevo San Salvador [= Santa Tecla]: SMF
42313, 42618 (tadpoles), 42708, 42849, 42875, 42941;
Río Chilama, W of La Libertad: SMF 42398–99,
42408, 44495–516; 8 km E La Libertad, Hacienda
San Diego: SMF 52184–85; road San Salvador–
Sonsonate, turnoff to Santa Ana: SMF 52186–88;
Hacienda Zapotitán, 457 m: MVZ 39807; Finca La
Giralda, 13°39.34´N, 89°22.47´W, 1080 m: KU
289949; Club Atami (near Playa El Palmarcito,
Municipio Tamanique): AMNH 125856, UF 48509;
10 km E La Libertad: KU 184706; Hacienda
Belmar, ca. La Libertad: LACM 9371–72;
Guadalupe, 640 m: KU 291371, 291373, MUHNES
C–30–1429–30; 2 km S Zaragoza, Cantón
Guadalupe, 13°33.1´N, 89°17.3´W, 740 m: YPM
6446. La Paz: 6 km N La Herradura: SMF 44541–
50; Amatecampo: SMF 47953–56. La Unión: Laguna
de Olomega: KU 184694–705; Puente Goascoran:
TCWC 55672–73. Morazán: Montecristo Mine, 213
m: MVZ 39793–94; Perquín, 13°57.17´N,
88°10.01´W, 1150 m: KU 290032–34, 291338–39,
291350, MUHNES C–30–1431–32. San Miguel:
Laguna de Olomega, 61 m: MVZ 39780, 39785–91.
San Salvador: San Salvador, Parque Zoológico
Nacional, 13°58.8´N, 89°11.9´W, 700 m: KU 289772,
289812–13, 289822–24, MUHNES C–30–1239–41, C–
30–1247–50, SMF 81456–58; San Salvador, Instituto
Tropical de Investigaciones Científicas: SMF 44517–
19, 47943–47, 52189, 81365–66; San Salvador,
Colónia America, Villa Margarita: SMF 44918–20;
San Salvador, Barranca on 65 Avenida Sur: SMF
42579; Lago de Ilopango near Asino: SMF 44520–39;
Río Acelhuate near Apopa, 500 m: SMF 42473; Lago
de Ilopango: SMF 47939; 1.6 km NW San Salvador:
KU 42474; 3 km SE Ilopango, Cantón Asino: KU
184707, 184717–22; San Salvador, Ciudad
Universitaria, 700 m: KU 184713–14. Santa Ana:
Municipio Metapán, ca. Lago Güija, 450 m: YPM
6445; Hacienda San José near Metapán: SMF
47936–38; Lago Coatepeque: AMNH 62214, 62218,
62222; 6 km S Metapán: KU 184708–12. San
Vicente: road San Salvador–San Miguel, turnoff to
San Vicente: SMF 52190–92; San Lorenzo, near Río
Lempa, 1 km N Pan Am Highway: FMNH 197987–
88. Sonsonate: Hacienda San Antonio near
Sonsonate: SMF 42494, 47948–52; Hacienda
Chilata, 5 km S of San Julián, 550 m: SMF 52178–
81; same locality at 610 m: MVZ 39795, 39800–06;
Hacienda Cuyan-Cuya, near Izalco, 380 m: SMF

43005–09; Acajutla: UF 45085–87; Bosque Las
Lajas, 13°50.04´N, 89°33.56´W, 920 m: KU 289868.
Usulután: Cerro del Tigre, 13°28.37´N, 88°26.21´W,
1100 m: KU 289846–49, MUHNES C–30–1242–46,
C–30–1251; Río Lempa at RR bridge: USNM 66944–
45.

Published locality records: Ahuachapán: Parque
Nacional El Imposible: YPM 6443 (Leenders &
Watkins-Colwell 2004); Município San Pedro Puxtla,
Cantón La Concepción, Cooperativa Concepción
Miramar (13.810°N, 89.807°W), 1000 m (Leenders &
Watkins-Colwell 2004). La Libertad: Município La
Libertad, 2 km S Zaragoza, Río San Antonio
(13.552°N, 89.288°W), 740 m: YPM 6446–47
(Leenders & Watkins-Colwell 2004). Morazán:
Município Arambala, Cantón Cumaro, Bailadero del
Diablo (13.931°N, 88.102°W), 696 m: YPM 7224
(Leenders & Watkins-Colwell 2004); Município
Arambala, Cantón Cumaro, Río Sapo (13.959°N,
88.132°W), 1118 m: YPM 7223, 7225–26 (Leenders &
Watkins-Colwell 2004). San Salvador: 3.2 km SW of
a bridge over the Río Lempa on the highway
between San Salvador and La Palma, 270 m
(Greding & Hellebuyck 1980). Santa Ana: Município
Metapán, E side Volcán San Diego, Area Protegida
San Diego y La Barra (14.262°N, 89.470°W), 450 m:
YPM 6445 (Leenders & Watkins-Colwell 2004).
Sonsonate: Município Izalco, Cantón Las Lajas,
Bosque Las Lajas (13.829°N, 89.567°W), 750 m:
YPM 6417–18, 6425, 6441–42, 6444 (Leenders &
Watkins-Colwell 2004); Município Izalco, Cantón
Cruz Grande, Finca Nuevos Horizontes (13.821°N,
89.653°W), 1250 m (Leenders & Watkins-Colwell
2004).

Bufo valliceps Wiegmann 1833
(Sapo Costero)
Plate 20, Map 12, Figure 4e

1833 *Bufo valliceps* Wiegmann, Isis von Oken 26:
657–659; type locality: "Mexico and Vera Cruz,
Mexico."
Bufo valliceps: McCranie & Wilson 2002, Köhler
2003a, Leenders 2003, D. Frost 2004.
Geographic distribution: Along the Atlantic
versant from central Veracruz (south of Palma
Sola), Mexico, to northern Costa Rica, and on the
Pacific versant from the Isthmus of Tehuantepec to
extreme western El Salvador (Mulcahy &
Mendelson 2000).
Ecological distribution: Subtropical humid forest
around 700 m.

Plate 20: *Bufo valliceps* (KU 55905) GUATEMALA:
Alta Verapaz: Chinajá. Photo: W. E. Duellman (KU CT
1279).

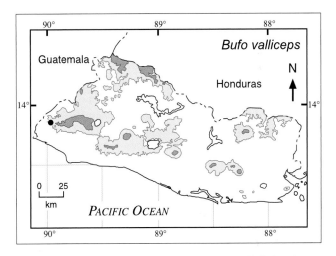

Map 12: Distribution of *Bufo valliceps* in El Salvador.
Closed circles represent examined-specimen locality records;
open squares are published locality records. Light shading
indicates 600–1200 m elevation; dark shading indicates elevations ≥ 1200 m; large bodies of freshwater are outlined in bold,
black lines.

Description: The only known specimen of this
species from El Salvador (SMF 81319) has a SVL of
52.4 mm; HW/SVL 0.35; HL/SVL 0.31; shank
length/SVL 0.44; foot length/SVL 0.43; tympanum
diameter/SVL 0.05; parotoid gland length/SVL 0.14;
parotoid gland width/SVL 0.09; interparietal crest
width/SVL 0.14; supratympanic crest length/SVL
0.06. Snout pointed in dorsal view, truncate in
profile; canthal, preorbital, supraorbital, postorbital, parietal, supratympanic and pretympanic
crests distinct; supralabial crest distinct, extending
from the point under the anterior border of orbit to
the corner of the jaw; nostrils directed

dorsolaterally, canthus rostralis distinct; loreal region slightly concave; tympanum distinct, ovoid, about 1/2 diameter of eye. Forelimbs relatively robust; fingers short and stout, relative length of fingers IV ~ II < I < III; finger webbing absent; tips of fingers not enlarged; palmar tubercle distinct, large, ovoid and flat; thenar tubercle ovoid, low, about half size of palmar tubercle; subarticular tubercles distinct only on first two fingers, enlarged, raised. Numerous supernumerary tubercles, differing in size, rounded, subconical; in sexually active males nuptial thumb pad with dark-brown excrescences. Hind limbs short, slender, inner tarsal fold absent, replaced by row of keeled, subconical tubercles; outer metatarsal tubercle small, rounded, flat, smaller than inner metatarsal tubercle which is almost spade-shaped; toes short, stout, relative length of toes: I < II < V < III < IV; toe webbing moderately developed, subarticular tubercles small, single, spinelike; supernumerary tubercles subconical, small, equal in size. Dorsum smooth with numerous small conical tubercles, most lateral ones and those on limbs bearing single, keratinized apices; parotoid glands ovoid to slightly triangular, of moderate size, slightly larger than area of upper eyelid; distinct lateral row of slightly enlarged tubercles present; skin on throat and venter covered with minute conical tubercles. Males with relatively large bilateral vocal slits.

In preservative, ground color of head, body, and limbs brown with a narrow dark brown interorbital bar and a pair of dark brown paramedian middorsal blotches; dorsal surface of shank with an oblique dark brown bar.

Call: Porter (1964b) noted the overall mean pulse rate for this species was 38.44 notes per second, and the mean frequency was 1828 Hz. Length of calls ranged from 1.96 to 7.13 seconds after correcting for temperature. Campbell (1998a) described the call of this species as a "short trill."

Natural history: Campbell (1998a) noted that breeding occurs from February–July, but this species might breed throughout the year. McCranie & Wilson (2002) commented that this species is often found in "open areas," including human-disturbed areas. Calling males were recorded from small ponds from June–November; tadpoles were noted from June–July.

Conservation status: GAA: Least concern (LC).

Specimens examined: <u>Ahuachapán</u>: Parque Nacional El Imposible, La Fincona, 13°50.8´N, 89°58.8´W, 720 m: SMF 81319.

Family Centrolenidae

The Glass Frogs are distributed from southern Mexico to Bolivia, southeastern Brazil and north-eastern Argentina, and are represented by approximately 140 species in three genera (McCranie & Wilson 2002, Wild 2003). One genus is represented in El Salvador.

Genus *Hyalinobatrachium*

Thirty-seven species are included in this genus, which has a distribution identical to the family Centrolenidae (D. Frost 2004). McDiarmid & Altig (1999) classified the larvae of this genus as exotrophic, lotic burrowers. One species is found in El Salvador.

Hyalinobatrachium fleischmanni (Boettger 1893)
(Rana de Vidrio Norteña)
Plate 21, Map 13, Figure 15d

1893 *Hylella fleischmanni* Boettger, Ber. Senckenb. Naturforsch. Ges. 1892–1893(1893): 251; type locality: San José, Costa Rica.
Centrolenella fleischmanni: Hidalgo 1982a, Villa et al. 1988.
Hyalinobatrachium fleischmanni: Dueñas et al. 2001.

Geographic distribution: From Guerrero and Veracruz, Mexico, through Central America to Colombia, Guyana, and Surinam (D. Frost 2002, 2004).

Ecological distribution: Subtropical humid forest around 1200 m.

Description: The only known specimen of this species from El Salvador (MUHNES 30-859; not examined by us) is a male with a SVL of 24.9 mm (Hidalgo 1982a). Morphometric data for Honduran and Nicaraguan specimens (SMF collection) are HW/SVL 0.34–0.42; HL/SVL 0.27–0.33; snout length/SVL 0.12–0.16; shank length/SVL 0.50–0.59; foot length/SVL 0.40–0.49. Rounded head with a weakly pointed snout in dorsal view (truncate in lateral view), eyes not protuberant, tympanum not evident externally, webbing between outer fingers III 2 – 1½ IV, webbing on foot I 1 – 2⁻ II 0 – 2 III 1 – 2⁺ IV 2⁺ – 1 V, absence of dermal folds along arms and legs, bones white, absence of vomerine teeth, a clear parietal peritoneum, and a white visceral peritoneum (Lynch & Duellman 1973, Starrett & Savage 1973). This species is

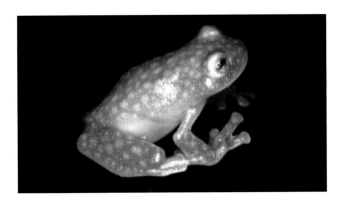

Plate 21: *Hyalinobatrachium fleischmanni* COSTA RICA: Cartago: Tapantí (1200 m). Photo: W. E. Duellman (KU CT 1492).

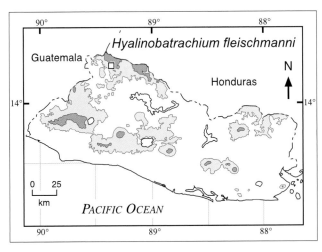

Map 13: Distribution of *Hyalinobatrachium fleischmanni* in El Salvador.
Closed circles represent examined-specimen locality records; open squares are published locality records. Light shading indicates 600–1200 m elevation; dark shading indicates elevations ≥ 1200 m; large bodies of freshwater are outlined in bold, black lines.

pale green with pale yellow spots in life (cream with faint brown flecks in preservative).
Call: Campbell (1998a) described the mating call of this species as a short, high-pitched peep which can be distinguished from the "mew-like" peeps of the territorial calls. Described as "a single rising untrilled wheet" by Starrett & Savage (1973).
Natural history: The only specimen of this species collected in El Salvador was found under a leaf of a bush along a fast-moving stream in December (Hidalgo 1982a). This species does not persist in areas that are disturbed by human activities (J. Campbell pers. comm.) and might explain why it

has been found at only one locality in El Salvador. This widespread species usually occurs in tropical and subtropical wet forest near streams; breeding is noted from May–October, and males are territorial (Campbell 1998a). This author also noted that females lay 14–90 greenish and yellow eggs per clutch. McCranie & Wilson (2002) noted that males call in vegetation from 2–10 m above flowing streams in Honduras (July–August), which makes them difficult to locate. Savage (2002) commented that males are territorial; clutches of 10–50 eggs are laid on the underside of leaves. Males exhibit hydric brooding behavior of the eggs at night; larvae are fossorial.
Conservation status: GAA: Least concern (LC).
Published locality records: <u>Santa Ana</u>: Cantón Montenegro, 14.1 km W Metapán, 1686 m: MUHNES 30-859 (Hidalgo 1982a). **NOTE:** The preceding locality is erroneous. According to V. J. Hellebuyck (pers. comm.), this specimen was collected 15.0 km E Metapán, Cantón Montenegro, Municipio de Metapán, 1200 m.

Family Hylidae

Forty-two genera and approximately 855 species of this family are located from Canada to Argentina in the New World (excluding Arctic North America and southern Argentina), the Greater Antilles, Eurasia, northern Africa, the Australo-Papuan region, and several islands in the Atlantic Ocean (McCranie & Wilson 2002, Duellman 2003c). The phylogenetic relationships of these primarily arboreal frogs are poorly known (Duellman 2003c). New species have been described every year in the last few decades, and many more undoubtedly await description. Seven genera and ten species of hylids occur in El Salvador.

Genus *Agalychnis*

This genus of colorful Leaf Frogs occurs from southern Mexico to Amazonian Ecuador. Eight species are included in this genus, one of which occurs in El Salvador (D. Frost 2002, 2004).

Agalychnis moreletii (Duméril 1853)
(Rana-hoja de Montaña)
Plate 22, Map 14, Figures 5ab, 15e

1853 *Hyla moreletii* Duméril, Ann. Sci. Nat., Paris, 19(3): 169; type locality: Verapaz, Guatemala.

Plate 22: *Agalychnis moreletii* (KU 289773–75) EL SALVADOR: Santa Ana: Finca El Milagro (1300 m). Pair in amplexus. Photo: E. Greenbaum.

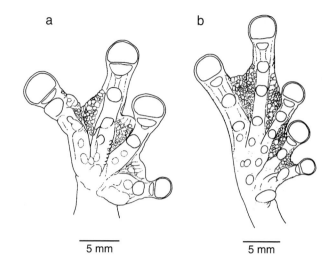

Figure 5: *Agalychnis moreletii* (SMF 78932): a. ventral view of right hand, b. ventral view of right foot.

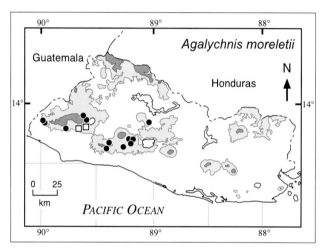

Map 14: Distribution of *Agalychnis moreletii* in El Salvador.

Closed circles represent examined-specimen locality records; open squares are published locality records. Light shading indicates 600–1200 m elevation; dark shading indicates elevations ≥ 1200 m; large bodies of freshwater are outlined in bold, black lines.

Agalychnis moreletii: Mertens 1952d, Duellman 1970, 2001, Villa et al. 1988, Campbell 1998a, Dueñas et al. 2001, D. Frost 2002, 2004, McCranie & Wilson 2002, Leenders 2003, Leenders & Watkins-Colwell 2004.

Geographic distribution: From northeastern Puebla and south-central Veracruz, Mexico, to northwestern Honduras on the Atlantic versant; from south-central Guerrero, Mexico, to central El Salvador on the Pacific versant (McCranie & Wilson 2002).

Ecological distribution: Dry forest, premontane evergreen forest, and subtropical humid forest, usually near streams, ponds, and lakes at elevations of 200–1795 m.

Description: Largest Salvadoran specimen is 75.0 mm SVL (Leenders & Watkins-Colwell 2004); HW/SVL 0.31–0.37; HL/SVL 0.33–0.37; shank length/SVL 0.43–0.51; foot length/SVL 0.36–0.39; tympanum diameter/SVL 0.05–0.06. Snout acuminate in dorsal aspect, sloping in profile; top of head flat or slightly concave, nostrils directed laterally, situated about two thirds of the distance between eyes and tip of snout; canthus rostralis rounded; loreal area concave; supratympanic fold present, extending from the posterior edge of eye around the upper and posterior margin of ear, almost touching angle of jaw; tympanum visible. Forelimbs robust, large; rounded disc on all fingers, equal or slightly larger than tympanum (except digit I is smaller); subarticular tubercles medium-sized and rounded, the distal ones on digits III and IV bifid; no distinct palmar tubercle; thumb pad in sexually active males bearing brown nuptial excrescences dorsally; relative length of fingers I < II < IV < III, finger webbing formula I 2⁻ – 2 II 1½ – 2⁺ III 2⁻ – 2⁻ IV. Hind limbs slender; weak dermal ridge extending along posterior ventrolateral edge of tarsus; inner tarsal fold generally present, but sometimes barely visible; relative length of toes I < II < III < V < IV; terminal disc slightly increasing in size from toe I to toe V; subarticular tubercles moderately large, rounded; inner metatarsal tubercle distinctly

keeled; modal webbing formula of toes I 2⁻ –
2 II 1⁺ – 3 III 3⁻ – 3 IV 3⁻ – 1 V; skin on dorsum,
head and dorsal surfaces of limbs smooth, skin on
belly and ventral surface of thighs granular; 10–16
vomerine teeth on small, widely separated processes between choanae; vocal sac single, median.

In life, dorsum bright green with or without
several white flecks; venter creamy yellow; flanks,
anterior and posterior surfaces of thighs, inner
surface of shanks, tarsi and forearms, upper arms,
first three fingers and first four toes orange; stripes
on the outer edges of forearm and tarsi white; iris
dull red or maroon; palpebral membrane reticu-
lated with gold. In preserved specimens, dorsum
dark to pale blue; the rest creamy white. White
flecks on dorsum remain without color changes.
Call: The call of this species resembles "woorp"
which may be repeated at intervals of one to
several minutes. The notes last for 0.09–0.27
second, and have a pulse rate of 55–61 pulses per
second; each note consists of 3–6 pulses. The
frequency spectrum is 1000–7500 Hz (Duellman
1970, 2001).

Natural history: E. Greenbaum (field notes)
recorded great numbers of this species calling
and in amplexus in man-made water basins (i.e.,
"pilas") in coffee plantations at Finca El Milagro,
Depto. Santa Ana at night in the rainy season;
Physalaemus pustulosus were breeding in these
same pools. Mertens (1952d) described how
these frogs sleep while attached to green leaves
during the day. According to his observations, the
calls of male *Agalychnis moreletii* are heard only
during the rainy season. On 7 September, he found
the egg masses (each the size of a human thumb
and containing 60–200 eggs) between the leaves of
Gliricidia sepium overhanging water. About eight
days after egg deposition, the larvae hatched and
dropped or jumped into the water beneath the
leaves (Mertens 1952d). Campbell (1998a) noted
breeding from May–August; females lay 25–75
greenish and cream eggs per clutch. McCranie &
Wilson (2002) recorded adults on vegetation overhanging a lake in Honduras. Leenders (2003)
commented that this species is often found at
night near man-made water basins and natural
pools at Parque Nacional El Imposible, Depto.
Ahuachapán. Leenders & Watkins-Colwell (2004)
noted calling males in January, February,
October, and November; gravid females were noted
in January and February in El Salvador.
Metamorphs were found in January and November

suggesting this species breeds year-round in El
Salvador.
Conservation status: GAA: Critically endangered
(CR A3e).
Specimens examined: Ahuachapán: Finca
Concepción Miramar, 13°48.46′N, 89°48.03′W, 920
m: KU 289920 (tadpoles); El Refugio, vicinity of
Mariposario of Francisco Serrano, 13°49.46′N,
89°59.98′W, 225 m: SMF 78932; Parque Nacional El
Imposible, La Fincona, 13°50.8′N, 89°58.8′W, 720
m: SMF 81328–29. Cuscatlán: Tenancingo, Cantón
El Tablón, 1500 m: KU 184724. La Libertad: near
Finca Los Angeles, La Cumbre, 1500 m: SMF
42851–63 (tadpoles), 42931 (tadpole), 43122–30
(juv.); Finca El Paraíso near Nuevo San Salvador [=
Santa Tecla]: SMF 42204, 42668–71, 42673, 42682–
99 (tadpoles), 42700–01, 42703, 42714, 42716,
42717–91 (tadpoles), 42818–42 (tadpoles), 42935,
43121; Finca La Giralda, 13°39.34′N, 89°22.47′W,
1080 m: KU 289955, 289963, 289964 (tadpoles). San
Salvador: San Antonio near San Salvador: SMF
43162; San Salvador, Instituto Tropical de
Investigaciones Científicas: SMF 49624; San Salvador: ZMB 35723. Santa Ana: Volcán de Santa Ana,
Finca Los Andes, 13°52.1′N, 89°37.2′W: MUHNES
1215, SMF 81330, VH 75; Finca El Milagro,
13°53.29′N, 89°37.17′W, 1300 m: KU 289773–78,
289782 (tadpoles), 289785, 290050, MUHNES C–30–
1422–28.
Published locality records: Ahuachapán: Parque
Nacional El Imposible: YPM 6414, 6422–23, 6457,
7222, 7286–89 (Leenders & Watkins-Colwell 2004);
Município San Pedro Puxtla, Cantón La
Concepción, Cooperativa Concepción Miramar
(13.810°N, 89.807°W), 950 m (Leenders & Watkins-
Colwell 2004). Santa Ana: Município Santa Ana,
Cantón Los Flores, Parque Nacional Los Andes and
Volcán Santa Ana (13.869°N, 89.620°W), 1795 m:
YPM 7249–64, 7291 (Leenders & Watkins-Colwell
2004). Sonsonate: Município Izalco, Cantón Cruz
Grande, Finca Nuevos Horizontes (13.821°N,
89.653°W), 1250 m: YPM 6458 (Leenders &
Watkins-Colwell 2004).

Genus *Hyla*

This very large (ca. 334 species) genus of
treefrogs is distributed from Canada to Argentina in
the New World, the Greater Antilles, extreme
northwestern Africa, eastern Asia, and southern
and central Europe (D. Frost 2004). Only one
species is known from El Salvador.

Hyla robertmertensi Taylor 1938
(Rana Arborícola Grillo de Mertens)
Plate 23, Map 15, Figure 6ab

1938 *Hyla robertmertensi* Taylor, Proc. Biol. Soc.
Washington, 50: 43; type locality: near Tapachula,
Chiapas, Mexico.
Hyla robertmertensi: Mertens 1952d, Duellman
1970, 2001, Greding & Hellebuyck 1980, Villa et al.
1988, Dueñas et al. 2001, D. Frost 2002, 2004.
Geographic distribution: Pacific lowlands from
eastern Oaxaca, Mexico, to El Salvador; also in
Cintalapa Valley in Chiapas, Mexico (D. Frost 2002,
2004).
Ecological distribution: Dry forest and savanna
from sea level to 400 m.
Description: Largest Salvadoran specimen examined is 24.6 mm SVL; HW/SVL 0.27–0.28; HL/SVL
0.26–0.32; shank length/SVL 0.48–0.50; foot length/
SVL 0.40–0.43; tympanum diameter/SVL 0.04.
Snout slightly narrowed anteriorly, rounded to
almost truncate terminally, truncate in profile; top
of head flat, canthus rostralis rounded and indistinct, loreal region slightly concave; nostrils situated about 2/3 of distance from the eyes to the tip of
snout; a narrow dermal fold extending from the
posterior corner of the eye to a point above the
insertion of arms, touching the upper border of
tympanum; tympanum diameter about 1/2 of eye
diameter; arms moderately short; fingers possessing discs in size almost equal to tympanum; fingers
relatively short, relative length of fingers I < II < IV
< III, modal webbing formula of fingers I 2⁺ – 3 II 2
– 3 III 3⁻ – 2 IV; subarticular tubercles large and
rounded, distal ones on fingers III and IV bifid;
palmar tubercle indistinct, pollical tubercle ovoid;
no nuptial excrescence in breeding males; relative
length of toes I < II < III ~ V < IV; terminal discs
slightly larger than those on fingers; subarticular
tubercles rounded, small; inner metatarsal tubercle
elongate, outer one small, round, indistinct; modal
webbing formula of toes I 2⁺ – 2⁻ II 1⁺ – 2 III 1⁺ – 2⁻
IV 2⁺ – 1 V; skin on dorsum smooth, that on belly
and ventral surfaces of thighs finely granular;
vomerine teeth on two small, rounded, narrowly
separated processes between choanae.

Dorsum pale grayish tan bordered by two thin
dorsolateral white stripes extending from tip of
snout to vent; pale brown lateral bands from the tip
of snout to groin; venter creamy yellow or white.
Call: Porter (1962) noted the call of this species as
an irregular clicking sound, with a dominant

Plate 23: *Hyla robertmertensi* MEXICO: Oaxaca: 7.2
km NNW Zanatepec. Photo: W. E. Duellman (KU CT
918).

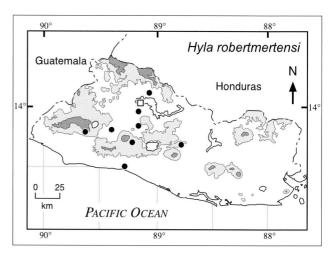

Map 15: Distribution of *Hyla robertmertensi* in El
Salvador.
Closed circles represent examined-specimen locality records;
open squares are published locality records. Light shading
indicates 600–1200 m elevation; dark shading indicates elevations ≥ 1200 m; large bodies of freshwater are outlined in bold,
black lines.

frequency of 6500 Hz and a pulse rate of 7 notes per
second. The duration of the call ranged from one
second to "several" seconds. Duellman (1970, 2001)
noted that the call of this species resembles an
insect and sounds like "cree-eek-eek-eek."
Natural history: Duellman (1970, 2001) noted this
species inhabits humid and subhumid lowlands. In
the rainy season, adults congregate in large numbers at temporary ponds, where males call from
grasses, bushes, and small trees.
Conservation status: GAA: Least concern (LC).
Specimens examined: <u>Chalatenango</u>: 16.5 km
WNW Chalatenango: KU 184725–46; 44 km N San

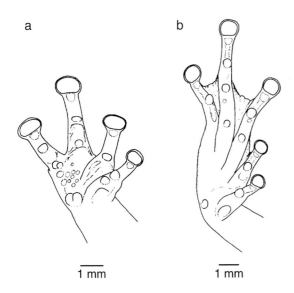

a   b

1 mm   1 mm

Figure 6: *Hyla robertmertensi* (SMF 81350): a. ventral view of right hand, b. ventral view of right foot.

Salvador: KU 140012. Cuscatlán: Colima: AMNH 125859–60. La Libertad: 16.1 km NW Nuevo San Salvador [= Santa Tecla]: KU 44112; Puerto de La Libertad: USNM 192606. San Salvador: 11.3 km N San Salvador: UTA A-1405; 22.1 km N San Salvador on rd to Citalá: UMMZ 119983. San Vicente: Carreterra to San Miguel, behind desvío to San Vicente: SMF 81350. Sonsonate: Hacienda Cuyan-Cuya near Izalco, 380 m: SMF 44566.
Published locality records: San Salvador: 3.2 km SW of a bridge over the Río Lempa on the highway between San Salvador and La Palma, 270 m (Greding & Hellebuyck 1980).

Genus *Phrynohyas*

This genus, commonly known as Golden-eyed Treefrogs, includes six species found from Mexico to Argentina (D. Frost 2002, 2004). One species is known from El Salvador.

Phrynohyas venulosa (Laurenti 1768)
(Rana Lechosa)
Plate 24, Map 16, Figures 7ab, 15f

1768 *Rana venulosa* Laurenti, Synops. Rept.: 31; type locality: America.
Hyla modesta: Mertens 1952d.
Phrynohyas venulosa: Duellman 1970, 2001, Greding & Hellebuyck 1980, Villa et al. 1988, Dueñas et al. 2001.

Plate 24: *Phrynohyas venulosa* EL SALVADOR: La Libertad: Club Atami (40 m). Photo: M. Veselý.

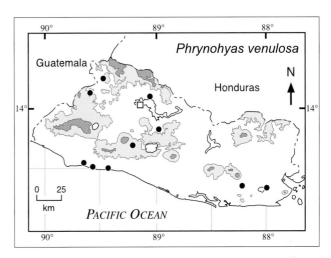

Map 16: Distribution of *Phrynohyas venulosa* in El Salvador.
Closed circles represent examined-specimen locality records; open squares are published locality records. Light shading indicates 600–1200 m elevation; dark shading indicates elevations ≥ 1200 m; large bodies of freshwater are outlined in bold, black lines.

Geographic distribution: From the lowlands of Mexico and Central America to the Amazon Basin of Brazil, Guianas, and south to Paraná (Brazil), Paraguay, and northern Argentina; also in Trinidad and Tobago (D. Frost 2002, 2004).
Ecological distribution: Dry forest and savanna between sea level and 700 m.
Description: Largest Salvadoran specimen examined is 74.7 mm SVL; HW/SVL 0.33–0.36; HL/SVL 0.30–0.36; shank length/SVL 0.46–0.52; foot length/SVL 0.38–0.43; tympanum diameter/SVL 0.05–0.06. Snout bluntly rounded in dorsal view, in profile

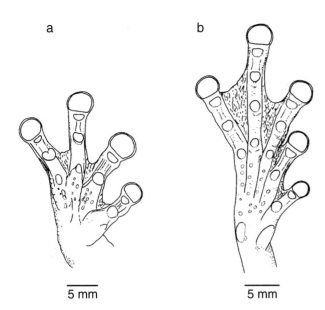

Figure 7: *Phrynohyas venulosa:* a. ventral view of right hand (SMF 81422), b. ventral view of right foot (SMF 81421).

sloping (males) or almost truncate (females); top of head flat, nostrils directed laterally, situated at a point about 4/5 distance from eyes to tip of snout; canthus rostralis rounded, distinct; loreal region barely concave; dermal fold extending from posterior margin of eye to a point above insertion of forelimb, only narrowly covering upper part of tympanum; arms as well as fingers short, robust, fingers bearing large discs, those on fingers III–V equal in size to tympanum, with swollen pads; relative length of fingers I < II < IV < III; heels smooth, subarticular tubercles large, round, projecting; no distinct palmar tubercle; large nuptial thumb pads bearing brown excrescences in sexually active males; finger webbing formula I 2½ – 2½ II 2⁻ – 3⁻ III 2½ – 2 IV. Legs longer and robust; relative length of toes I < II < III < V < IV; toe webbing formula I 1½ – 2 II 1 – 2 III 1⁺ – 2 IV 2⁻ – 1 V; toe discs smaller than those on fingers; transverse dermal fold present on heels; tarsal fold present; dorsum smooth, weakly tuberculate anteriorly, especially on head and upper eyelids; skin on throat, belly and posteroventral surface of thighs heavily granular, other ventral areas smooth; vomerine teeth 10–27, on two slightly curved prevomeral processes, processes narrowly separated from each other, situated between the posterior margins of choanae.

Dorsal ground color brown or reddish brown with darker irregular pattern on dorsum and limbs; ventral surfaces dirty white; iris deep golden bronze with black flecks; color of preserved specimens a bit darker; belly and thighs dirty yellow to pale bronze.

Call: Duellman (1970, 2001) noted that the call of this species resembles a low growl or raucous note repeated at rapid intervals. There are 42–52 notes per minute, and the duration of each note is from 0.23–0.36 second. There are 150–175 pulses per second. The dominant frequency varies from 1392–1946 Hz.

Natural history: M. Veselý (field notes) observed calling males in swimming pools, on coconut palms, and the leaves of trees during heavy rains at Club Atami, Depto. La Libertad in late May. Duellman (1970, 2001) noted that this species can be active during the dry season because of a sticky glandular secretion that may retard water loss. This sticky substance is usually exuded when the frog is handled. Campbell (1998a) noted that this species eats orthopterans, coleopterans, dipterans, homopterans, spiders, and small vertebrates; breeding occurs after the first heavy rains in May–June or July–August. McCranie & Wilson (2002) found breeding choruses of this species in temporary pools and inundated lowlands from June–August in Honduras. Solitary individuals were found in tree holes or vegetation in the dry season. Savage (2002) warned the toxic substance of this species can cause extreme irritation, swelling, or pain if it contacts human mucous membranes. The author also commented on the parachuting ability of this species; tadpoles are nektonic.

Conservation status: GAA: Least concern (LC).
Specimens examined: <u>Chalatenango</u>: 16.5 km WNW Chalatenango: KU 184783. <u>Cuscatlán</u>: 1 km E Tenancingo: KU 184763–71, 184775–82. <u>La Libertad</u>: Club Atami (near Playa El Palmarcito, Municipio Tamanique), 13°30.2´N, 89°25.0´W, 40 m: SMF 81421–23; Mizata, km 89, Carretera Del Litoral: KU 184772. <u>La Unión</u>: Laguna de Olomega: KU 184773–74. <u>San Miguel</u>: Laguna El Jocotal, S of Volcán San Miguel, 50 m: SMF 43161, 43177. <u>San Salvador</u>: San Salvador: ZMB 35721–22. <u>Santa Ana</u>: 15 km SSE Candelaria: KU 129859; 6 km S Metapán: KU 184784. <u>Sonsonate</u>: 9.2 km SE Jct Hwys 12/2: TCWC 55902–22.

Published locality records: <u>San Salvador</u>: 3.2 km SW of a bridge over the Río Lempa on the highway between San Salvador and La Palma, 270 m (Greding & Hellebuyck 1980).

Genus *Plectrohyla*

Eighteen species of Spikethumb Frogs are
known from disjunct highland habitats from
Chiapas, Mexico, to northern El Salvador and
Honduras; an "undetermined" larvae and subadult
are known from north-central Nicaragua (D. Frost
2004). McDiarmid & Altig (1999) classified the
larvae of this genus as exotrophic, lotic claspers.
Three species are known from El Salvador.

Plectrohyla guatemalensis **Brocchi 1877**
(Rana Combatiente de Guatemala)
Plate 25, Map 17, Figure 8ab

1877 *Plectrohyla guatemalensis* Brocchi, Bull. Soc.
Philomath. Paris, 1(7): 92; type locality: "Pacicilla"
(= Patzicia), Depto. Chimaltenango, Guatemala.
Plectrohyla guatemalensis: Mertens 1952d, Rand
1957, Duellman 1970, 2001, Villa et al. 1988,
Duellman & Campbell 1992, Dueñas et al. 2001, D.
Frost 2002, 2004, McCranie & Wilson 2002.
Geographic distribution: From southeastern
Chiapas, Mexico, to southwestern Guatemala and
east-central Honduras (D. Frost 2002, 2004,
McCranie & Wilson 2002).
Ecological distribution: Pine-oak forest and
cloud forest at elevations of 1830–2800 m.
Description: Largest Salvadoran specimen examined is 50.0 mm SVL; HW/SVL 0.31–0.35; HL/SVL
0.27–0.33; shank length/SVL 0.48–0.54; foot length/
SVL 0.42–0.51; tympanum diameter/SVL 0.03–0.04.
Snout bluntly rounded in dorsal aspect, sloping to
rounded in profile; frontal region flat or slightly
concave, canthus rostralis distinct and angular,
loreal region concave, nasal openings directed
laterally, situated about 3/5 of distance from eyes to
tip of snout; distinct dermal fold extending from
orbit, obscuring upper part of tympanum and
terminating at a point above insertion of arms;
arms short and robust, distinct transverse fold on
the wrist; finger discs large, much larger than
tympanum; relative length of fingers I < II < IV <
III, webbing of fingers vestigial; subarticular
tubercles large and subconical, supernumerary
tubercles distinct, palmar tubercle large, flat, bifid;
thenar tubercle bifid; enlarged prepollex with two
curved spines (the outer one longer) in both males
and females; hind limbs moderately long, toe discs
slightly smaller than those on fingers, relative
length of toes I < II < V < III < IV, modal webbing
formula of toes I 1½ – 2 II 1⁺ – 2 III 1½ – 2 IV 2 – 1

Plate 25: *Plectrohyla guatemalensis* (USNM 523204)
HONDURAS: Ocotepeque: Cerro El Pital. Photo: J. R.
McCranie.

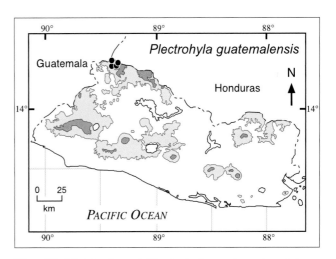

Map 17: Distribution of *Plectrohyla guatemalensis* in
El Salvador.
Closed circles represent examined-specimen locality records;
open squares are published locality records. Light shading
indicates 600–1200 m elevation; dark shading indicates elevations ≥ 1200 m; large bodies of freshwater are outlined in bold,
black lines.

V; subarticular tubercles large, round, inner
metatarsal tubercle ovoid, flat; outer metatarsal
tubercle indistinct, rounded, subconical; skin on
dorsum smooth with many scattered tubercles
laterally, posteriorly and on head, skin on throat,
belly and ventral surfaces of thighs granular;
vomerine teeth on narrowly separated transverse
ridges between posterior parts of choanae; numerous maxillary and premaxillary teeth.

Dorsum dull olive-brown with reddish brown
markings. In preserved specimens, the dorsal color
is dark brown or gray, with darker mottling; venter
dull tan to grayish brown.

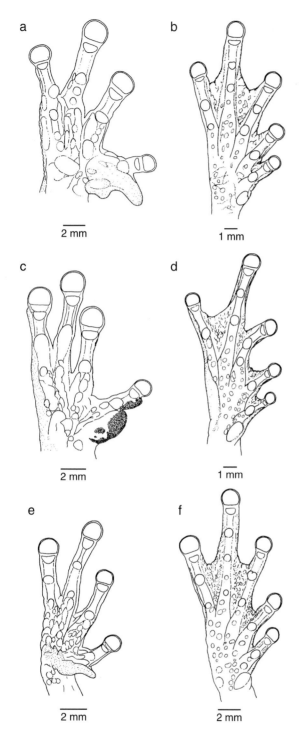

Figure 8: *Plectrohyla guatemalensis:* a. ventral view of right hand (male; SMF 81356), b. ventral view of right foot (female; SMF 81361). *Plectrohyla psiloderma:* c. ventral view of right hand (male; SMF 78041), d. ventral view of right foot (male; SMF 78042). *Plectrohyla sagorum* (female; KU 94030): e. ventral view of right hand, f. ventral view of right foot.

Call: Adult males of this species do not have vocal slits or a vocal sac and thus have been presumed to be mute (Duellman 1970, 2001); however, McCranie et al. (1987:72) reported the mating call of *Plectrohyla guatemalensis* to consist of "a single low pitched note best described as a grunt which is repeated at intervals of about two min."

Natural history: According to Mertens (1952d), these frogs can be found in water, leaf litter, and *Tillandsia.* Rand (1957) noted a juvenile found in the leaf axil of a tree bromeliad and two adults among rocks in a stream at Cerro Miramundo (2200 m), Depto. Santa Ana in February. Duellman (1970, 2001) noted adults on vegetation overhanging a stream during the day and at night in Guatemala. McCranie & Wilson (2002) found individuals of this nocturnal species on vegetation above streams from April–August and October–February in Honduras. Adults were collected during the day from bromeliads, under moss mats, and in rock crevices. Females with eggs were found in July and August.

Conservation status: GAA: Critically endangered (CRA3e).

Specimens examined: <u>Santa Ana</u>: Hacienda Los Planes, Metapán mountains, 1830 m: SMF 43032–38; 44941–42, 52234; Hacienda Los Planes, Cerro Miramundo, 2000 m: SMF 43165, KU 61951; same locality at 2200 m: FMNH 65116–18; "cloud forest" on Montecristo, 2200 m: SMF 44943–44, 81353–54, 81356–63; Hacienda Montecristo, Cordillera de Metapán, 2200 m: VH 45, UMMZ 118411–12, KU 61945–48; Trifino, 2800 m: KU 61949; Metapán Mt, 2200 m: KU 61950, 61953–54.

Plectrohyla psiloderma McCranie & Wilson 1999

(Rana Combatiente de Dorso Liso)
Plate 26, Map 18, Figure 8cd

1999 *Plectrohyla psiloderma* McCranie & Wilson, Senckenbergiana biol. 78: 232; type locality: Río Arcáqual (14°33´N, 88°40´W), Cerro Celaque, 2530 m elevation, Depto. Lempira, Honduras.
Plectrohyla glandulosa: Duellman 1970, Villa et al. 1988, Duellman & Campbell 1992, Dueñas et al. 2001.
Plectrohyla psiloderma: Duellman 2001, D. Frost 2002, 2004, McCranie & Wilson 2002.

Geographic distribution: Northwestern El Salvador and southwestern Honduras (McCranie & Wilson 2002).

Ecological distribution: Pine-oak forest and

Plate 26: *Plectrohyla psiloderma* (SMF 78041) HONDURAS: Lempira: Cerro Celaque (2530 m). Photo: G. Köhler.

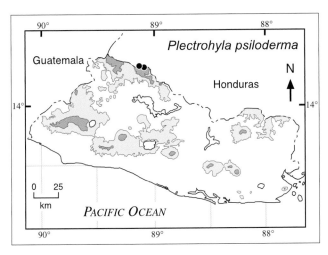

Map 18: Distribution of *Plectrohyla psiloderma* in El Salvador.
Closed circles represent examined-specimen locality records; open squares are published locality records. Light shading indicates 600–1200 m elevation; dark shading indicates elevations ≥ 1200 m; large bodies of freshwater are outlined in bold, black lines.

cloud forest around 2400 m. McCranie & Wilson (1999) noted that the Salvadoran specimens of this species were collected 50 km from the type locality of *Plectrohyla psiloderma*, with most of the intervening area consisting of unsuitable habitat.

Description: (extracted from McCranie & Wilson 1999): Maximum SVL 49.0 mm; HW/SVL 0.31–0.37; HL/SVL 0.29–0.35; shank length/SVL 0.47–0.58; foot length/SVL 0.44–0.54. Snout semicircular in dorsal aspect, obtuse in profile; canthus rostralis slightly thickened, nearly angular, loreal region slightly concave, nasal openings directed

dorsolaterally; distinct dermal fold extending from orbit, obscuring upper part of otherwise very indistinct tympanum and merging with body contour above point of insertion of arm; arms robust, distinct transverse fold on the wrist; finger discs large; relative length of fingers I < II < IV < III, webbing basal between fingers I and II, remaining webbing formula II 2 – 3$^+$ III 3$^-$ – 2 ⅓ IV; subarticular tubercles large and globular, supernumerary tubercles absent on fingers; prepollex enlarged, distal end blunt proximal to finger, rounded anterolaterally, lateral edge flat for about proximal 1/3 of its length, distal end of prepollex extending to point about midlevel of subarticular tubercle on finger I; hind limbs moderately long, toe discs slightly smaller than those on fingers, relative length of toes I < II < V ~ III < IV, modal webbing formula of toes I 1⅓ – 2 II 1$^+$ – 2½ III 1⅓ – 3$^-$ IV 2½ – 1 V; subarticular tubercles moderately large, globular; skin on dorsum smooth, except a few small pustules present on upper eyelids and forearms; 1–2 vomerine teeth on somewhat rounded ridges between ovoid choanae; vocal slits and sac absent.

Dorsal surfaces variable shades of green in life; flanks and anterior and posterior surfaces of thighs maroon in life.

Call: McCranie & Wilson (1999) noted that this species does not have vocal slits or a vocal sac; a mating call has not been reported.

Taxonomic comments: McCranie & Wilson (1999) note that the prepollical width/prepollical length ratio of the single known male from El Salvador falls within the range of variation for *Plectrohyla glandulosa*. Additional specimens from El Salvador are needed to evaluate the taxonomic status of this group.

Natural history: McCranie & Wilson (2002) noted the presence of this nocturnal species from low vegetation and rocks adjacent to a river from April–August in Honduras; tadpoles were also present at this locality during the same months, but many of them had deformed mouthparts.

Conservation status: GAA: Endangered (EN B1ab[iii]).

Specimens examined: <u>Chalatenango</u>: Los Esesmiles, Cerro El Pital, 2438–2454 m: MVZ 39858; Cerro El Pital: KU 184948.

***Plectrohyla sagorum* Hartweg 1941**
(Rana Combatiente de Rostro Quillado)
Plate 27, Map 19, Figure 8ef

Plate 27: *Plectrohyla sagorum* (KU 103164) GUATE-MALA: Quetzaltenango: Granja Lorena. Photo: W. E. Duellman (KU CT 2248).

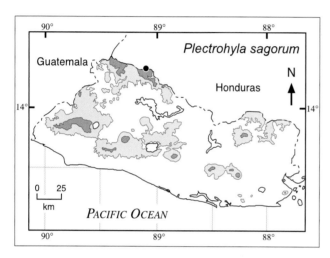

Map 19: Distribution of *Plectrohyla sagorum* in El Salvador.
Closed circles represent examined-specimen locality records; open squares are published locality records. Light shading indicates 600–1200 m elevation; dark shading indicates elevations ≥ 1200 m; large bodies of freshwater are outlined in bold, black lines.

1941 *Plectrohyla sagorum* Hartweg, Occas. Pap. Mus. Zool. Univ. Michigan, 437: 2; type locality: Cerro Ovando, 1800 m, Distrito Soconusco, Chiapas, Mexico.
Plectrohyla sagorum: Duellman 1970, 2001, Villa et al. 1988, Duellman & Campbell 1992, Dueñas et al. 2001, D. Frost 2002, 2004.
Geographic distribution: Highlands from southeastern Chiapas, Mexico, to southwestern Guatemala; a single record from the highlands of northwestern El Salvador (D. Frost 2002, 2004).

Ecological distribution: Cloud forest around 2400 m.
Description: Maximum SVL 45.5 mm (Duellman & Campbell 1992); morphometric ratios are from three specimens collected at Volcán Tacaná, Chiapas, Mexico (KU 94021, 94025, 94030): HW/SVL 0.31–0.35; HL/SVL 0.32–0.33; shank length/SVL 0.51–0.53; foot length/SVL 0.45–0.47; tympanum diameter/SVL 0.04–0.05. Canthus rostralis prominent, loreal region slightly concave, nasal openings directed dorsolaterally; tubercles present on dorsal surfaces of head and limbs; vertical rostral keel present; distinct dermal fold extending from orbit, obscuring upper part of otherwise indistinct tympanum and merging with body contour above point of insertion of arm; arms robust; finger discs large; relative length of fingers I < II < IV < III, webbing of fingers vestigial; prepollical spine pointed; hind limbs moderately long, toe discs slightly smaller than those on fingers, relative length of toes I < II < V ~ III < IV, modal webbing formula of toes I 2⁻ – 2 II 1 – 2⁺ III 1½ – 2⁺ IV 2⁺ – 1 V; subarticular tubercles moderately large, globular; vocal slits present.

Dorsum dull brown with small, irregular, darker brown spots; flanks tan with fine dark brown reticulations or small dark brown flecks.
Call: Taylor & Smith (1945:598) noted that the call of this species resembles a "slightly drawn out, coarsely trilled, nasal *quaaacck.*"
Natural history: Duellman (1970, 2001) noted this species spends its days in bromeliads and calls at night near cascading mountain streams in cloud forest. Calling and breeding take place throughout the year.
Conservation status: GAA: Endangered (EN B1ab[iii]).
Specimens examined: Chalatenango: Los Esesmiles: MVZ 39859.

Genus *Ptychohyla*

There are 12 species of Mountain Stream Frogs distributed from southern Mexico to western Panama (D. Frost 2002, 2004). Two species are known from El Salvador.

Ptychohyla euthysanota (Kellogg 1923)
(Ranita de Quebrada de la Montaña)
Plate 28, Map 20, Figure 9acd

1923 *Hyla euthysanota* Kellogg, Proc. Biol. Soc.

Plate 28: *Ptychohyla euthysanota* GUATEMALA: San Marcos: Finca La Paz (1325 m). Photo: W. E. Duellman (KU CT 1465).

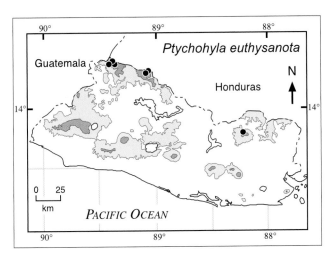

Map 20: Distribution of *Ptychohyla euthysanota* in El Salvador.

Closed circles represent examined-specimen locality records; open squares are published locality records. Light shading indicates 600–1200 m elevation; dark shading indicates elevations ≥ 1200 m; large bodies of freshwater are outlined in bold, black lines.

Washington, 41: 123; type locality: Los Esesmiles, Cerro El Pital, Depto. Chalatenango, El Salvador.
Hyla euthysanota: Mertens 1952d, Rand 1957.
Ptychohyla euthysanota euthysanota: Duellman 1963, 1970, 2001.
Ptychohyla euthysanota: Villa et al. 1988, Campbell & Smith 1992, Duellman 2001, Dueñas et al. 2001, D. Frost 2002, 2004, McCranie & Wilson 2002, Leenders & Watkins-Colwell 2004.
Geographic distribution: Highlands from the Pacific versant of southeastern Mexico (extreme eastern Oaxaca and Chiapas) to Guatemala and El Salvador (D. Frost 2002, 2004).

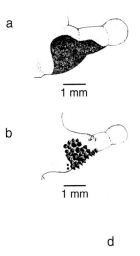

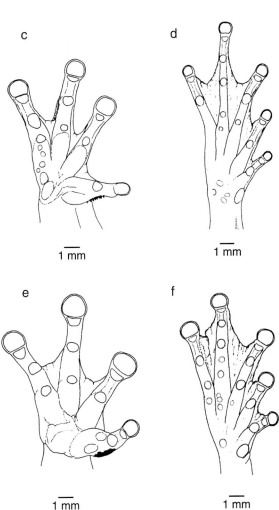

Figure 9: A comparison of thumb nuptial tubercles in males of a. *Ptychohyla euthysanota* (SMF 43040); b. *Ptychohyla salvadorensis* (SMF 43045). *Ptychohyla euthysanota* (SMF 43040): c. ventral view of right hand, d. ventral view of right foot. *Ptychohyla salvadorensis* (SMF 43045): e. ventral view of right hand, f. ventral view of right foot.

Ecological distribution: Premontane evergreen forest, subtropical humid forest, pine-oak forest, and cloud forest at elevations of 800–2200 m.

Description: Largest Salvadoran specimen examined is 33.1 mm SVL (Leenders & Watkins-Colwell 2004); HW/SVL 0.32–0.36; HL/SVL 0.32–0.35; shank length/SVL 0.51–0.56; foot length/SVL 0.41–0.44; tympanum diameter/SVL 0.06–0.07. Snout bluntly pointed in dorsal view, truncate to bluntly rounded in profile; top of head flat; nostrils directed laterally, situated at a point about 2/3 of distance between the anterior corner of orbit to tip of snout; canthus rostralis slightly elevated, angular; loreal region concave; distinct dermal fold extending from eye along upper margin of tympanum to a point above insertion of arm; tympanum distinct; arms short, robust, an indistinct ridge present on ventrolateral surface formed by small white tubercles; a distinct transverse fold on upper surface of wrist; finger discs smaller than tympanum, relative length of fingers I < II < IV < III, modal webbing formula of fingers I 2½ – 2½ II 2⁻ – 3⁻ III 2⁺ – 2 IV; subarticular tubercles large, subconical, rounded to bifid, no distinct palmar tubercle, supernumerary tubercles present; thumb bearing numerous distinct black spines in sexually active males; legs moderately long, relative length of toes I < II < III < V < IV; modal webbing formula of toes I 1½ – 2 II 1 – 2 III 1 – 2⁻ IV 2⁻ – 1 V; terminal discs slightly smaller than those on fingers; subarticular tubercles round, large, outer metatarsal tubercle small, indistinct; inner metatarsal tubercle ovoid, raised; inner tarsal fold present; skin on dorsum smooth, that on throat, belly and posterior part of thighs granular; ventrolateral glands moderately developed; vomerine teeth on two small triangular, narrowly separated processes between choanae. Rand (1957) noted that two specimens collected from Cerro Miramundo, Depto. Santa Ana have dermal wrist folds, which are not mentioned in the type description of this species.

Dorsum reddish brown or brown with irregular dark brown markings extending onto limbs; creamy white stripes around vent and on upper lips; ventral surfaces creamy yellow to pale brown; flanks decorated with small dark brown spots.

Call: Duellman (1970, 2001) noted that the call of this species sounds like a soft noted "wraaaack" that is repeated every 3–4 seconds. Each note has a duration of 0.60–0.65 second, with 91–102 pulses per second. The dominant frequency is between 3000–3200 Hz.

Natural history: Mertens (1952d) found an individual of this frog in a muddy garden covered with *Zantedeschia aethiopica* in El Salvador. Rand (1957) collected two specimens in leaf axils of aerial bromeliads in cloud forest at Cerro Miramundo (2200 m), Depto. Santa Ana in February. Duellman (1970, 2001) noted this cloud-forest species breeds in clear mountain streams. It is possible this species breeds throughout the year. Leenders & Watkins-Colwell (2004) noted an adult female at night from epiphytic vegetation ca. 80 cm above the ground at Parque Nacional Montecristo (1840 m), Depto. Santa Ana.

Conservation status: GAA: Near threatened (NT).

Specimens examined: <u>Chalatenango</u>: E slope Los Esesmiles, Cerro El Pital, 2225 m: MVZ 39856; SW slope Los Esesmiles, Cerro El Pital, 1829 m: MVZ 39857. <u>Morazán</u>: N slope Mt. Cacahuatique: MVZ 39855. <u>Santa Ana</u>: Hacienda San José, Metapán mountains, 800 m: SMF 44571; Hacienda Los Planes, Metapán mountains, 1830 m: SMF 43040; Cerro Miramundo, Metapán mountains, 2200 m: SMF 44188, FMNH 65120.

Published locality records: <u>Santa Ana</u>: Município Metapán, Cantón Metapán, Parque Nacional Montecristo (14.401°N, 89.362°W), 1840 m: YPM 7239 (Leenders & Watkins-Colwell 2004).

Ptychohyla salvadorensis (Mertens 1952)
(Ranita de Quebrada Salvadoreña)
Plate 29, Map 21, Figure 9bef

1952 *Hyla salvadorensis* Mertens, Senckenb. biol. 33: 169; type locality: Hacienda San José, Sierra Metapán, Depto. Santa Ana, El Salvador.
Hyla salvadorensis: Mertens 1952d, Duellman 1970, Villa et al. 1988, Savage 2002.
Ptychohyla salvadorensis: Campbell & Smith 1992, Duellman 2001, Dueñas et al. 2001, D. Frost 2002, 2004, McCranie & Wilson 2002, Leenders & Watkins-Colwell 2004.

Geographic distribution: Pacific versant from central El Salvador to south-central Honduras and southeastern Guatemala; also from southwestern Honduras near Continental Divide to northeastern El Salvador (McCranie & Wilson 2002).

Ecological distribution: Dry forest, premontane evergreen forest, subtropical humid forest, and pine-oak forest at elevations of 700–1800 m.

Description: Largest Salvadoran specimen examined is 36.5 mm SVL (Leenders & Watkins-Colwell 2004); HW/SVL 0.31–0.35; HL/SVL 0.34–0.36;

Plate 29: *Ptychohyla salvadorensis* (KU 289952) EL SALVADOR: La Libertad: Finca La Giralda (1080 m). Photo: E. Greenbaum.

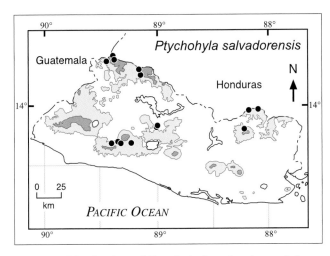

Map 21: Distribution of *Ptychohyla salvadorensis* in El Salvador.
Closed circles represent examined-specimen locality records; open squares are published locality records. Light shading indicates 600–1200 m elevation; dark shading indicates elevations ≥ 1200 m; large bodies of freshwater are outlined in bold, black lines.

shank length/SVL 0.52–0.54; foot length/SVL 0.401–0.42; tympanum diameter/SVL 0.05–0.06. Snout rounded in both dorsal view and profile; top of head slightly convex, nostrils barely protuberant, situated at a point about 2/3 distance between anterior corner of orbit and tip of snout; loreal region concave, canthus rostralis rounded; a moderately developed dermal fold extending from eye to a point above insertion of arm, narrowly obscuring upper part of tympanum which is otherwise distinct, tympanum about 2/3 diameter of eye; arms rela-

tively short, robust, with white line formed by small, flattened tubercles on the ventrolateral edge of arms; finger discs slightly smaller than tympanum; relative length of fingers I < II < IV < III, modal webbing formula of fingers I 3 – 3 II 1½ – 2½ III 2 – 2 IV; tiny excrescences present on pollex of breeding males; relative length of toes I < II < V ~ III < IV, modal subarticular tubercles round, distinct, palmar tubercle large, ovoid and flat, granular; webbing formula of toes I 1 – 2⁻ II 1⁺ – 2 III 1½ – 2 IV 2 – 1½ V; toe discs slightly smaller than those on fingers; subarticular tubercles round; inner metatarsal tubercle distinct, ovoid, flat; outer metatarsal tubercle minute and conical; a weak inner tarsal fold present; dorsal surfaces of head and body smooth; skin on belly, throat and ventral surfaces of thighs granular; vomerine teeth on two widely separated transverse ridges.

Ground color dull brown or green above and creamy white below; dorsum sometimes with several irregularly scattered minute white spots; thin white stripes above the vent and on the tarsal keels. In life, the iris is coppery bronze (Duellman 2001; E. Greenbaum pers. obs.).

Call: The call of this species resembles a short series of low pitch notes repeated rapidly; each note sounds like "wraaack" (E. Greenbaum pers. obs.). Duellman (1970, 2001) noted that the call of this species "consists of a short series of short notes. Call groups consist of two to six notes; the duration of each call group varies from 0.27 to 0.78 (mean, 0.38) of a second, ... the dominant frequency varies from 2200 to 2700 (mean, 2345) cycles per second [Hz]." He also noted that frogs from Rancho San José, Depto. Santa Ana produced 3–6 notes in each call group.

Natural history: E. Greenbaum (field notes) found males calling at night in vegetation 1–2 m from the ground adjacent to streams at Finca La Giralda, Depto. La Libertad and Perquín, Depto. Morazán in August. O. Komar (field notes) found males calling at night from banana leaves near a creek at Cerro Cacahuatique, Depto. Morazán in May. Mertens (1952d) found three individuals of this frog in vegetation 2.0–2.5 m above the ground along a fast running stream close to a waterfall in El Salvador. Duellman (1970, 2001) noted this species is also known from cloud forest; tadpoles were noted from Rancho San José, Depto. Santa Ana in July. McCranie & Wilson (2002) noted calling males from low vegetation and thick grasses near streams and seepage areas from June–August in Honduras;

tadpoles were found during the same months. Leenders & Watkins-Colwell (2004) observed calling males and amplexus in November, and a metamorph in late May in El Salvador.

Conservation status: GAA: Vulnerable (VU B1ab[iii]).

Specimens examined: <u>Chalatenango</u>: road near La Palma, 1100 m: SMF 48023; El Tunel 6.9 km S La Palma: UTA A-13544. <u>Cuscatlán</u>: 1.5 km N Tenancingo: KU 184926–27; 1.3 km N Tenancingo: KU 184933, 184937; Tenancingo, El Sitio de los Sánchez: KU 184928–32. <u>La Libertad</u>: Los Chorros, between Nuevo San Salvador [= Santa Tecla] and Colón, 700 m: SMF 42438, 44940 (tadpole), MUHNES 178–79; Finca La Giralda, 13°39.34´N, 89°22.47´W, 1080 m: KU 289950–52, 289957, MUHNES C–30–1299–1301; Nueva San Salvador, 1300 m: KU 184936; Puerto de La Libertad: USNM 192607. <u>Morazán</u>: Cerro Cacahuatique: MUHNES 151, 851; same locality at 1010 m: KU 291294, 291317–18; same locality at 1100 m: MUHNES C–30–1454–56; Perquín, 13°57.17´N, 88°10.01´W, 1150 m: KU 290007, 290039–40, 291355, MUHNES C–30–1298. <u>San Salvador</u>: 1.6 km NW San Salvador: KU 43121. <u>Santa Ana</u>: Hacienda San José (7 km N Metapán), Metapán mountains, 850 m: SMF 42461, 42455–56, 42704, 43056 (tadpole); same locality at 800 m: KU 65019–20, SMF 43045; Hacienda Los Planes, Metapán mountains, 1800 m: SMF 44933–38, MUHNES 172–74, AMNH 125861; Cerro Montecristo: MUHNES 175–77, 180–81, 297–99, 620.

Published locality records: <u>Morazán</u>: Cerro Cacahuatique: YPM 6456 (Leenders & Watkins-Colwell 2004); Município Arambala, Cantón Cumaro, Nahuaterique, near border crossing with Honduras (13.995°N, 88.093°W), 1310 m: YPM 7235–38 (Leenders & Watkins-Colwell 2004).

Genus *Scinax*

There are approximately 85 species of Snouted Treefrogs distributed from eastern and southern Mexico to eastern Argentina and Uruguay, Trinidad and Tobago, and St. Lucia (Barrio-Amorós et al. 2004, Faivovich 2002, D. Frost 2002, 2004). One species occurs in El Salvador.

Scinax staufferi (Cope 1865)
(Ranita de Stauffer)
Plate 30, Map 22, Figure 10ab

1865 *Hyla staufferi* Cope, Proc. Acad. Nat. Sci.

Plate 30: *Scinax staufferi* HONDURAS: Intibucá: Santa Lucía (370 m). Photo: G. Köhler.

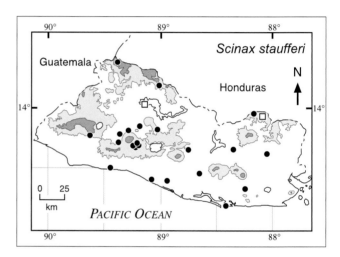

Map 22: Distribution of *Scinax staufferi* in El Salvador. Closed circles represent examined-specimen locality records; open squares are published locality records. Light shading indicates 600–1200 m elevation; dark shading indicates elevations ≥ 1200 m; large bodies of freshwater are outlined in bold, black lines.

Philadelphia, 17: 195; type locality: Orizaba, Veracruz, Mexico.

Hyla staufferi: Mertens 1952d, Rand 1957, Nelson & Hoyt 1961, Duellman 1970, Greding & Hellebuyck 1980.

Ololygon staufferi: Villa et al. 1988.

Scinax staufferi: Duellman 2001, Dueñas et al. 2001, Leenders 2003, Leenders & Watkins-Colwell 2004.

Geographic distribution: From Mexico (Tamaulipas and Guerrero) southward through Central America to Costa Rica on the Atlantic and Pacific versants, including islands in Honduras, El Salvador and Nicaragua (McCranie & Wilson 2002).

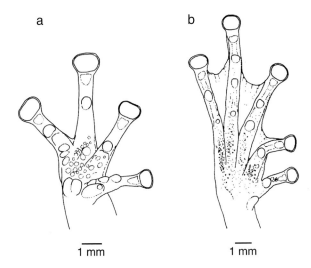

a   b

1 mm   1 mm

Figure 10: *Scinax staufferi* (SMF 43000): a. ventral view of right hand, b. ventral view of right foot.

Ecological distribution: Dry forest and savanna between sea level and 1150 m.

Description: Largest Salvadoran specimen examined is 30.3 mm SVL; HW/SVL 0.27–0.33; HL/SVL 0.29–0.36; shank length/SVL 0.44–0.51; foot length/ SVL 0.37–0.43; tympanum diameter/SVL 0.04–0.06. Dorsal outline of snout rounded to subovoid, snout more or less distinctly protruding in profile; canthus rostralis rounded; frontal area rather convex as is loreal region; tympanum distinct, about 1/2 eye diameter; supratympanic fold thin; males with single median vocal sac. Forelimbs slender; outer finger discs (III, IV) equal to or larger than tympanum; webbing vestigial; subarticular tubercles rounded, projecting; relative length of fingers I < II < IV < III, palmar tubercle large, bifid; hind limbs relatively short and robust; relative length of toes I < II < III ~ V < IV; toe webbing formula I 2 – 2½ II 1⁺ – 3⁻ III 1½ – 3⁻ IV 2½ – 1 V; outer metatarsal tubercle rounded, small, barely visible; inner metatarsal tubercle ovoid, about twice as large as outer metatarsal tubercle; skin on dorsal surfaces tuberculate, that on venter granular; vomerine teeth present on almost fused vomerine processes between choanae.

Dorsal ground color pale brown or gray-yellow with darker longitudinal stripes formed by concentrated black flecks, flecks otherwise present on whole dorsal surface; outer dorsal stripes ending at midbody, the inner ones extending to 3/4 of body; barely visible darker lines also on canthus rostralis and dorsomedian line of head; venter creamy yellow.

Call: Duellman (1970, 2001) noted that the call of this species "consists of a series of short nasal notes, 'ah-ah-ah-ah.'" Call groups range from 2–77 notes with a duration of 0.13–0.23 second, and a pulse rate of 100–130 pulses per second. Two harmonics of equal intensity occur at 1743 and 3056 Hz.

Natural history: E. Greenbaum (field notes) collected calling males at night from inside and around water tanks in a village, and 1–2 m above ground in vegetation during a heavy rain at Isla San Sebastián, Depto. Usulután in July. Calling males and adults in amplexus were collected from a flooded field adjacent to a road at night at Perquín, Depto. Morazán in August; *Physalaemus pustulosus* were also calling from this water. O. Komar (field notes) collected adults in amplexus at night at Perquín, Depto. Morazán in June. Rand (1957) noted calling males in mid-June at Instituto Tropical, Depto. San Salvador. Nelson & Hoyt (1961) reported calling males at night during heavy rains in rain-filled temporary pools at San Salvador, Depto. San Salvador in June. Greding & Hellebuyck (1980) noted Isoptera and Lepidoptera in the diet of 19 frogs collected at night at a pond in Depto. San Salvador in June. Campbell (1998a) noted breeding from May–July, but females with eggs have been observed as late as September. McCranie & Wilson (2002) noted breeding choruses around temporary pools from June–August and October in Honduras; females with eggs were collected in August. Savage (2002) noted the larvae are nektonic. Leenders & Watkins-Colwell (2004) collected tapoles from a stagnant pool of water (along with *Rana maculata* tadpoles) in November at Río Sapo (662 m), Depto. Morazán.

Conservation status: GAA: Least concern (LC).
Specimens examined: <u>Cuscatlán</u>: Colima: MUHNES 201–202; 1 km E Tenancingo: KU 184747–50. <u>La Libertad</u>: road San Salvador–San Juan Opico, turnoff to Quetzaltepeque: SMF 52220– 31; Quetzaltepeque: CAS 94799; Club Atami (near Playa El Palmarcito, Municipio Tamanique), 13°30.2′N, 89°25.0′W, 40 m: SMF 81444; 16.1 km NW Nuevo San Salvador [= Santa Tecla]: KU 43540–41. <u>La Paz</u>: swamp 6 km N of La Herradura: SMF 44570; 7.5 km SW San Luis Talpa: KU 184751–62. <u>Morazán</u>: Divisadero: USNM 73290; Perquín, 13°57.17′N, 88°10.01′W, 1150 m: KU 290008–11, 290020, 291332–34, MUHNES C–30– 1321–25, C–30–1470–72. <u>San Miguel</u>: Laguna El Jocotal: MUHNES 198. <u>San Salvador</u>: San Salvador,

Instituto Tropical de Investigaciones Científicas:
SMF 44567–69, 52232–33, 54154–55, KU 61932–92;
San Salvador: MUHNES 199, UMMZ 118391,
118393–94; San Salvador near west edge of city:
UMMZ 117588; 22.1 km N San Salvador on rd to
Citalá: UMMZ 118392; 1.6 km NW San Salvador:
KU 43162–63; San Salvador, 670 m: FMNH 65101–
06. Santa Ana: Hacienda Montecristo: MUHNES 33.
San Vicente: 5 km off main road CAI, Lago
Apastepeque: CAS 139996–97. Sonsonate: Hacienda
Cuyan-Cuya near Izalco, 380 m: SMF 43000.
Usulután: Nancuchiname: MUHNES 203–207; Isla
San Sebastián, 13°10.01´N, 88°24.49´W, 20 m: KU
289897–98, 289914–15, MUHNES C–30–1326–27.
Depto. unknown: 2.4 km E Santa Rosa: TCWC
16669–70 (*).

Published locality records: Morazán: Município
Arambala, Cantón Cumaro, Río Sapo (13.959°N,
88.132°W), 662 m: YPM 7293–99 (Leenders &
Watkins-Colwell 2004). San Salvador: 3.2 km SW of
a bridge over the Río Lempa on a highway between
San Salvador and La Palma, 270 m (Greding &
Hellebuyck 1980).

Genus *Smilisca*

D. Frost (2002, 2004) noted the six species of
this treefrog genus are distributed from extreme
southern Texas (USA), to northwestern South
America (exclusive of the Amazon Basin). Duellman
(2001) noted this genus is paraphyletic with respect
to *Pternohyla* and *Triprion*. One common species is
found in El Salvador.

Smilisca baudinii (Duméril & Bibron 1841)
(Rana Arborícola de Baudin)
Plate 31, Map 23, Figure 11ab

1841 *Hyla Baudinii* Duméril & Bibron, Erp. Gén., 8:
564; type locality: Mexico; restricted to Córdoba,
Veracruz, Mexico, by Smith & Taylor, 1950, Univ.
Kansas Sci. Bull. 33: 347; restricted (in error) to
"Mexico City" by Schmidt, 1953, Check List N. Am.
Amph. Rept. Ed. 6: 69.
Hyla baudinii: Mertens 1952d, Rand 1957.
Smilisca baudinii: Nelson & Hoyt 1961, Duellman
1968, 1970, 2001, Greding & Hellebuyck 1980, Villa
et al. 1988, Dueñas et al. 2001, Leenders 2003,
Leenders & Watkins-Colwell 2004.
Geographic distribution: From extreme south-
ern Texas (USA) to southern Costa Rica on the
Atlantic versant and from southern Sonora, Mexico,

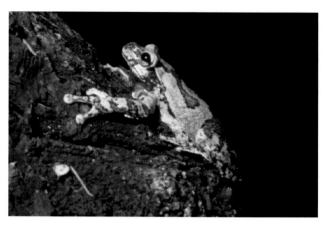

Plate 31: *Smilisca baudinii* (KU 289891–96) EL
SALVADOR: Usulután: Isla San Sebastián (20 m).
Photo: E. Greenbaum.

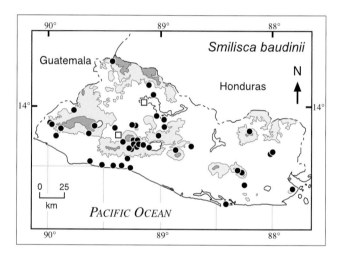

Map 23: Distribution of *Smilisca baudinii* in El Salvador.
Closed circles represent examined-specimen locality records;
open squares are published locality records. Light shading
indicates 600–1200 m elevation; dark shading indicates elevations ≥ 1200 m; large bodies of freshwater are outlined in bold,
black lines.

to northwestern Costa Rica on the Pacific versant,
including several islands in Mexico, Honduras, and
El Salvador (McCranie & Wilson 2002).
Ecological distribution: Dry forest, premontane
evergreen forest, subtropical humid forest, and
savanna between sea level and 1240 m.
Description: Largest Salvadoran specimen examined is 71.0 mm SVL; HW/SVL 0.33–0.39; HL/SVL
0.30–0.36; shank length/SVL 0.44–0.53; foot length/
SVL 0.42–0.50; tympanum diameter/SVL 0.04–0.07.
Dorsal outline of snout rounded, snout round to

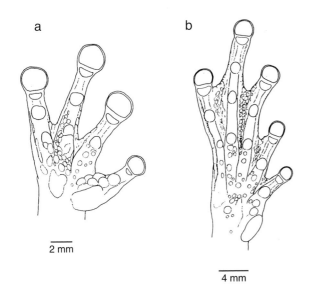

a

b

2 mm

4 mm

Figure 11: *Smilisca baudinii:* a. ventral view of right hand (SMF 81452), b. ventral view of right foot (SMF 81455).

almost sloping in profile; canthus rostralis rounded but distinct; frontal area flat; loreal region noticeably concave; dermal fold extending posteriorly from posterior corner of eye to a point above insertion of forelimbs, concealing upper edge of tympanum; tympanum distinct, diameter 1/2 to 2/3 of eye diameter; male vocal sacs paired, lateral; outer finger discs about 2/3 of tympanum diameter; relative length of fingers I < II < IV < III, modal webbing formula of fingers I 2 – 2 II 2⁻ – 3 III 2⁺ – 2⁺ IV; subarticular tubercles rounded to bifid on outer fingers (III, IV); no nuptial thumb pads; palmar tubercle flat, irregular in shape, equal in size to ovoid, raised thenar tubercle; toe discs present, relative length of toes I < II < V < IV < III; modal webbing formula of toes I 1⁺ – 2 II 0 – 2 III 1⁺ – 2⁺ IV 2 – 1 V; inner metatarsal tubercle large, oblong; outer metatarsal tubercle absent or very small, rounded; subarticular tubercles rounded, sometimes bifid on outer toes; distinct inner tarsal fold; heel surface smooth or slightly warty; skin granular on belly and ventral surfaces of thighs, dorsal surfaces smooth; vomerine teeth on fused, triangular processes situated transversally between choanae.

Dorsum uniform or spotted pale green, brown, or gray with irregular dark brown or blackish spots or blotches; limbs with dark brown transverse bars; a dark brown or black band extending from tympanum laterally onto anterior third of body; a dark

brown line present on canthus rostralis; flanks yellow in life, white or cream in preserved specimens, with brown or black mottling; venter dirty white or yellowish white.

Call: Porter (1962) described the call of this species as a loud monotonous repetition of the same notes with a dominant frequency at 2500 Hz and 0.2 second between notes. Duellman (1970, 2001) added that each note has a duration of 0.09–0.13 second, with 15 seconds to several minutes between call groups. The notes have 140–195 pulses per second and a fundamental frequency of 135–190 Hz. Lee (1996) noted the distinctive call of this species is a loud and nasally "wonk, wonk, wonk" repeated in rapid succession.

Natural history: E. Greenbaum (field notes) encountered calling males of this species at night in numerous lowland localities in El Salvador from July–August. Adults were collected from trees (1–2 m above ground) at night at Bosque Las Lajas, Depto. Sonsonate in July. A large breeding chorus was observed in a flooded depression of grass at night at Isla San Sebastián, Depto. Usulután in July. A pair was collected in amplexus at night ca. 1 m above the ground at Bosque Cinquera, Depto. Cabañas in August. M. Veselý (field notes) observed numerous calling males at night in a public fountain among houses in San Salvador, Depto. San Salvador in late May. Mertens (1952d) observed breeding activity from July through September and recorded egg laying in small ponds and water tanks in El Salvador. Rand (1957) noted Salvadoran frogs will call during the day if it is raining. Greding & Hellebuyck (1980) noted Coleoptera and Lepidoptera in the diet of 13 frogs collected at night in a pond in Depto. San Salvador in June. McCranie & Wilson (2002) noted breeding adults on mainland Honduras from May–October; tadpoles were collected from May–September and in November. Savage (2002) noted that high-pitched distress calls are emitted when the species is attacked. Females lay 2500–3000 black and cream eggs, and tadpoles are pelagic.

Conservation status: GAA: Least concern (LC).

Specimens examined: <u>Ahuachapán</u>: Parque Nacional El Imposible, La Fincona, 13°50.8′N, 89°58.8′W, 720 m: SMF 81433–34; Ausoles near San José: SMF 48032; El Refugio: VH 81; Finca Santa Luisa, 13°49′N, 89°52′W, 900 m: MUHNES C–30–1333–34. <u>Cabañas</u>: Bosque Cinquera, 13°53.13′N, 88°57.36′W, 400 m: KU 289989–90, 290003–04. <u>Chalatenango</u>: 1.6 km N Tejutla:

UTA A-50517; 16.5 km WNW Chalatenango. Cuscatlán: 22 km E San Salvador, 920 m: KU 107081, 1 km E Tenancingo: KU 184786–93; Tenancingo, Cantón El Tablón, Río Mazacuayo: KU 184805; Suchitoto: TCWC 23611; 2.9 km N Suchitoto: UU 4804. La Libertad: Quetzaltepeque: CAS 94798, UTA A-50535; Club Atami (near Playa El Palmarcito, Municipio Tamanique), 13°30.2′N, 89°25.0′W, 40 m: SMF 81445–54; Río Chilama near La Libertad: SMF 42393–96, 42672; Finca El Paraíso near Nuevo San Salvador [= Santa Tecla]: SMF 42235–36, MVZ 39860; road San Salvador–Sonsonate, turnoff to Santa Ana: SMF 52193–202; road San Salvador–Sonsonate, turnoff to Talnique, 520 m: SMF 52203–04; Playa El Balsamar, approx. 30 km W La Libertad, 10 m: VH 71; 16.1 km NW Nuevo San Salvador [= Santa Tecla]: KU 43542–44; 10 km E La Libertad: KU 184808–12; Los Chorros, 4.8 km W La Libertad: UF 20416–21; 1 km S Comasagua: TCWC 23805; Guadalupe, 640 m: KU 291376–77; 2 km S Zaragoza, Cantón Guadalupe, 13°33.1′N, 89°17.3′W, 740 m: YPM 6448–49. La Paz: road San Salvador–La Herradura, km 9 behind turnoff to Zacatecoluca, 50 m: SMF 52219. La Unión: 4 km S La Unión, Volcán de Conchagua: UU 4780. Morazán: Montecristo Mine, 213 m: MVZ 39861; Divisadero, 244 m: USNM 73284; Cerro Cacahuatique, 995 m: KU 291313, 1035 m: KU 291303–05, MUHNES C–30–1483. San Miguel: Laguna El Jocotal, below El Borbollón village: SMF 44565; Volcán de San Miguel, Hacienda Calle Nueva: UTA A-50532–33; Volcán de San Miguel, 740 m: MUHNES C–30–1477–82, KU 291262. San Salvador: 3.2 km S Río Lempa Bridge at intersection Guazapa Hwy: UTA A-50526; San Salvador, 65 Avenida Sur: SMF 42230–31, 42452, 42578, 42580, 43119–20; San Salvador, 65 Avenida Sur, pool near Barranca: SMF 42271–79, 42467–68 (tadpoles), 42515–21 (tadpoles); San Salvador, 65 Avenida Sur, Bougainvillia, hedge on the house of Reich: SMF 42409, 42419; San Salvador, Instituto Tropical de Investigaciones Científicas: KU 61955–88, SMF 43180–83, 44563–64, 47176, 47569, 47714, 48031, 48043, 50032, 52205–17, 52643, 54134, 58274, 61552, 81352; San Salvador, Río Acelhuate, near Instituto Tropical de Investigaciones Científicas: SMF 52218; San Salvador: MUHNES 1150–55, UMMZ 118380; same locality at 670 m: FMNH 65092, 65088–99; San Salvador on west edge of city: UMMZ 117586; San Salvador, Parque Zoológico Nacional: KU 289820, 289974, MUHNES C–30–1335–39; San Salvador, Parque Saburo-Hirao: AMNH 125858,

UF 48516; San Salvador, Ciudad Universitaria, 700 m: KU 184800–04, 184813–20; 3 km SE Ilopango, Cantón Asino: KU 184794–99, 184806–07. San Vicente: San Vicente: MUHNES 21; Finca El Carmen, 13°36.8′N, 88°50.3′W, 1240 m: SMF 81435; km 67.5 road San Salvador–Río Lempa, Barranca Sisimico, 480 m: SMF 42945. Santa Ana: Parque Nacional Montecristo, oficinas de Parques Nacionales, 800 m: MUHNES 699, SMF 81455. Sonsonate: Hacienda Cuyan–Cuya near Izalco: SMF 42561; 9.2 km SE Jct Hwys 12/2: TCWC 55897; Bosque Las Lajas, 13°50.04′N, 89°33.56′W, 920 m: KU 289875, 289877, 289880–84, MUHNES C–30–1328–29, C–30–1340. Usulután: Isla San Sebastián, 13°10.01′N, 88°24.49′W, 20 m: KU 289891–96, 289912, MUHNES C–30–1330–32.

Published locality records: La Libertad: Município La Libertad, 2 km S Zaragoza, Río San Antonio (13.552°N, 89.288°W), 740 m: YPM 6448–49 (Leenders & Watkins-Colwell 2004). San Salvador: 3.2 km SW of bridge over Río Lempa on highway between San Salvador and La Palma, 270 m (Greding & Hellebuyck 1980). Sonsonate: Município Izalco, Cantón Las Lajas, Bosque Las Lajas (13.829°N, 89.567°W), 750 m: YPM 6424 (Leenders & Watkins-Colwell 2004).

Family Leptodactylidae

Over 1120 species (45 genera) of frogs are included in this family. Distributed from Texas (USA) to the Straits of Magellan in South America, southern Florida (USA), Hispaniola, Puerto Rico, and throughout the West Indies. Although seven subfamilies are recognized, the systematics of this group remains in a state of flux (Duellman 2003d). New species continue to be described, especially from South America (e.g., Caramaschi et al. 2003, Verdade & Rodrigues 2003). Four species in two genera occur in El Salvador.

Genus *Eleutherodactylus*

Most of the 690 species of frogs in this genus lay eggs that hatch into froglets with no larval stage, but at least one species (*Eleutherodactylus jasperi*) gives birth to live young (Duellman 2003d). Distributed from the southwestern USA to southern Argentina and Brazil, throughout the West Indies, and introduced to several American states outside their natural range (D. Frost 2002, 2004). Two species occur in El Salvador.

Eleutherodactylus rhodopis (Cope 1867)
(Rana Hojarasquera Común)
Plate 32, Map 24

1867 *Lithodytes rhodopis* Cope, Proc. Acad. Nat.
Sci. Philadelphia, 18: 323; type locality: Orizaba and
Cordóba, Veracruz (Mexico).
Eleutherodactylus rhodopis: Mertens 1952d, Rand
1957, Villa et al. 1988, Dueñas et al. 2001, Leenders
& Watkins-Colwell 2004.
Eleutherodactylus loki: Lynch 2000, D. Frost 2002,
2004, McCranie & Wilson 2002, Leenders 2003.
Geographic distribution: Western Veracruz and
adjacent Hidalgo and Puebla, Mexico; from north-
ern San Luis Potosí, Mexico, to northwestern
Honduras on the Atlantic versant; from southern
Chiapas and Oaxaca, Mexico, to central El Salvador
on the Pacific versant (D. Frost 2002, McCranie &
Wilson 2002).
Ecological distribution: Dry forest, premontane
evergreen forest, subtropical humid forest, and
pine-oak forest between sea level and 1720 m.
Description: Largest Salvadoran specimen examined is 43.7 mm SVL; HW/SVL 0.31–0.43; HL/SVL
0.32–0.42; shank length/SVL 0.42–0.57; foot length/
SVL 0.39–0.53; tympanum diameter/SVL 0.06–0.11;
2nd toe disc width/SVL 0.02–0.03; 3rd toe disc
width/SVL 0.02–0.03. Snout nearly rounded in
dorsal aspect, rounded in profile; top of head flat,
canthus rostralis rounded, distinct; loreal region
concave; nostrils directed laterally, situated at a
point about 3/4 distance between anterior border of
eye and tip of snout; supratympanic fold distinct,
continuing to flanks, narrowly obscuring upper
edge of tympanum; narrow discs on fingers III–IV;
no nuptial thumb pads; relative length of fingers II
< IV < I < III or II < IV < I ~ III; heels smooth to
rugose, lacking tubercles; subarticular tubercles
rounded, projecting, usually obtuse in profile;
thenar tubercle equal in size to palmar tubercle,
ovoid, raised; discs present on all toes; inner
metatarsal tubercle slightly elliptical in outline,
projecting in profile; outer metatarsal tubercle
rounded, projecting; relative length of toes I < II <
V < III < IV; webbing absent between toes; inner
metatarsal fold weak; dorsum smooth to tubercular
with narrow longitudinal skin folds; upper eyelids
rugose and tubercular; skin of belly and ventral
surfaces of thighs coarsely areolate; vomerine tooth
patches on elevated, somewhat triangular ridges
between and posterior to choanae, each ridge separated by distance smaller than size of either patch.

Plate 32: *Eleutherodactylus rhodopis* EL SALVADOR:
Ahuachapán: El Refugio (225 m). Photo: G. Köhler.

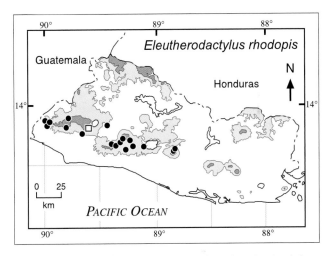

Map 24: Distribution of *Eleutherodactylus rhodopis* in
El Salvador.
Closed circles represent examined-specimen locality records;
open squares are published locality records. Light shading
indicates 600–1200 m elevation; dark shading indicates elevations ≥ 1200 m; large bodies of freshwater are outlined in bold,
black lines.

Dorsal ground color brown or reddish brown,
sometimes with irregular dark brown blotching on
body and limbs. Ventral surfaces opaque, yellowish
gray in coloration. More or less distinct dark brown
stripe extending from tip of snout through nasal
opening and orbits, terminating beyond posterior
margin of tympanum. Small creamish spots present
on posterior surface of thigh in some individuals.
Call: The call of this species resembles two
whistles followed by a chick-like peep, repeated
intermittently (E. Greenbaum, pers. obs.).
Taxonomic comments: Leenders & Watkins-
Colwell (2004) discussed the dubious taxonomic
changes of Lynch (2000), who examined only one

Salvadoran specimen of this species. Samples of *Eleutherodactylus loki* from several localities (including some near the type locality) interdigitated with *E. rhodopis* at a very low sequence divergence in a recent molecular phylogenetic analysis (E. N. Smith, pers. comm.). Thus, we do not agree with the findings of Lynch (2000) who recognized *E. loki* as a valid taxon.

Natural history: E. Greenbaum (field notes) observed calling males at Parque Nacional El Imposible, Depto. Ahuachapán in July; most individuals were calling on the ground during a heavy rain at night, but one individual was discovered calling from vegetation 2 m off the ground in a tree. Other males were calling from leaf litter among coffee plants at night during a light rain at Finca La Giralda, Depto. La Libertad in August. Mertens (1952d) reported *Eleutherodactylus rhodopis* in the stomach of a *Pliocercus elapoides* (Serpentes: Colubridae) collected in El Salvador. Rand (1957) collected *E. rhodopis* (together with *E. rupinius*) under stones and leaf litter at the bottom of a brush-grown gully in pasture at San Salvador, Depto. San Salvador in March. Leenders (2003) commented this species is diurnal and common in humid leaf litter in Parque Nacional El Imposible, Depto. Ahuachapán. The only specimen known from Honduras was collected in 1923 in an area that has been severely altered by anthropogenic activity (McCranie & Wilson 2002). Leenders & Watkins-Colwell (2004) noted high densities of this species in leaf litter of dried riverbeds during the dry season in El Salvador.

Conservation status: GAA: Least concern (LC). Taxon listed as *E. loki*.

Specimens examined: Ahuachapán: Finca Concepción Miramar, 13°48.46´N, 89°48.03´W, 920 m: KU 290049; Parque Nacional El Imposible, El Caschal, 500 m: SMF 79060–61; Parque Nacional El Imposible, Piedra Sellada, 500 m: SMF 79062; Parque Nacional El Imposible, Finca San Benito, 730 m: SMF 78931; Parque Nacional El Imposible, Finca San Benito, 600 m: VH 89; same locality near Río Guayapa, 480 m: KU 289837–38, MUHNES C–30–1256; Parque Nacional El Imposible, La Fincona, 13°50.8´N, 89°58.8´W, 720 m: KU 289751–54, 289756, 289767, 290048, MUHNES C–30–1252–55, C–30–1258–60, SMF 81402, 81404, 81475, VH 61, 79, 91; Laguna de Las Ninfas, 13°52.4´N, 89°47.8´W, 1720 m: SMF 81401; El Refugio, vicinity of Mariposario of Francisco Serrano, 13°49.46´N, 89°59.98´W, 225 m: SMF 79069–70, VH 54, 57;

Finca Santa Luisa, 13°49´N, 89°52´W, 900 m: MUHNES C–30–1261. La Libertad: Finca San José, 1200 m: SMF 42375: SMF 44395–96; Finca Alicante, Cumbre de Nuevo San Salvador [= Santa Tecla], 1100 m: SMF 44397; Finca El Paraíso near Nuevo San Salvador [= Santa Tecla]: SMF 42591–95, 42604–06, 42677–81, 42846; Los Chorros: MUHNES 64, 323, 455; Finca La Giralda, 13°39.34´N, 89°22.47´W, 1080 m: KU 289960–62, MUHNES C–30–1257. San Salvador: Los Planes de Renderos near San Salvador, 975 m: SMF 44398; 2.4 km SE Ilopango, Cantón Asino: KU 184415; San Salvador, 670 m: FMNH 65107–08. San Vicente: Finca Santa Magdalena, 1000 m: SMF 44399; Las Iglasias, Finca El Rudal, 1145 m: SMF 44400. Sonsonate: Finca Los Guates, Izalco: MUHNES 38; Hacienda Chilata, 610 m: MVZ 39836–47.

Published locality records: Ahuachapán: Município San Pedro Puxtla, Cantón La Concepción, Cooperativa Concepción Miramar (13.810°N, 89.807°W), 950 m: YPM 6430–32 (Leenders & Watkins-Colwell 2004); Parque Nacional El Imposible: YPM 6427–29, 7244–48 (Leenders & Watkins-Colwell 2004). Sonsonate: Município Izalco, Cantón Cruz Grande, Finca Nuevos Horizontes (13.821°N, 89.653°W), 1200 m: YPM 6415–16, 6433 (Leenders & Watkins-Colwell 2004).

Eleutherodactylus rupinius Campbell & Savage 2000
(Rana de Riachuelo del Pacífico)
Plate 33, Map 25

2000 *Eleutherodactylus rupinius* Campbell & Savage, Herpetol. Monogr. 14: 213; type locality: Finca El Faro, S slope Volcán Santa María, 4.0 km N El Palmar, 875 m, Quetzaltenango, Guatemala.
Eleutherodactylus rugulosus: Mertens 1952d, Rand 1957, Lynch 1965, Savage 1975, Villa et al. 1988, Dueñas et al. 2001.
Eleutherodactylus rupinius: D. Frost 2002, 2004, Leenders 2003, Leenders & Watkins-Colwell 2004.

Geographic distribution: From southeastern Chiapas, Mexico, southeastward along the Pacific versant through southern Guatemala to eastern El Salvador (D. Frost 2002, 2004).

Ecological distribution: Dry forest, premontane evergreen forest, subtropical humid forest, and pine-oak forest at elevations of 200–1800 m.

Description: Largest Salvadoran specimen examined is 63.8 mm SVL; HW/SVL 0.37–0.43; HL/SVL 0.36–0.42; shank length/SVL 0.49–0.61; foot length/

Plate 33: *Eleutherodactylus rupinius* EL SALVADOR: Ahuachapán: El Refugio (225 m). Photo: G. Köhler.

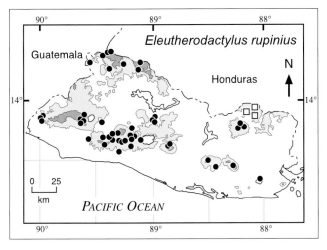

Map 25: Distribution of *Eleutherodactylus rupinius* in El Salvador.Closed circles represent examined-specimen locality records; open squares are published locality records. Light shading indicates 600–1200 m elevation; dark shading indicates elevations ≥ 1200 m; large bodies of freshwater are outlined in bold, black lines.

SVL 0.45–0.54; tympanum diameter/SVL 0.05–0.08; 2nd toe disc width/SVL 0.02–0.03; 3rd toe disc width/SVL 0.03–0.05. Snout rounded or nearly rounded in dorsal aspect, almost rounded in profile; nostrils directed laterally; canthus rostralis distinct, sharp; tympanum distinct; finger discs definite, about twice width of digits just proximal to discs on fingers III and IV; relative length of fingers II < I < IV < III; subarticular tubercles rounded, distinct; palmar tubercle flat, bifid, about two times larger than thenar tubercle which is ovoid and raised; strong inner tarsal fold; toe discs definite, on toes III and IV at least 1.5 times wider than digits; toe relative length: I < II < V < III < IV; weak marginal

ridge on toes evident; toe webbing definite, basal to moderate; outer metatarsal tubercle small, rounded; inner metatarsal tubercle spade-like, much larger than outer metatarsal tubercle; subarticular tubercles rounded, small. Dorsal skin smooth; distinct supratympanic fold extending from posterior margin of orbit to tympanum, terminating at point above the insertion of forelimbs; posterior surface of thighs slightly granular; vomerine teeth present on triangular processes situated posterior to the choanae.

Dorsum uniform grayish brown, with or without minute irregular black spots in dorsolateral regions. On the flanks, the dorsal color gradually grades into white or creamy yellow ventral coloration. Gular area may be uniformly dark grayish brown or creamy yellow with grayish brown spots. Upper lip dark brown with four or five creamish bands on each side, in some specimens banding may be extremely faint. The two posterior bands touch the orbit. A black line extends from posterior edge of orbit around the dorsal and posterior borders of tympanum, ending beyond corner of mouth. Posterior thigh surface variegated with numerous creamish spots and small blotches on a dark brown background. Some specimens have a white line from the tip of the snout to the posterior margin of the dorsum above the vent.

Call: Campbell & Savage (2000) noted that in this species "vocal slits [are] present or absent in large adult males," but no information on the mating call in this species was provided.

Natural history: E. Greenbaum (field notes) collected two adults as they hopped across a road at night during a light rain at Cerro del Tigre, Depto. Usulután in July; the surrounding habitat was coffee plantation and human habitations. Mertens (1952d) noted that these frogs are common along streams where they can be observed on rock walls in El Salvador. Rand (1957) collected this species (together with *Eleutherodactylus rhodopis*) under stones and leaf litter at the bottom of a brush-grown gully in pasture at San Salvador, Depto. San Salvador in March. Juveniles were collected between April and May in several Salvadoran localities.

Conservation status: GAA: Least concern (LC).
Specimens examined: Ahuachapán: El Refugio, vicinity of Mariposario of Francisco Serrano, 13°49.46′N, 89°59.98′W, 225 m: SMF 79071–76; Parque Nacional El Imposible, Finca San Benito, 600 m: VH 85, 87, 90; Parque Nacional El

Imposible, La Fincona, 13°50.8´N, 89°58.8´W, 720
m: MUHNES 43, 858–59, 872, 878, 885, SMF 81403;
Parque Nacional El Imposible: MUHNES 34, 44, 54,
57, 63, 138, 140, 875, 879, 883. Chalatenango: 11 km
E La Palma, Cantón El Aguacatal: KU 184412; San
José del Sacaré, 1097 m: USNM 73279–82; Los
Esesmiles, Cerro El Pital: USNM 73295. Cuscatlán:
Tenancingo, El Sitio de los Sánchez: KU 184402–04;
3 km SE Tenancingo, Río Tizapa: KU 184405; 1.3
km N Tenancingo, Cantón Copalchan: KU 184408; 2
km NNE Tenancingo, Sitio de José Santiago: KU
184413–14. La Libertad: Los Chorros, between
Colón and Nuevo San Salvador [= Santa Tecla], 700
m: SMF 42382–91, 42436, 44414, 44945, MUHNES
35, 452–54; Finca Los Angeles, Cumbre de Jayaque,
1500 m: SMF 42850, 44415; Finca San José,
Cumbre de Nuevo San Salvador [= Santa Tecla],
1200 m: SMF 44416; Finca Alicante, Cumbre de
Nuevo San Salvador [= Santa Tecla], 1100 m: SMF
44417–18; Finca El Paraíso near Nuevo San Salvador [= Santa Tecla]: SMF 42596–97, 42599–601,
42607–11, 42709, 42715, 42796–99, 42807, 42869,
42884; Ayagualo on km 15, road San Salvador–La
Libertad, 835 m: SMF 43079; Los Chorros near
Colón: SMF 52268–83; La Libertad, cave near
Hacienda San Diego, 17 m: SMF 52284–85; Hacienda Zapotitán, 457 m: MVZ 39815; 4.4 km E Colón:
UMMZ 131114, 137911–14; 2.3 km E Colón: UMMZ
131115, 137915–17; near Colón: MCZ 28857; 16.1
km NW Nuevo San Salvador [= Santa Tecla]: KU
44111; 2 km SE Colón: KU 61875–76; 4.2 km W
Nuevo San Salvador [= Santa Tecla]: KU 61877–78;
Nueva San Salvador, 1300 m: KU 184409–10; 3 km
from Comasagua: KU 184411; Guadalupe, 640 m:
KU 291369–70, MUHNES C–30–1434–35. Morazán:
N slope Mt. Cacahuatique, 1402 m: MVZ 39851;
1158 m: MVZ 39878–80, 39808–24, 39826, 39828; E
slope Mt. Cacahuatique, 1219 m: MVZ 39852–53;
same locality at 1128 m: 39854; 39827; W slope Mt.
Cacahuatique, 1280 m: MVZ 39825. San Miguel:
Volcán de San Miguel, 13°26.2´N, 88°16.2´W, 1600
m: SMF 81428; Volcán de San Miguel, 740 m: KU
291264; Laguna de Olomega, 61 m: MVZ 39848,
39809. San Salvador: Río Acelhuate near Apopa:
SMF 42431, 42475; Colónia Modelo near San
Salvador: SMF 48025; Tubo Milingo near San
Salvador: SMF 48052–55; San Salvador, 670 m:
FMNH 65110–14; Lago de Ilopango, 400 m: FMNH
65100, 65115. San Vicente: Volcán San Vicente,
Finca Santa Magdalena, 1000 m: SMF 44419–25;
Volcán San Vicente, Finca El Carmen, 1319 m: SMF
44426, 48026, 81429–32. Santa Ana: Laguna de

Güija, 700 m: SMF 44401; Hacienda San José,
Metapán: SMF 44402–09, 42457–60; Volcán de
Santa Ana, Finca Los Andes, 13°52.1´N, 89°37.2´W,
1500 m: MUHNES C–30–1209; Hacienda Los
Planes, 1830 m: SMF 43043; San Juan Mine, 12.1
km SE Metapán, 488 m: MVZ 39811; Hacienda
Montecristo, Metapán Mt: KU 61879, 62001;
Hacienda San José, 800 m: KU 66019–20.
Sonsonate: Cerro Verde, Hacienda Buena Vista,
1200 m: SMF 44410–13; Hacienda Cuyan-Cuya near
Izalco, 380 m: SMF 43011; Hacienda Chilata, 610 m:
MVZ 39835, 39850, 39882–85, 39812–14, 39816–19,
USNM 73293–94. Usulután: Volcán Tecapa, north-
ern side of crater lake, 13°29.3´N, 88°29.9´W, 860
m: SMF 81427; Cerro del Tigre, 13°28.37´N,
88°26.21´W, 1100 m: KU 289843–44, 289861,
MUHNES C–30–1262.

Published locality records: Ahuachapán: Parque
Nacional El Imposible, Río Guayapa: YPM 6419
(Leenders & Watkins-Colwell 2004). Sonsonate:
Município Izalco, Cantón Cruz Grande, Finca
Nuevos Horizontes (13.821°N, 89.653°W), 1130 m:
YPM 6410–13, 6434–39 (Leenders & Watkins-
Colwell 2004).

Genus *Leptodactylus*

This large genus of frogs (approximately 64
species) is distributed from southern Texas (USA) to
south-central Argentina, the Lesser Antilles,
Hispaniola, Puerto Rico, and the Virgin Islands
(McCranie & Wilson 2002, D. Frost 2004).
McDiarmid & Altig (1999) classified the larvae of
this genus as exotrophic, lentic, and benthic. Two
species occur in El Salvador.

Leptodactylus fragilis (Brocchi 1877)
(Ranita Espumera Labioblanco)
Plate 34, Map 26, Figures 12a, 15g

1877 *Cystignathus fragilis* Cope, Bull. Soc. Philo.
Paris 1: 182; type locality: Tehuantepec, Mexico.
Leptodactylus labialis: Mertens 1952d, Rand 1957;
Heyer 1971, Dueñas et al. 2001, Leenders 2003,
Leenders & Watkins-Colwell 2004.
Leptodactylus fragilis: Heyer 1978, Villa et al. 1988,
Heyer 2002.
Geographic distribution: From extreme south-
ern Texas (USA) to central Colombia and northern
Venezuela on the Atlantic versant; from Colima,
Mexico, to central Panama on the Pacific versant
(McCranie & Wilson 2002).

Plate 34: *Leptodactylus fragilis* NICARAGUA: Chontales: Bartola (340 m). Photo: G. Köhler.

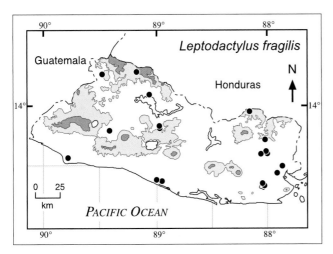

Map 26: Distribution of *Leptodactylus fragilis* in El Salvador.Closed circles represent examined-specimen locality records; open squares are published locality records. Light shading indicates 600–1200 m elevation; dark shading indicates elevations ≥ 1200 m; large bodies of freshwater are outlined in bold, black lines.

Ecological distribution: Dry forest and savanna between sea level and 1150 m.

Description: Largest Salvadoran specimen examined is 39.0 mm SVL; HW/SVL 0.32–0.38; HL/SVL 0.34–0.42; shank length/SVL 0.40–0.53; foot length/SVL 0.46–0.59; tympanum diameter/SVL 0.05–0.07. Snout pointed in dorsal and lateral views; canthus rostralis rounded; frontal area slightly convex; loreal region concave; tympanum distinct, about 2/3 of eye diameter; supratympanic fold weak; fingers and toes with slightly expanded tips lacking discs; webbing absent; subarticular tubercles rounded, projecting; palmar tubercle slightly bifid, larger than thenar tubercle; relative length of fingers II ~

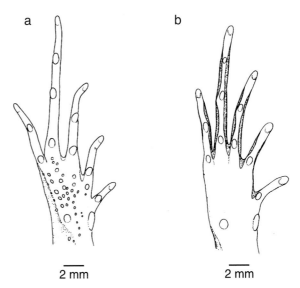

2 mm   2 mm

Figure 12: Ventral view of right feet of a. *Leptodactylus fragilis* (SMF 48049); b. *Leptodactylus melanonotus* (SMF 81425).

IV < I < III; toes I < II < V < III < IV; outer metatarsal tubercle relatively small, ovoid, equal in size to inner metatarsal tubercle; subarticular tubercles small, rounded; inner tarsal fold present; skin of body smooth; a distinct ventral disc present; vomerine tooth patches on elevated ridges between and posterior to choanae, ridges separated by distance about 1/2 size of each patch.

Dorsum brown, tan, or gray with irregular dark brown blotches in more or less distinct longitudinal lines; dark brown line on canthus continuing behind eye around upper and posterior border of ear, ending above point of insertion of forelimbs; three to four darker transverse blotches on legs; usually a conspicuous white labial stripe present, obscured in some specimens; cream longitudinal stripe on the posterior part of thighs; venter immaculate cream, sometimes spotted in gular region.

Call: Straughan & Heyer (1976) described the calls of 17 Costa Rican individuals at ca. 25°C as follows: the call consists of two notes separated by a short time gap (6 msec). The first note lasts about 170 msec and consists of 24–29 pulses, with 141–167 pulses per second (1000–1100 Hz). The second note lasts about 23 msec (1700 Hz). Campbell (1998a) described the call of this species as a short, high-pitched, upwardly inflected peep or whistle, sounding like "boing" and given at irregular intervals.

Taxonomic comments: Because of a mistake in

Dubois & Heyer (1992) *Leptodactylus labialis* was used as the erroneous name for this taxon from 1992–2002. Heyer (2002) discussed the confusion regarding the valid name for this species.

Natural history: E. Greenbaum (field notes) collected this species from a flooded field adjacent to a road at night at Perquín, Depto. Morazán in August; calling *Scinax staufferi* and *Physalaemus pustulosus* were also in this water. O. Komar (field notes) collected an adult under a log during the day in pine-oak forest at Perquín, Depto. Morazán in June. M. Veselý (field notes) found three Salva-doran adult males at a pasture at night after rain at the end of May; the frogs were calling from well-hidden chambers under grass tussocks that already contained eggs. Mertens (1952d) found this species in water canals near Cerro Montecristo, Depto. Santa Ana. Rand (1957) collected specimens along a forest edge and under bark 6 km N of Los Blancos, Depto. La Paz in May and June. Campbell (1998a) noted that males whip eggs, jelly capsules, and seminal fluid into a foam and construct nest cham-bers 1–3 m from shorelines during periods of increasing rain; clutches range in size from 25–250 bright yellow eggs. McCranie & Wilson (2002) found individuals at night from June–August; tadpoles were found from July–August in Honduras. Savage (2002) noted this species feeds mainly on arthropods.

Conservation status: GAA: Least concern (LC).

Specimens examined: Chalatenango: La Palma, 1000 m: SMF 48051; 16.5 km WNW Chalatenango: KU 184425. Cuscatlán: 1 km E Tenancingo, El Manguito: KU 184416–17; 1 km E Tenancingo, Cantón El Llano: KU 184419–24. La Libertad: Hacienda Zapotitán, 457 m: MVZ 39871. La Paz: 6 km N of La Herradura: SMF 44467–78; 6 km N Los Blancos: FMNH 65121–22. La Unión: km 198 road La Unión–Pasaquina: SMF 44483–88; Hacienda San Cajetano: SMF 48050; 24.1 km N, 3.2 km E La Unión: KU 42862–63. Morazán: Montecristo Mine, 213 m: MVZ 39862–65; 1.6 km SE Divisadero, 259 m: MVZ 39866–67; 4 km N of Divisadero, quarry Flamenco: SMF 42955; Divisadero, 244 m: USNM 73285–86; Perquín, 13°57.17´N, 88°10.01´W, 1150 m: KU 290013, 290042, 291331, 291348–49, 291357, MUHNES C–30–1263, C–30–1440, C–30–1442. San Miguel: km 155 road San Miguel–La Unión: SMF 44479–82; San Miguel: SMF 48049; Laguna de Olomega, 61 m: MVZ 39868. Santa Ana: 6 km S Metapán: KU 184418. Sonsonate: Morrotal on road to Los Cobanos, 1 km S road Sonsonate–Acajutla: SMF 44464–66.

Published locality records: Morazán: Município Arambala, Cantón Cumaro, Bailadero del Diablo (13.931°N, 88.102°W), 696 m: YPM 7232 (Leenders & Watkins-Colwell 2004); Município Arambala, Cantón Cumaro, Nahuaterique, near border crossing with Honduras (13.995°N, 88.093°W): YPM 7233; Município Arambala, Cantón Cumaro, Río Sapo (13.959°N, 88.132°W), 1120 m: YPM 7234.

Leptodactylus melanonotus (Hallowell 1861)
(Ranita Espumera Común)
Plate 35, Map 27, Figures 12b, 15h

1861 *Cystignathus melanonotus* Hallowell, Proc. Acad. Nat. Sci. Philadelphia 12: 485; type locality: Nicaragua.
Leptodactylus melanonotus: Mertens 1952d, Rand 1957, Heyer 1970b, Greding & Hellebuyck 1980, Villa et al. 1988, Dueñas et al. 2001, Leenders 2003.

Geographic distribution: From Tamaulipas, Mexico, to central Panama on the Atlantic versant; from Sonora, Mexico, to central Ecuador on the Pacific versant (D. Frost 2002, 2004, McCranie & Wilson 2002).

Ecological distribution: Dry forest and savanna between sea level and 1150 m.

Description: Largest Salvadoran specimen exam-ined is 45.4 mm SVL; HW/SVL 0.29–0.38; HL/SVL 0.28–0.41; shank length/SVL 0.38–0.48; foot length/SVL 0.39–0.55; tympanum diameter/SVL 0.05–0.07. Snout bluntly rounded in dorsal as well as lateral view; canthus rostralis widely rounded, indistinct; frontal area flat, loreal region slightly concave; tympanum visible, about 2/3 of eye diameter; no supratympanic fold; limbs short, robust; fingers and toes lack webbing, but narrow dermal fringes present on digits, especially on toes; relative length of fingers II < I < IV < III; subarticular tubercles small, rounded; males possessing two black kerati-nized spines at the bases of thumbs; palmar tu-bercle bifid; relative length of toes I < II < V < III < IV; outer metatarsal tubercle rounded, smaller than inner metatarsal tubercle, which is ovoid and prominent; skin generally smooth, that of dorsum covered by tiny black pustulation; vomerine teeth present on triangular, separated processes, situated posteriorly from and between choanae.

Dorsal color dark brown, gray, or almost black, often with indistinct darker markings and a trian-gular interorbital bar; ventral coloration creamy yellow, sometimes spotted or flecked to form a dark-er reticulum; ventral part of limbs often yellowish.

Plate 35: *Leptodactylus melanonotus* EL SALVADOR: Ahuachapán: El Refugio (225 m). Photo: G. Köhler.

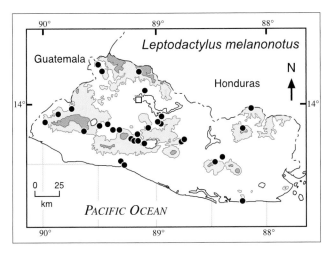

Map 27: Distribution of *Leptodactylus melanonotus* in El Salvador.
Closed circles represent examined-specimen locality records; open squares are published locality records. Light shading indicates 600–1200 m elevation; dark shading indicates elevations ≥ 1200 m; large bodies of freshwater are outlined in bold, black lines.

Call: Straughan & Heyer (1976) described the calls of 25 Costa Rican individuals at ca. 25°C as follows: the call is a single note repeated at an average of 150–160 calls per minute. The minimum average time between calls is 0.2 second. The note has two parts—the first part lasts 7–8 msec, 1100–2600 Hz; the second part lasts 23–26 msec, 2000–2400 Hz. Campbell (1998a) distinguished between a soft single-noted territorial call and a higher pitched breeding call of this species. Described as "a simple but well-modulated 'tuc, tuc, tuc-tuc'" by Lee (1996).
Natural history: E. Greenbaum (field notes) collected adults from a temporary pond in a meadow at night at Bosque Cinquera, Depto. Cabañas in August; calling *Physalaemus pustulosus*

were collected from the same pond. M. Veselý (field notes) collected several adults during the day on the banks of Laguna Chalchuapa, Depto. Santa Ana in June. Mertens (1952d) noted this species prefers small ponds, water canals, and swampy grassland in El Salvador. Most breeding activity was observed during the rainy season and metamorphs were recorded on 8 October. Rand (1957) described calling behavior, larvae, and recently transformed juveniles at localities in Depto. San Salvador. Greding & Hellebuyck (1980) noted Coleoptera and Lepidoptera in the diet of three frogs collected at night at a pond in Depto. San Salvador in June. Campbell (1998a) noted breeding from the months of April, October, and November. McCranie & Wilson (2002) noted adults in breeding choruses in May, July, August, and October in mainland Honduras; males were heard calling during the day in the height of the breeding season. Tadpoles were noted from mainland Honduras from June–August. Savage (2002) noted that males are territorial and fights can occur if leg-raising displays do not dissuade challengers to resident males. Males construct foam nests, which may contain 1000–2000 eggs.
Conservation status: GAA: Least concern (LC).
Specimens examined: Ahuachapán: El Refugio, vicinity of Mariposario of Francisco Serrano, 13°49.46´N, 89°59.98´W, 225 m: SMF 81117–18; 1.6 km S Ahuachapán, Lago de Espino: TCWC 37878. Cabañas: Bosque Cinquera, 13°53.13´N, 88°57.36´W, 400 m: MUHNES C–30–1264, C–30–1268–70, KU 289982–87. Chalatenango: San Ignacio, 920 m: SMF 44493; 16.5 km WNW Chalatenango: KU 184477–88. Cuscatlán: Tenancingo: MUHNES 659, 661, 663; 3 km ENE Tenancingo, Río Quezalapa: KU 184427–49, USNM 211433. La Libertad: Río Joya S of Ciudad Arce, Chilamatal: SMF 44490; Laguna de Chanmico, 480 m: SMF 42627–32, UMMZ 123613; 9 km N La Libertad on Carretera Litoral: AMNH 62937; 16 km NW Nuevo San Salvador [= Santa Tecla]: KU 41915–23, 48973–78; 10 km E La Libertad: KU 184474–76; Río El Jute flowing beneath Carretera Sur 4 km N of La Libertad (ca. km 33): AMNH 62938. Morazán: Cerro Cacahuatique: MUHNES 772–74; Perquín: KU 291328, MUHNES C–30–1441, C–30–1443. San Salvador: Villa Margarita, Colónia America, San Salvador: SMF 44881–901; San Salvador, 700 m: FMNH 65077, 65085–86; Asino, Lago de Ilopango: SMF 42936–40; Lago de Ilopango, 400 m: FMNH 65071, 65073–74, 65078, 65080–82, 65084–85; road San Salvador–Suchitoto, at bridge over Río Las

Canas: SMF 44492; 11.3 km N San Salvador: UTA
A-1403; San Salvador, Parque Zoológico Nacional:
KU 289814, 289819, 289828–32, MUHNES C–30–
1265–67; km 29 near Ateos, N of San Salvador:
MCZ 28858, 28862; 3 km SE Ilopango, Cantón
Asino: KU 184450–55, 184460–73. Santa Ana:
Gameros brook in Cantón La Joya: SMF 44491;
Chalchuapa, Laguna Cuscachapa, 13°58.8´N,
89°40.5´W, 690 m: SMF 81424–26; San Juan Mine,
12.1 km SE Metapán, 488 m: MVZ 39869–70; 6 km
S Metapán: KU 184457–59. San Vicente: 5 km off
main rd. CAI, Lago Apastepeque: CAS 139992–95;
Laguna de Apastepeque: SMF 44494; Laguna Ciega:
SMF 43027–28; brook near the Laguna de
Apastepeque: SMF 47958–63. Sonsonate: Hacienda
Cuyan-Cuya near Izalco, 380 m: SMF 42483; 42529–
47; 43012–24, 43114–17. Usulután: limestone
quarry 8 km S of km 99, road San Salvador–San
Miguel: SMF 42996; Playa El Espino, Municipio de
Jucuarán: VH 77.

Published locality records: San Salvador: 3.2
km SW of a bridge over the Río Lempa, on highway
between San Salvador and La Palma, 270 m
(Greding & Hellebuyck 1980).

Genus *Physalaemus*

The 45 species in this genus are distributed
from central Veracruz and southern Oaxaca,
Mexico, to central Argentina (McCranie & Wilson
2002, Caramaschi et al. 2003, D. Frost 2004, Ron et
al. 2004). McDiarmid & Altig (1999) classified the
larvae of this genus as exotrophic, lentic, and
benthic. One species is ubiquitous in El Salvador's
lowlands.

Physalaemus pustulosus (Cope 1864)
(Sapito Tungara)
Plate 36, Map 28

1864 *Paludicola pustulosa* Cope, Proc. Acad. Nat.
Sci. Philadelphia 16: 180; type locality: New
Granada on the River Truando, Colombia.
Eupemphix pustulosus: Sokol 1949.
Engystomops pustulosus: Mertens 1952d, Rand
1957, Nelson & Hoyt 1961.
Physalaemus pustulosus: Greding & Hellebuyck
1980, Villa et al. 1988, Dueñas et al. 2001, Leenders
2003.
Geographic distribution: From central Veracruz,
Mexico, to Guyana on the Atlantic versant; from
southern Oaxaca, Mexico, to eastern Panama on

Plate 36: *Physalaemus pustulosus* HONDURAS:
Intibucá: Santa Lucía (370 m). Photo: G. Köhler.

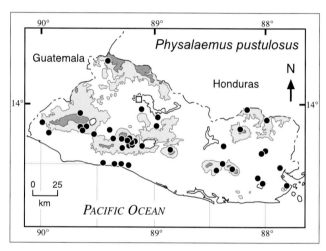

Map 28: Distribution of *Physalaemus pustulosus* in
El Salvador.
Closed circles represent examined-specimen locality records;
open squares are published locality records. Light shading
indicates 600–1200 m elevation; dark shading indicates elevations ≥ 1200 m; large bodies of freshwater are outlined in bold,
black lines.

the Pacific versant (McCranie & Wilson 2002).
Ecological distribution: Dry forest and savanna
between sea level and 1300 m. This species occurs
in many areas of El Salvador that have been
severely altered by human activities.
Description: Largest Salvadoran specimen examined is 31.8 mm SVL; HW/SVL 0.29–0.37; HL/SVL
0.27–0.33; shank length/SVL 0.38–0.45; foot length/
SVL 0.37–0.47. Snout acuminate, but blunt on tip in
dorsal view, truncate in profile; top of head slightly
convex; loreal region concave; nostrils directed
posterolaterally, situated at a point about 4/5
distance between anterior border of eye and tip of
snout; tympanum absent; narrow fold in
supratympanic region; fingers unwebbed, relative

length of fingers I < II < IV < III; subarticular tubercles large, rounded, projecting; palmar tubercle ovoid to almost bifid; thenar tubercle elliptical and raised, smaller than palmar tubercle; a conspicuous inner tarsal tubercle present; relative length of toes I < II < V < III < IV; subarticular and outer metatarsal tubercles small, rounded; inner metatarsal tubercle ovoid, projecting; toe webbing absent or at best basal between toes II–IV; narrow lateral skin fringe on digits; skin generally verrucose with numerous tubercles in dorsal region, tubercles less numerous but present on venter; dorsal tubercles with no definite arrangement or arranged in longitudinal rows and dermal ridges; no vomerine teeth; vocal sac single.

Coloration variable, generally brown, reddish brown, or gray with darker blotches and spots or even longitudinal lines; sometimes a thin creamish longitudinal line is present on the posterior part of body; darker transverse bands on limbs; creamish spot in interscapular area in some specimens; venter pale yellow with irregular darker blotches; gular region usually dark brown with creamish midventral longitudinal line.

Call: The call of this species is very distinctive and consists of several "beeee–yooop" whines followed occasionally by a few short "chuck" sounds (Campbell 1998a). Described as "a *pow*, whine whose dominant frequency begins at about 900 Hz and sweeps downward to about 400 Hz" by Lee (1996).

Natural history: E. Greenbaum (field notes) recorded this species at nearly every human-disturbed, lowland habitat visited in the rainy season from July–August. Numerous males congregated and called at very shallow pools in roadside ditches. Great numbers of this species were found calling and breeding in man-made water basins (i.e., "pilas") in coffee plantations at Finca El Milagro, Depto. Santa Ana at night; *Agalychnis moreletii* were breeding in these same pools. M. Veselý (field notes) encountered numerous individuals at Finca El Carmen (1240 m), Depto. San Vicente. Sokol (1949) reported calling behavior and egg masses of frogs in Depto. La Libertad in July. Mertens (1952d) noted that calls of this frog can be heard from late April through early October. Axillary amplexus was observed at night in El Salvador. Rand (1957) described the habitat, calling behavior, and egg masses of Salvadoran animals in detail; during the day specimens were found under logs and leaf litter. Nelson & Hoyt (1961) reported

calling males at night during heavy rains in rain-filled temporary pools at San Salvador, Depto. San Salvador in June. Campbell (1998a) noted that males construct foam nests from the egg jelly to prevent dessication and predation. McCranie & Wilson (2002) noted breeding choruses in temporary ponds and puddles in June–August and October in Honduras; tadpoles were found in August. Savage (2002) noted adults of this species are arthropod generalists, whereas larvae are detritivores. Between 80 and 450 unpigmented eggs are deposited by females. Leenders (2003) commented that this species is common in the early rainy season and calls in shallow pools at Parque Nacional El Imposible, Depto. Ahuachapán.

Conservation status: GAA: Least concern (LC).

Specimens examined: <u>Ahuachapán</u>: Ausoles in front of San José: SMF 48027–30; Finca Concepción Miramar, 13°48.46´N, 89°48.03´W, 920 m: KU 289921–24, MUHNES C–30–1281–82, C–30–1286; Parque Nacional El Imposible: MUHNES 1111. <u>Cabañas</u>: Bosque Cinquera, 13°53.13´N, 88°57.36´W, 400 m: KU 289978–81, 289999–290002, MUHNES C–30–1276, C–30–1292; La Chorrera del Guayabo, Cantón San Nicolás: SMF 48058. <u>Cuscatlán</u>: Hacienda Colima, S of Punta Lempira, 240 m: SMF 44458; 1 km E Tenancingo, Cantón El Llano: KU 184569. <u>La Libertad</u>: Club Atami (near Playa El Palmarcito, Municipio Tamanique), 13°30.2´N, 89°25.0´W, 40 m: SMF 81413; Cumbre de Nuevo San Salvador [= Santa Tecla], Finca San José, 1200 m: SMF 44429; Finca El Paraíso near Nuevo San Salvador [= Santa Tecla]: SMF 42874, SMF 44430 (900 m elevation); Colón: SMF 52259–60; 16.1 km NW Nuevo San Salvador [= Santa Tecla]: KU 41965–42000, 43471–72; 5.3 km E La Libertad, 20 m: KU 85080–83; 10 km E La Libertad: KU 184546–50. <u>La Unión</u>: km 198 road La Unión–Pasaquina: SMF 44461–63; 24.1 km N, 3.2 km E La Unión: KU 42782–89; La Unión: CAS-SU 9499–500. <u>Morazán</u>: Montecristo Mine, 213 m: MVZ 39829–33, 39849; Divisadero: USNM 73287; Perquín, 13°57.17´N, 88°10.01´W, 1150 m: KU 290012, 290018–19, 290041, 291323–27, MUHNES C–30–1274, C–30–1290; Cerro Cacahuatique, 1035 m: KU 291295–301, MUHNES C–30–1446. <u>San Miguel</u>: km 155 road San Salvador–La Unión, 60 m: SMF 44459–60; Laguna de Olomega, 61 m: MVZ 39834; Volcán de San Miguel, 740 m: MUHNES C–30–1444–45, MUHNES C–30–1447–49, MUHNES C–30–1450–53, KU 291263. <u>San Salvador</u>: San Salvador, Parque Zoológico Nacional, 13°58.8´N, 89°11.9´W, 700 m: MUHNES C–30–1283,

C–30–1288–89, KU 289799, 289816–18, 289825–27, SMF 81408–12; San Salvador, Instituto Tropical de Investigaciones Científicas: SMF 44431–57, 48045–48, 52261, KU 61880–927; San Salvador, La Rabida: SMF 42885–86; San Salvador, 65 Avenida Sur: SMF 42215, 42233–34, 42266–70, 42392, 42410, 42420–27, 42466, 42571–73, 42509 (tadpoles), 42514 (spawn), 42280–300 (tadpoles), 42522–28 (tadpoles), 42314–73 (tadpoles), 42469–72 (tadpoles), 42598 (tadpoles); San Salvador near west edge of city: UMMZ 117587; San Salvador, Parque Saburo-Hirao: AMNH 125857; 1.6 km S Los Planes de Renderos: KU 42778–80; 9.7 km E San Salvador: KU 42790–846; San Salvador, Ciudad Universitaria, 700 m: KU 184490–545, 184551–68; San Salvador, 670 m: FMNH 65057, 65061–70; same locality at 700 m: FMNH 65058–60. San Vicente: Finca El Carmen, 13°36.8´N, 88°50.3´W, 1240 m: SMF 81407, 81417–19; road San Salvador–San Miguel, turnoff to San Vicente: SMF 52262–63. Santa Ana: Parque Nacional Montecristo, Hacienda San José, oficinas de Parques Nacionales, 800 m: SMF 44427, 81414–16; Finca El Milagro, 13°53.29´N, 89°37.17´W, 1300 m: KU 289779, 289781 (tadpoles), 289784, MUHNES C–30–1277–78, C–30–1293. Sonsonate: Hacienda Cuyan-Cuya near Izalco: SMF 42562; km 43 road San Salvador–Sonsonate, 683 m: SMF 44428; Bosque Las Lajas, 13°50.04´N, 89°33.56´W, 920 m: KU 289867, 289869–74, 289876, MUHNES C–30–1273, C–30–1280, C–30–1284, C–30–1291. Usulután: Beneficio San José, near Jucuapa, 650 m: SMF 42923–26; Cerro del Tigre, 13°28.37´N, 88°26.21´W, 1100 m: KU 289845, 289851, 289862, MUHNES C–30–1271, C–30–1275, C–30–1279, C–30–1285, C–30–1287. Depto. unknown: 2.4 km E Santa Rosa: TCWC 16330 (*).
Published locality records: San Salvador: 3.2 km SW of a bridge over the Río Lempa on the highway between San Salvador and La Palma, 270 m (Greding & Hellebuyck 1980).

Family Microhylidae

A recent tally of this family attributed 362 species (67 genera) to this group, which is distributed from eastern North America to Argentina and Brazil in the New World, subsaharan Africa and Madagascar, and most of Southeast Asia to northern Australia. Approximately 30% of microhylids have direct development, but the other species have derived tadpoles that lack cornified denticles (Zweifel 2003). Not all researchers agree that the family Scaphiophrynidae, which includes 11

Madagascan species in two genera, should be considered a distinct group from Microhylidae (Savage 2002, Glaw 2003, Vences et al. 2003). Numerous recent species descriptions continue to increase the size of this family (e.g., Kraus & Allison 2002, Rainer 2003, Vences et al. 2003).

Genus *Gastrophryne*

The five species of frogs in this genus are distributed from the southeastern United States to southeastern Costa Rica (D. Frost 2002, 2004, Savage 2002). McDiarmid & Altig (1999) described the tadpoles of this genus as exotrophic, lentic suspension feeders. One species occurs in El Salvador.

Gastrophryne usta (Cope 1866)
(Termitero de la Costa)
Plate 37, Map 29, Figure 16c

1866 *Engystoma ustum* Cope, Proc. Acad. Nat. Sci. Philadelphia, 18: 131; type locality: "Guadalaxara" (= Guadalajara), Jalisco, Mexico; apparently in error, according to Nelson, 1972, J. Herpetol., 6: 119, who corrected the type locality to "Tecoman, Colima, Mexico."
Gastrophryne usta gadovi: Legler 1964.
Gastrophryne usta: Nelson & Cuellar 1968, Nelson 1972a, b, Nelson & Altig 1972, Villa et al. 1988, Dueñas et al. 2001, D. Frost 2002, 2004.
Geographic distribution: Central Sinaloa, the Balsas Depression, and central Veracruz to Chiapas, Mexico, and El Salvador on the Pacific versant (D. Frost 2002, 2004).
Ecological distribution: Dry forest between sea level and 700 m.
Description: Largest Salvadoran specimen examined is 24.8 mm SVL; HW/SVL 0.25–0.34; HL/SVL 0.22–0.31; shank length/SVL 0.38–0.52; foot length/SVL 0.39–0.50. Tip of snout slightly truncated in dorsal aspect, protruding in profile; top of head flat; loreal region barely concave; canthus rostralis rounded; nostrils directed laterally, situated at a point about 2/3 distance between anterior border of eye and tip of snout; tympanum absent; no supratympanic fold; a distinct transverse skin fold present immediately behind eyes. Tips of digits not expanded; forelimbs short; subarticular tubercles rounded, projecting; no nuptial thumb pads in males; relative length of fingers I < II ~ IV < III; fingers unwebbed; palmar and thenar tubercles

Plate 37: *Gastrophryne usta* MEXICO: Guerrero: El Ocoliuto. Photo: W. E. Duellman (KU CT 1125).

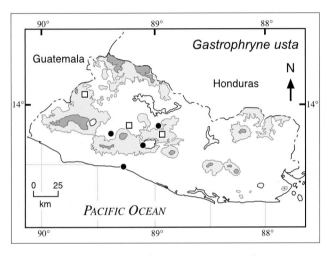

Map 29: Distribution of *Gastrophryne usta* in El Salvador.
Closed circles represent examined-specimen locality records; open squares are published locality records. Light shading indicates 600–1200 m elevation; dark shading indicates elevations ≥ 1200 m; large bodies of freshwater are outlined in bold, black lines.

barely visible; toes relatively short; relative length of toes I < II < V < III < IV; modal webbing formula of toes I 1½ – 2⁺ II 2 – 3⁺ III 3 – 4 IV 4⁺ – 2½ V (males), I 2 – 2½ II 2 – 3½ III 3⁺ – 4⁺ IV 4⁺ – 2½ V (females); subarticular tubercles small; outer metatarsal tubercle rounded, protruding, smaller than the blade-shaped inner metatarsal tubercle; inner and outer metatarsal tubercles separated from each other by 0.3–0.7 times width of outer metatarsal tubercle; no tarsal folds; skin generally smooth, lacking warts, pustules, or tubercles; no vomerine teeth.

Dorsum dark, deep purplish brown (darker markings very faintly indicated in liquid), having sharply defined hair-fine whitish line from the tip of snout to apex of cloacal fold; dorsal surfaces of arms and thighs having slightly paler ground color, creamish lines on posterior surfaces of thighs and legs and on tarsus less distinct; venter nearly uniform grayish tan, having faint paler maculations; a fine creamish line on throat (Legler 1964).
Call: According to Nelson (1973b) the call of *G. usta* consists of a single prolonged note of 3400–4750 Hz with a harmonic interval of 70–130 Hz and a duration of 0.5 to 8.2 seconds.
Natural history: Nelson (1972a) commented this species is known from open tropical deciduous formations, marshes, and savannas. Nelson (1972b) noted this species eats ants and has been collected from under tree trunks and palm fronds. Gravid females and chorusing have been noted in July and August.
Conservation status: GAA: Least concern (LC).
Specimens examined: <u>Cuscatlán</u>: 1 km E Tenancingo, Cantón El Llano: KU 184824; 1 km E Tenancingo, El Manguito: KU 184489. <u>La Libertad</u>: 1.6 km SE La Libertad on Pan American Hwy: UMMZ 131902–03; 16.1 km NE Nuevo San Salvador [= Santa Tecla]: KU 43557–58. <u>San Salvador</u>: 3 km SE Ilopango, Cantón Asino: KU 184825–52.
Published records: <u>Cuscatlán</u>: 7.2 km WNW Cojutepeque (Nelson & Cuellar 1968). <u>Santa Ana</u>: 5–15 km ESE Candelaria (Nelson 1972a).

Genus *Hypopachus*

The two species of this genus are distributed from southern Texas (USA) to central Costa Rica (D. Frost 2002, 2004, Savage 2002). McDiarmid & Altig (1999) described the tadpoles of this genus as exotrophic, lentic suspension feeders. Both species occur in El Salvador.

***Hypopachus barberi* Schmidt 1939**
(Termitero de Montaña)
Plate 38, Map 30, Figures 13a, 16a

1939 *Hypopachus barberi* Schmidt, Field Mus. Nat. Hist. Publ., Zool. Ser., 24: 1; type locality: Tecpán, Sololá (in error Chimaltenango), Guatemala.
Hypopachus aquae: Mertens 1952d.
Hypopachus barberi: Nelson 1973a, Villa et al. 1988, Dueñas et al. 2001, D. Frost 2002, 2004, McCranie & Wilson 2002, Leenders 2003.

Plate 38: *Hypopachus barberi* (KU 291248) EL SALVA-DOR: Chalatenango: Cerro El Pital (2300 m). Photo: O. Komar.

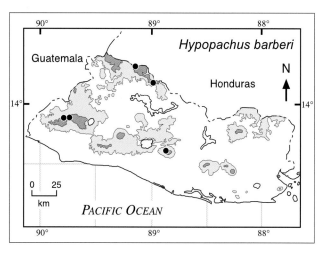

Map 30: Distribution of *Hypopachus barberi* in El Salvador.

Closed circles represent examined-specimen locality records; open squares are published locality records. Light shading indicates 600–1200 m elevation; dark shading indicates elevations ≥ 1200 m; large bodies of freshwater are outlined in bold, black lines.

Geographic distribution: Disjunct distribution from highlands of Chiapas, Mexico, to eastern Guatemala on the Atlantic versant; from western Guatemala to southwestern Honduras and east-central El Salvador (McCranie & Wilson 2002).
Ecological distribution: Pine-oak forest and cloud forest at elevations of 1300–2300 m.
Description: Largest Salvadoran specimen examined is 46.0 mm SVL; HW/SVL 0.29–0.34; HL/SVL 0.22–0.29; shank length/SVL 0.37–0.46; foot length/SVL 0.43–0.58. Snout pointed in dorsal aspect,

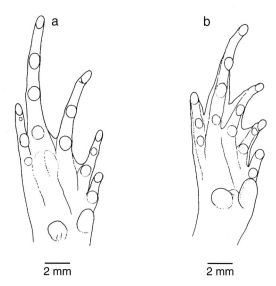

Figure 13: Ventral view of right feet of a. *Hypopachus barberi* (SMF 44615); b. *Hypopachus variolosus* (KU 62018). **NOTE:** Differences in webbing might be a consequence of sexual dimorphism and not interspecific variation.

protruding in profile; top of head slightly convex; loreal region barely concave; canthus rostralis rounded; nostrils directed laterally, situated at a point about 2/3 distance between anterior border of eye and tip of snout; tympanum absent; no supratympanic fold; a distinct transverse skin fold present immediately behind eyes, absent or weak in some specimens. Tips of digits not expanded; forelimbs short; subarticular tubercles rounded, projecting; no nuptial thumb pads in males; relative length of fingers I < II ~ IV < III; fingers unwebbed; palmar and thenar tubercles barely visible; toes relatively short; relative length of toes I < II < V < III < IV; modal webbing formula of toes I 1⅔ – 2⁺ II 1⅔ – 3⁺ III 2⅔ – 3⅔ IV 4⁻ – 2⅓ V (males), I 2 – 2⅓ II 2 – 3⁺ III 3 – 4 IV 4⁺ – 2½ V (females); subarticular tubercles small; outer metatarsal tubercle rounded, protruding, smaller than the blade-shaped inner metatarsal tubercle; inner and outer metatarsal tubercles separated from each other by 0.9–1.7 times width of outer metatarsal tubercle; no tarsal folds; skin generally smooth, dorsally with tiny pustulation; no vomerine teeth.

Dorsum brown, reddish brown, or grayish brown with series of dark brown or black markings on the sides, on the waists, and dorsal surfaces of the limbs; a creamy white, thin stripe may extend from posterior edge of eye ventrally to anterior base of forelimb; a thin yellow or creamy middorsal line extends from tip of snout to above vent; venter cream or pale yellow with dark brown or black blotches (most blotches larger than eye) that can fuse to form a dark brown or black reticulum.

Call: According to Nelson (1973b) the call of *H. barberi* consists of a single prolonged note of 1750–2900 Hz with a harmonic interval of 110–180 Hz and a duration of 0.8 to 8.2 seconds.

Natural history: O. Komar (field notes) collected an adult in a pitfall trap in cloud forest at Cerro El Pital, Depto. Chalatenango in May. McCranie & Wilson (2002) noted calling males at night after heavy rains in May, July, and August in Honduras; tadpoles were found in July and August.

Conservation status: GAA: Vulnerable (VU B1ab[iii]).

Specimens examined: <u>Ahuachapán</u>: Laguna de Las Ranas, 1720–1730 m: SMF 44653; Laguna de Las Ninfas, 1630 m: SMF 44572–73, 44574–651, FMNH 67432. <u>Chalatenango</u>: La Montañona, Municipio La Laguna, 1300 m: VH 59; Cerro El Pital, 2300 m: KU 291248. <u>San Vicente</u>: E part of Vólcan San Vicente, forest over 1700 m: SMF 44654.

Hypopachus variolosus (Cope 1866)
(Termitero Balador)
Plate 39, Map 31, Figures 13b, 16b

1866 *Engystoma variolosum* Cope, Proc. Acad. Nat. Sci. Philadelphia 18: 131; type locality: "Arriba" [see comment under *Bufo coccifer*], Costa Rica.
Hypopachus championi: Nelson & Hoyt 1961.
Hypopachus variolosus: Dueñas et al. 2001.

Geographic distribution: From southern Texas, USA, to northern Costa Rica on Atlantic versant; from southern Sonora, Mexico, to central Costa Rica on the Pacific versant (McCranie & Wilson 2002).

Ecological distribution: Dry forest between 700 and 1240 m.

Description: Largest Salvadoran specimen examined is 44.6 mm SVL; HW/SVL 0.27–0.31; HL/SVL 0.20–0.25; shank length/SVL 0.35–0.42; foot length/SVL 0.41–0.51. Snout pointed in dorsal aspect, protruding in profile; top of head slightly convex; loreal region barely concave; canthus rostralis rounded; nostrils directed laterally, situated at a point about 2/3 distance between anterior border of eye and tip of snout; tympanum absent; no supratympanic fold; a distinct transverse skin fold present immediately behind eyes. Tips of digits not

Plate 39: *Hypopachus variolosus* EL SALVADOR: San Miguel: Volcán San Miguel (740 m). Photo: O. Komar.

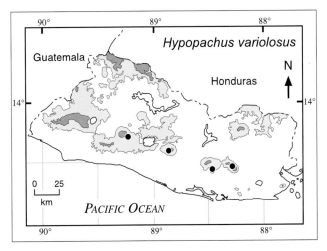

Map 31: Distribution of *Hypopachus variolosus* in El Salvador.
Closed circles represent examined-specimen locality records; open squares are published locality records. Light shading indicates 600–1200 m elevation; dark shading indicates elevations ≥ 1200 m; large bodies of freshwater are outlined in bold, black lines.

expanded; forelimbs short; subarticular tubercles rounded, projecting; no nuptial thumb pads in males; relative length of fingers I < II ~ IV < III; fingers unwebbed; palmar and thenar tubercles barely visible; toes relatively short; relative length of toes I < II < V < III < IV; modal webbing formula of toes I 2⁻ – 2 II 1½ – 2⁺ III 2 – 3⁺ IV 3⅓ – 2⁻ V (males), I 2 – 2⁺ II 2 – 3⅔ III 3⁻ – 4 IV 4 – 2⅓ V (females); subarticular tubercles small; outer metatarsal tubercle rounded, protruding, almost the same size as the blade-shaped inner metatarsal tubercle; inner and outer metatarsal tubercles separated from each other by 0.3–0.6 times width of outer metatarsal tubercle; no tarsal folds; skin generally smooth, dorsally with tiny pustulation; no vomerine teeth.

Dorsum brown, reddish brown, or grayish brown with a series of dark brown or black markings on the sides, on the waists, and dorsal surfaces of the limbs; a pair of dark brown or black blotches present on the dorsolateral surface just anterior to base of legs; a creamy white, thin stripe extends from posterior edge of eye ventrally to anterior base of forelimb; sides with dark brown or gray stripe, irregular, broad, extends from posterior border of eye to inguinal area; a thin yellow or creamy middorsal line extends from tip of snout to above vent and bifurcates into two lines that continue onto the legs almost to the metatarsal tubercles; venter cream or pale yellow with either no blotches (rarely), or small dark brown or black blotches that may fuse to form a dark brown or black reticulum. Color description for specimens from Volcán de San Miguel, Depto. San Miguel: dorsum is rusty reddish brown with increasingly brighter orange coloration towards the posterior side of the body and hind limbs; middorsal stripe bright yellow, sides black, venter white with black blotches that may fuse to form a reticulum; eye light bronze.

Call: O. Komar (field notes) remarked that the call of this species at Volcán de San Miguel, Depto. San Miguel resembles the mew of a calf. According to Nelson (1973b) the call of *H. variolosus* consists of a single prolonged note of 1500–3600 Hz with a harmonic interval of 100–220 Hz and a duration of 0.8 to 6.0 seconds. Campbell (1998a) described the call as a loud, distinct "*baaaaaaaaaa.*" Described as "a nasal, sheep-like bleat" by Lee (1996).

Natural history: E. Greenbaum (field notes) collected an adult of this species in grass (near human habitations) at night during a light rain at Cerro del Tigre, Depto. Usulután in July. O. Komar (field notes) observed several individuals calling from an artificial pond (3 × 1.5 m) at a coffee finca at night at Volcán de San Miguel, Depto. San Miguel in May. *Physalaemus pustulosus* and *Smilisca baudinii* were breeding in the same pond, but presumably, both of these species died from *H. variolosus* secretions when placed in the same collection bag. M. Veselý (field notes) observed calling males from concrete water tanks at night at Finca El Carmen, Depto. San Vicente in late June. Nelson & Hoyt (1961) reported calling males at night during heavy rains in rain-filled temporary pools at San Salvador, Depto. San Salvador in June. Campbell (1998a) noted this species aestivates underground most of the year; prey items include ants, termites, and other insects. Breeding occurs from May–August following heavy rains. McCranie & Wilson (2002) found breeding choruses in temporary ponds and inundated areas from June–August after heavy rains in Honduras; tadpoles were found from July–August. Savage (2002) noted breeding males have spicules or pustules under the chin and gravid females have pericloacal spicules. Females lay 600–800 pigmented eggs. Mucous secretions are probably used as an anti-ant and termite repellant, but they can be irritating to human skin and mucous membranes.

Conservation status: GAA: Least concern (LC).

Specimens examined: <u>San Miguel</u>: Volcán de San Miguel, 740 m: KU 291269–72, 291387, MUHNES C–30–1436–39. <u>San Salvador</u>: Instituto Tropical de Investigaciones Científicas: KU 62004–23, UU 4908. <u>San Vicente</u>: Finca El Carmen, 13°36.8′N, 88°50.3′W, 1240 m: SMF 81310. <u>Usulután</u>: Cerro del Tigre, 13°28.37′N, 88°26.21′W, 1100 m: KU 289842.

Family Ranidae

Over 686 species (51 genera) of frogs are included in this family. This family has a nearly ubiquitous distribution throught the world with a few exceptions: central and southern South America, arid regions of Africa, and Australia. Although eleven subfamilies are recognized, the relationships of the major groups of frogs in this family are poorly resolved (Dubois 2003). One genus occurs in El Salvador.

Genus *Rana*

This genus currently includes approximately 240 species, which are distributed identical to the family Ranidae, except in southern Africa (D. Frost 2004). Two species occur in El Salvador.

Rana forreri Boulenger 1883
(Rana Leopardo del Pacífico)
Plate 40, Map 32, Figure 14b

1883 *Rana forreri* Boulenger, Ann. mag. Nat. Hist., 11(5): 343; type locality: Presidio, Sinaloa, Mexico. *Rana pipiens*: Mertens 1952d, Rand 1957, Greding & Hellebuyck 1980.

Plate 40: *Rana forreri* (KU 289994) EL SALVADOR: Cabañas: Bosque Cinquera (400 m). Photo: E. Greenbaum.

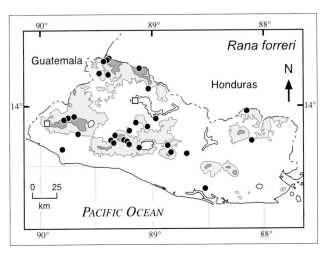

Map 32: Distribution of *Rana forreri* in El Salvador. Closed circles represent examined-specimen locality records; open squares are published locality records. Light shading indicates 600–1200 m elevation; dark shading indicates elevations ≥ 1200 m; large bodies of freshwater are outlined in bold, black lines.

Rana forreri: Villa et al. 1988, Dueñas et al. 2001, Leenders 2003.

Geographic distribution: From southern Sonora, Mexico, south along the Pacific coast to northwestern Costa Rica (McCranie & Wilson 2002).

Ecological distribution: Dry forest, premontane evergreen forest, subtropical humid forest, and pine-oak forest between sea level and 1960 m.

Description: Largest Salvadoran specimen examined is 94.4 mm SVL; HW/SVL 0.29–0.47; HL/SVL 0.28–0.52; shank length/SVL 0.49–0.66; foot length/SVL 0.49–0.95; tympanum diameter/SVL 0.06–0.11.

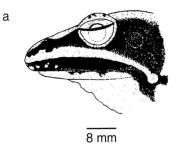

8 mm

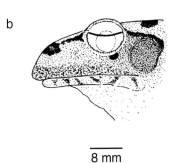

8 mm

Figure 14: Lateral view of head of a. *Rana maculata* (SMF 81280); b. *Rana forreri* (SMF 81269).

Snout acutely round, tip of snout blunt in dorsal aspect, sloping to rounded in profile; top of the head flat, nostrils directed dorsolaterally, situated about 3/5 of distance from orbit to tip of snout; canthus rostralis rounded, indistinct, loreal region slightly concave, more or less distinct skin fold extending along the upper jaw to a point above the insertion of arms, in adult males interrupted by vocal sacs; tympanum large, distinct; forelimbs moderately short, robust, fingers with small pads on tips, relative length of fingers II < I < IV < III, webbing vestigial, subarticular tubercles round, subconical, palmar tubercle flat, pollical tubercle ovoid, in breeding males enlarged pollex bearing nuptial excrescence; hind limbs long and robust, distinct transverse dermal fold on the heels; toes slender, long, with small pads on the tips, relative length of toes I < II < V < III < IV, modal webbing formula of toes I 1⁺ – 2⁺ II 1⁺ – 1½ III 1⁺ – 2⁺ IV 2 – 1 V; subarticular tubercles large, rounded, inner metatarsal tubercle large, elongated, spade-like; outer metatarsal tubercle rounded and subconical, equal in size to subarticular tubercles; distinct inner tarsal fold present; skin on dorsum smooth with two dorsolateral folds that are continuous, posterior portion not inset medially; irregular shorter parallel folds scattered between them; ventral skin smooth, granular on posterior part of thighs; vomerine teeth on two large, raised, narrowly separated ridges between choanae; rudimentary oviducts present in adult males.

Dorsum usually green (olive, or grayish brown in preserved specimens), dorsolateral skin folds usually creamy yellow; well-defined grayish brown spots on back, flanks, and limbs; usually two ovoid spots in frontal region, around nasal openings and canthus; venter creamy yellow; brown markings on posterior part of thighs.

Call: J. Frost (1982) described the call of this species as a guttural trill composed of two notes (each lasting 2.5 sec), with a pulse rate of 21–24/sec and dominant frequencies ranging from 0.7–1 kHz.

Natural history: E. Greenbaum (field notes) encountered an adult calling from a water tank near a stream at night at Bosque Cinquera, Depto. Cabañas in August. Mertens (1952d) noted breeding activity throughout the rainy season; he collected tadpoles with a total length of 90 mm in El Salvador. Rand (1957) noted several Salvadoran animals in habitats far from water. Greding & Hellebuyck (1980) noted Lepidoptera and a single *Smilisca baudinii* in the diet of frogs collected at night at a pond in Depto. San Salvador in June. McCranie & Wilson (2002) collected adults around permanent and temporary pools and a stream in March, July, and August in Honduras; tadpoles were found in July and August. Savage (2002) noted that about 1000 black-and-white eggs are laid by females.

Conservation status: GAA: Least concern (LC).

Specimens examined: Ahuachapán: Laguna de Las Ranas, 1676 m: MVZ 39900–04; Laguna de Las Ninfas, 13°52.4′N, 89°47.8′W, 1720 m: MUHNES 1185, SMF 44655–769, 81296–99; 3.2 km NW Apaneca, 1676 m: MVZ 39892–93, 39895–96, 39898. Cabañas: Bosque Cinquera, 13°53.13′N, 88°57.36′W, 400 m: KU 289994. Chalatenango: 24 km N Guazapa 1.6 km N bridge over Río Lempa: UTA A-49392, 49397; 16.5 km WNW Chalatenango: KU 184922–23; 10 km NE La Palma, Cantón Las Pilas: KU 184924–25. Cuscatlán: 1.2 km N Tenancingo: KU 184902. La Libertad: 4.4 km E Colón: UMMZ 118370; 2.3 km E Colón: UMMZ 118371; 16.1 km NW Nuevo San Salvador [= Santa Tecla]: KU 48990. Morazán: Mineral Encuentro near Río Gotera: SMF 52242–44; Perquín, 13°57.17′N, 88°10.01′W, 1150 m: KU 290035–36, 291319–20, 291358, MUHNES C–30–1302, C–30–1457–59. San Salvador: 3.2 km S Río Lempa Bridge and intersection Guazapa Hwy: UTA A-49371; Río Acelhuate

near Apopa: SMF 42432; Instituto Tropical de Investigaciones Científicas, Río Acelhuate: SMF 52236; Near Guazapa: UTA A-49391; 3 km SE Ilopango, Cantón Asino: KU 184913; San Salvador, 670 m: FMNH 65131; same locality at 700 m: FMNH 65130; Parque Zoológico Nacional: AMNH 125862. Santa Ana: Parque Nacional Montecristo, Hacienda San José, oficinas de Parques Nacionales, 800 m: MUHNES C–30–1210; Hacienda Montecristo: UTA A-50587–88, 50612; Hacienda Los Planes, Metapán mountains, 1830 m: SMF 43031, 52235; San Juan Mine, 12.1 km SE Metapán, 488 m: MVZ 39899; 6 km S Metapán: KU 184914–15. San Vicente: E part of Volcán de San Vicente (craterpool), 1960 m: SMF 44921–32 (tadpoles); km 80 on road San Salvador–San Miguel, 110 m: SMF 52237; km 60 road San Salvador–San Miguel, turn off to San Vicente: SMF 52238–41. Sonsonate: Hacienda San Antonio near Sonsonate: SMF 42482; Hacienda Cuyan-Cuya near Izalco: SMF 43010 (380 m elevation), 42553 (tadpoles). Usulután: Hacienda La Carrera, ca. 6.4 km NE Puerto El Triunfo: UTA A-49396.

Published locality records: Ahuachapán: Parque Nacional El Imposible (Leenders 2003). San Salvador: 3.2 km SW of a bridge over the Río Lempa on the highway between San Salvador and La Palma, 270 m (Greding & Hellebuyck 1980). San Vicente: Laguna Apastepeque, 500 m (Rand 1957).

Rana maculata Brocchi 1877
(Rana Montañera Enmascarada)
Plate 41, Map 33, Figure 14a

1877 *Rana maculata* Brocchi, Bull. Soc. Philomath. Paris, 1(7): 178; type locality: Totonicapan, Guatemala.
Rana macroglossa: Mertens 1952d, Rand 1957.
Rana maculata: Villa 1979, Hillis & de Sá 1988, Villa et al. 1988, Dueñas et al. 2001, McCranie & Wilson 2002, Leenders & Watkins-Colwell 2004.

Geographic distribution: From Chiapas, Mexico, to central Nicaragua on the Atlantic versant; from eastern Oaxaca, Mexico, to El Salvador and Honduras on the Pacific versant (McCranie & Wilson 2002).

Ecological distribution: Dry forest, premontane evergreen forest, subtropical humid forest, pine-oak forest, and cloud forest at elevations of 400–2200 m.

Description: Largest Salvadoran specimen examined is 94.6 mm SVL; HW/SVL 0.32–0.40; HL/SVL 0.35–0.44; shank length/SVL 0.48–0.60; foot length/

Plate 41: *Rana maculata* EL SALVADOR: Ahuachapán: El Refugio (225 m). Photo: G. Köhler.

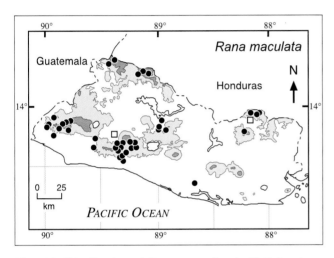

Map 33: Distribution of *Rana maculata* in El Salvador. Closed circles represent examined-specimen locality records; open squares are published locality records. Light shading indicates 600–1200 m elevation; dark shading indicates elevations ≥ 1200 m; large bodies of freshwater are outlined in bold, black lines.

SVL 0.50–0.64; tympanum diameter/SVL 0.05–0.09. Snout rounded in both dorsal view and profile; top of head flat, canthus rostralis indistinct, rounded, loreal region slightly concave; nostrils directed dorsolaterally, situated at a point about 3/5 of distance between anterior corner of orbit and tip of snout, short skin fold along posterior part of upper jaw to a point above insertion of arms; tympanum relatively small, distinct; forelimbs moderately long, robust; relative length of fingers II < I ~ IV < III, webbing vestigial; subarticular tubercles round, large; palmar tubercle indistinct; pollical tubercle ovoid and flat; hind limbs long, robust, relative length of toes I < II < III < V < IV, modal webbing formula of toes I 1 – 2⁻ II 1 – 2⁺ III 1 – 2 IV 2⁻ – 1 V;

toe tips slightly expanded, subarticular tubercles ovoid, large, inner metatarsal tubercle elongated, small, outer metatarsal tubercle indistinct; inner tarsal fold barely visible; skin generally smooth, but with distinct denticulations (small white tubercles, scattered throughout the dorsum, easily seen with the aid of a dissecting microscope), two dorsolateral dermal folds extend from the posterior edge of orbit to about 2/3 of body, subanal region slightly granular; vomerine teeth on two small ovoid processes between choanae.

Dorsum grayish tan or gray with irregular diffuse dark brown to olive-brown flecks scattered over dorsum and flanks; smaller spots present on limbs and head; dark-brown lines extend laterally from tip of snout through nasal opening to anterior edge of orbit and continuing along skin folds to posterior part of body; venter creamy white.

Call: Although Hillis & de Sá (1988) explained that numerous workers have reported this species calling year-round, no description of the call exists in the literature.

Natural history: E. Greenbaum (field notes) collected tadpoles and subadults from shallow pools (continuous with streams) at Parque Nacional El Imposible, Depto. Ahuachapán in July. Adults were collected from water tanks near streams at night at Bosque Cinquera, Depto. Cabañas in August. O. Komar (field notes) collected an adult on a rock next to a river in pine-oak forest during the day at Perquín, Depto. Morazán in June. Mertens (1952d) found this "nocturnal frog" in or near bodies of water in El Salvador. Rand (1957) noted juveniles and tadpoles in the latter part of the dry season, and "transforming" individuals in March and April in San Salvador, Depto. San Salvador. McCranie & Wilson (2002) collected specimens at night from montane streams in February and April–November in Honduras; tadpoles were collected from May– August and November. Leenders & Watkins-Colwell (2004) noted tadpoles, egg masses, and calling males from November–February in El Salvador; juveniles were collected in June but males lacked nuptial pads at this time.

Conservation status: GAA: Least concern (LC).
Specimens examined: <u>Ahuachapán</u>: Finca Concepción Miramar, 13°48.46´N, 89°48.03´W, 920 m: KU 289925–27, 289935–289941; Parque Nacional El Imposible, La Fincona, 13°50.8´N, 89°58.8´W, 720 m: KU 289744–48, 289755 (tadpoles), MUHNES C–30–1303, C–30–1305–08, SMF 81471–74; El Refugio, vicinity of Mariposario of Francisco Serrano,

13°49.46´N, 89°59.98´W, 225 m: SMF 81279–81;
Tacuba: MUHNES 154–55, 159, 162–63; Laguna
Verde, 1600 m: SMF 44870–72, 48033–35; Laguna
de Las Ninfas, 1630 m: SMF 44770–867; Ausoles of
San José: SMF 48037–40; 3.2 km NW Apaneca,
1676 m: MVZ 39894, 39897; Finca Santa Luisa,
13°49´N, 89°52´W, 900 m: MUHNES C–30–1314, C–
30–1316; Finca La Esperanza, 13°49´N, 89°52´W,
1000 m: KU 290052, MUHNES C–30–1315.
Cabañas: Bosque Cinquera, 13°53.13´N, 88°57.36´W,
400 m: KU 289993; 4.5 km SW Tejutepeque, Cantón
El Huilihuiste: KU 184908–12. Chalatenango: Río
La Palma near La Palma, 1000 m: SMF 52245–48;
10 km NE La Palma, Cantón Las Pilas: KU 184907;
E slope Los Esesmiles, Cerro El Pital, 2225 m: MVZ
39887–90; 1890 m: MVZ 39891. Cuscatlán:
Tenancingo, 1.3 km N Tenancingo: KU 184856; 1.2
km N Tenancingo: KU 184861–901. La Libertad:
km 15 road San Salvador–La Libertad, water
construction Ayagualo, 835 m: SMF 43068–78,
43179; km 15 road San Salvador–La Libertad, small
streams: SMF 44874–80; Finca San José near
Nuevo San Salvador [= Santa Tecla], 1200 m: SMF
42449–51, 43003; Finca El Paraíso near Nuevo San
Salvador [= Santa Tecla]: SMF 42440, 42615, 42620–
21, 42710–11, 42792–94, 42803–06, 42847–48, 43118
(1 juv.), 42612–14 (tadpoles), 43057–60 (tadpoles),
42795 (spawn), 52250–51; Colón: SMF 47731, 55044;
Los Chorros near Colón, 716 m: SMF 52249; km 25
road from San Salvador–La Libertad: SMF 52252–
58; Finca La Giralda, 13°39.34´N, 89°22.47´W, 1080
m: KU 289956, MUHNES C–30–1313; same locality
at 880 m: KU 289958–59, MUHNES C–30–1311; 2
km SE Colón: KU 61993; Guadalupe, 640 m: KU
291374–75, MUHNES C–30–1460–62; 2 km S
Zaragoza, Cantón Guadalupe, 13°33.1´N, 89°17.3'W,
740 m: YPM 6451–55. Morazán: Cerro
Cacahuatique: MUHNES 853; same locality at 1158
m: MVZ 39886; same locality at 995 m: KU 291312;
same locality at 1015 m: KU 291302, 291308,
291312, MUHNES C–30–1464–66; Perquín,
13°57.17´N, 88°10.01´W, 1150 m: KU 291329–30,
291353–54, MUHNES C–30–1310, C–30–1312, C–
30–1463, C–30–1467–68. San Salvador: San Salvador, Villa Margarita, Colónia America: SMF 44902–
17 (7 juv. and 9 tadpoles); San Salvador: MUHNES
165, CAS 188237; same locality at 700 m: FMNH
65123–28; San Salvador, Parque Zoológico Nacional:
KU 289810–11, MUHNES C–30–1304, C–30–1309;
1.6 km S Los Planes de Renderos: KU 43311. Santa
Ana: Hacienda Los Planes, Metapán mountains,
1830 m: SMF 43039, AMNH 125863; Hacienda San

José: SMF 43044 (800 m elevation), 44868–69 (1100
m elevation); Parque Nacional Montecristo:
MUHNES 156, 158, 160–61; same locality at 1350
m: KU 289802 (tadpoles); Hacienda San José, 800
m: KU 66092–93. San Vicente: San Judas:
MUHNES 26. Sonsonate: Finca near km 48 road
San Salvador–Sonsonate, 600 m: SMF 44873;
Hacienda Chilata, 610 m: MVZ 39872–77.
Published locality records: Ahuachapán: Parque
Nacional El Imposible: YPM 6420–21, 6426, 6440,
6459–72 (Leenders & Watkins-Colwell 2004). La
Libertad: Município La Libertad, 2 km S Zaragoza,
Río San Antonio (13.552°N, 89.288°W), 740 m: YPM
6450–55 (Leenders & Watkins-Colwell 2004).
Morazán: Município Arambala, Cantón Cumaro,
Bailadero del Diablo (13.931°N, 88.102°W), 696 m:
YPM 7268, 7270, 7280, 7282, 7303–12 (Leenders &
Watkins-Colwell 2004); Município Arambala, Cantón
Cumaro, Nahuaterique, near border crossing with
Honduras (13.995°N, 88.093°W), 1389 m: YPM
7271–75, 7278 (Leenders & Watkins-Colwell 2004);
Município Arambala, Cantón Cumaro, Río Sapo
(13.959°N, 88.132°W), 1118 m: YPM 7269, 7281,
7301–02 (Leenders & Watkins-Colwell 2004). Santa
Ana: Município Metapán, Cantón Metapán, Parque
Nacional Montecristo (14.401°N, 89.362°W), 1840
m: YPM 7265–67, 7276–77, 7279 (Leenders &
Watkins-Colwell 2004).

Family Rhinophrynidae

This ancient family includes one species distributed from southern Texas, USA, to northwestern
Honduras on the Atlantic versant, from southern
Michoacán, Mexico, to northwestern Costa Rica on
the Pacific versant, northeastern Nicaragua, and
the Río Grijalva Valley of Chiapas, Mexico (D. Frost
2002, 2004, McCranie & Wilson 2002). McDiarmid
& Altig (1999) described the tadpoles of this family
as exotrophic, lentic suspension feeders. Only one
species is included.

Genus *Rhinophrynus*

This genus includes one species, which is
distributed as described for the family
Rhinophrynidae. This fossorial species is rarely
encountered in El Salvador.

Rhinophrynus dorsalis Duméril & Bibron 1841
(Sapo Borracho)
Plate 42, Map 34, Figure 16d

Plate 42: *Rhinophrynus dorsalis* HONDURAS: Yoro: Tegucigalpita (1260 m). Photo: G. Köhler.

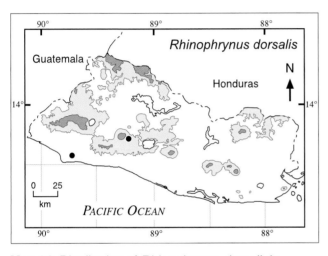

Map 34: Distribution of *Rhinophrynus dorsalis* in El Salvador.

Closed circles represent examined-specimen locality records; open squares are published locality records. Light shading indicates 600–1200 m elevation; dark shading indicates elevations ≥ 1200 m; large bodies of freshwater are outlined in bold, black lines.

1841 *Rhinophrynus dorsalis* Duméril & Bibron, Erp. Gén., 8: 758; type locality: Veracruz, Mexico. *Rhinophrynus dorsalis*: Nelson & Hoyt 1961, Fouquette 1969, Duellman 1971, Villa et al. 1988, Dueñas et al. 2001, D. Frost 2002, 2004.
Geographic distribution: Identical to family Rhinophrynidae.
Ecological distribution: Dry forest around 700 m.
Description: Largest Salvadoran specimen exam-

ined is 64.9 mm SVL; HW/SVL 0.21–0.23; HL/SVL 0.17–0.19; shank length/SVL 0.31–0.36; foot length/SVL 0.41–0.46. This toad-like frog has a stocky, rounded body with smooth, relatively loose skin and a small, narrow head that protrudes from the mass of the body; no external ear opening; arms are short with webbing between the fingers; hind limbs are largely enclosed by the skin of the body; four toes, with thick webbing; two elongate spade-like inner metatarsal tubercles present; tips of fingers and toes not expanded.

Dorsal ground color chocolate-brown, usually with a pale red, orange, or yellow vertebral stripe and irregular spots and flecks laterally; ventral surfaces grayish brown.
Call: Porter (1964b) noted the call of this species is similar to *Gastrophryne,* and sounds like a relatively long buzzing noise. The dominant frequency was noted at 2500 Hz; the length of each call lasted 3–4 seconds with 2-second intervals between calls. Field observations by W.E. Duellman (pers. comm.) noted that this frog's call resembles a retching sound (thus the name "drunken toad" in Spanish); the force of the call often pushes calling males backwards in the water. Described as an extremely loud "long-drawn-out 'whoop' with a rising inflection at the end" by Foster & McDiarmid (1983).
Natural history: Nelson & Hoyt (1961) reported calling males at night during heavy rains in rain-filled temporary pools at San Salvador, Depto. San Salvador in June. This species is an explosive breeder that may emerge only a few nights a year, whereas the tadpoles are present in shallow pools for longer periods (Duellman & Trueb 1986). Campbell (1998a) remarked that this frog spends most of its time underground where it feeds upon ants and termites. Breeding takes place following heavy downpours from June–September; egg clutch size ranges from 2000–8000 eggs. McCranie & Wilson (2002) recorded calling males following heavy rainfalls in August and October in Honduras. Savage (2002) noted males can be heard calling from underground burrows after the first heavy rains in May or June.
Conservation status: GAA: Least concern (LC).
Specimens examined: <u>San Salvador</u>: San Salvador, Instituto Tropical de Investigaciones Científicas: KU 60088–92, UU 4722. <u>Sonsonate</u>: 9.2 km SE Jct Hwys 12/2: TCWC 55532.

Larval Anurans

Tadpoles are an integral and abundant component of the ecosystems in El Salvador and an understanding of their biology and identification is needed to conduct thorough biodiversity invento-

ries. Frequently, anurans have been noted from specific localities, only on the basis of their larvae (see examples of *Agalychnis moreletii* noted above). McDiarmid & Altig (1999) provided an excellent review of the terminology related to tadpole morphology, which is useful for diagnosing the tadpoles

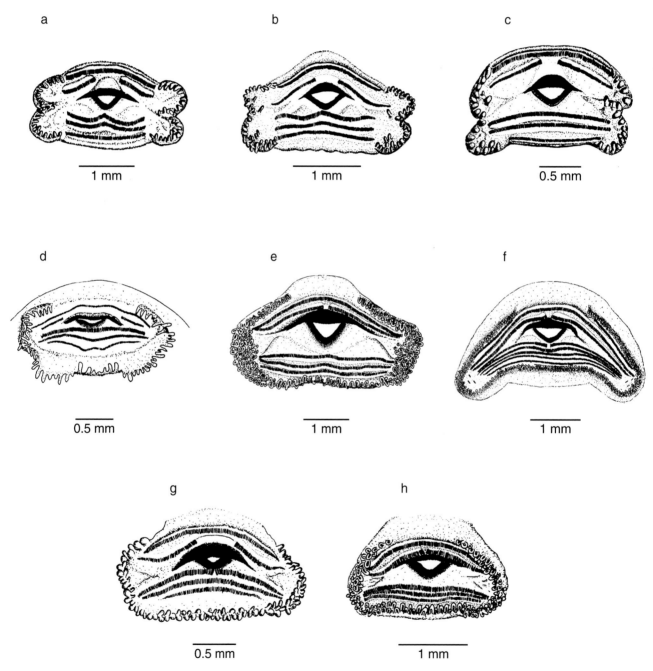

Figure 15: Oral discs of tadpoles of a. *Bufo coccifer* (KU 104111); b. *Bufo luetkenii* (KU 87694); c. *Bufo marinus* (KU 68328); d. *Hyalinobatrachium fleischmanni* (KU 68376); e. *Agalychnis moreletii* (SMF 81608); f. *Phrynohyas venulosa* (KU 124955); g. *Leptodactylus fragilis* (KU 104224); h. *Leptodactylus melanonotus* (SMF 42956).

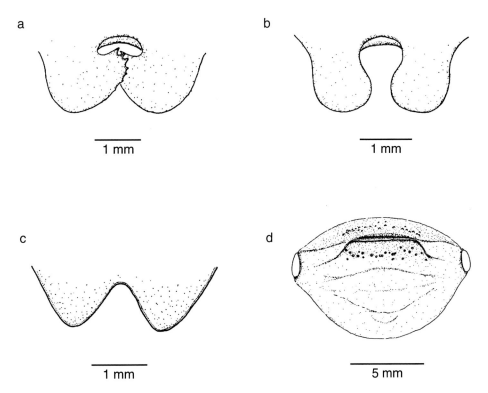

Figure 16: Oral flaps of tadpoles of a. *Hypopachus barberi* (KU 68565); b. *Hypopachus variolosus* (KU 104204); c. *Gastrophryne usta* (KU 139944). d. Anterior view of tadpole of *Rhinophrynus dorsalis* (KU 157684).

of El Salvador. Salvadoran frogs of the genus *Eleutherodactylus* exhibit direct development and therefore do not have free-swimming larvae. Although this key will apply to most anuran larvae in El Salvador, the tadpoles of two species are unknown, and therefore are not included here: *Bufo canaliferus* and *Hyla robertmertensi*. However, by inference from comparisons of general body shape and other morphological attributes, as well as a process of elimination, these species may be identified with closely related taxa (Starrett 1960; Duellman 1970; Altig 1987; Wilson & McCranie 1993; Lips & Savage 1996). Although the larvae of *Hypopachus barberi* and *H. variolosus* have been described, these species cannot be distinguished by morphological features of the tadpoles (Nelson 1966b; McCranie & Wilson, 2002).

The following key contains tadpoles from 20 species of the families Bufonidae (Limbaugh & Volpe 1957; Savage 1960; McDiarmid & Foster 1981; Köhler et al. 2000), Centrolenidae (Starrett 1960), Hylidae (Duellman 1970, 2001), Leptodactylidae (Heyer 1970a), Microhylidae (McDiarmid & Altig 1999), Ranidae (Campbell 1998a, McCranie & Wilson 2002), and Rhinophrynidae (Starrett 1960). Tooth row numbers refer to the number of upper tooth rows over number of lower tooth rows (eg. tooth rows 3/4 = three upper tooth rows and four lower tooth rows). A and P are abbreviations for anterior (upper) and posterior (lower) tooth rows; numbered superscripts refer to the order of tooth rows (eg., A^2 = second anterior tooth row).

Key to the Larval Anurans of El Salvador

1　a. Labial teeth absent **2**
　　b. Labial teeth present **4**
2　a. No oral flaps .... ***Rhinophrynus dorsalis***
　　b. Oral flaps present **3**

3 a. Oral flaps with irregular margins, converging or overlapping
      ventromedially .... *Hypopachus*
   b. Oral flaps with smooth margins, triangular, not converging
      ventromedially .... *Gastrophryne usta*
4 a. Vent tube medial **5**
   b. Vent tube dextral **12**
5 a. Two rows of marginal papillae **6**
   b. One row of marginal papillae **8**
6 a. Tooth rows 3–4/5–6, deep lateral folds in oral disc, dark brown
      lateral stripe .... *Phrynohyas venulosa*
   b. Tooth rows 2/3, oral disc without deep lateral folds, no lateral stripe **7**
7 a. Second anterior tooth row (A^2) tooth row with distinct, wide gap;
      light spot behind oral disk, body pigmentation light, without dark brown
      flecks ....*Leptodactylus fragilis*
   b. A^2 tooth row with narrow, almost invisible gap; body pigmentation heavy,
      pigment on spiracle and areas lateral to eyes pale .... *Leptodactylus melanonotus*
8 a. Anterior oral papillary gap present, posterior oral papillary gap absent;
      pale cream or white in preservative, reddish in life because of skin
      vascularization .... *Hyalinobatrachium fleischmanni*
   b. Anterior and posterior oral papillary gap present; pigmentation dark
      brown to black **9**
9 a. Lower tooth rows subequal in length and slightly shorter than upper
      tooth rows **10**
   b. Lower tooth rows not subequal in length, P^1 subequal with upper tooth rows **11**
10 a. Medial gap in A^2 tooth row 22 teeth wide, lateral surface of tail musculature
      uniformly dark brown, submarginal papillae present .... *Bufo luetkenii*
   b. Medial gap in A^2 tooth row five teeth wide, cream-colored mottling on
      lateral surface of tail musculature, submarginal papillae absent .... *Bufo valliceps*
11 a. P^1 and P^2 tooth rows not subequal in length, relatively wide medial gap
      in A^2 tooth row, tail musculature cream ....*Bufo coccifer*
   b. P^1 and P^2 tooth rows subequal in length, relatively narrow medial gap
      in A^2 tooth row, tail musculature dark brown to black with a narrow
      creamish region ventrally .... *Bufo marinus*
12 a. Oral disc emarginated (marginal indentation) laterally **13**
   b. Oral disc not emarginated laterally **14**
13 a. Lateral segments of A^2 tooth rows slightly longer than medial gap;
      tail musculature relatively slender .... *Physalaemus pustulosus*
   b. Lateral segments of A^2 tooth rows much less than medial gap;
      tail musculature relatively robust .... *Rana forreri*
14 a. 4–7 upper tooth rows, 4 lower tooth rows, dark brown blotches
      on fins ....*Rana maculata*
   b. 2–4 upper tooth rows, 3 **or** 5–6 lower tooth rows, no dark brown blotches
      on fins **15**
15 a. 3 lower tooth rows **17**
   b. 5 or 6 lower tooth rows **16**
16 a. Tooth rows 4/6, creamy tan crescent-shaped bar present on posterior
      margin of body ....*Ptychohyla euthysanota*
   b. Tooth rows 2–3/5; no crescent-shaped bar on side of body .... *Ptychohyla salvadorensis*
17 a. No gap in marginal papillae on anterior lip **20**
   b. Medial gap in marginal papillae on anterior lip **18**
18 a. P^1 tooth row without median gap .... *Smilisca baudinii*
   b. Narrow, distinct gap in P^1 tooth row **19**

19 a. Eyes lateral, gap in A^2 tooth row narrow, segmentation of caudal
        musculature distinct ....***Agalychnis moreletii***
    b. Eyes nearly dorsal, gap in A^2 tooth row broad, segmentation of caudal
        musculature indistinct ....***Scinax staufferi***
20 a. A^2 tooth row without median gap ....***Plectrohyla psiloderma***
    b. A^2 tooth row with narrow, distinct median gap **21**
21 a. Short, blunt serrations on beak, iris in life pale brown ....***Plectrohyla guatemalensis***
    b. Long, pointed serrations on beak, iris in life deep bronze with
        black reticulations ....***Plectrohyla sagorum***

Clave para los Renacuajos de El Salvador

1   a. Dientes labiales ausentes **2**
    b. Dientes labiales presentes **4**
2   a. Inflexiones orales ausentes ....***Rhinophrynus dorsalis***
    b. Inflexiones orales presentes **3**
3   a. Inflexiones orales con márgenes irregulares que convergen o se
        sobreponen ventromedialmente ....***Hypopachus***
    b. Inflexiones orales con forma triangular y márgenes lisos que no
        convergen ventromedialmente ....***Gastrophryne usta***
4   a. Tubo cloacal medial (alineado a la aleta ventral) **5**
    b. Tubo cloacal diestro (ubicado a la derecha del plano de la aleta ventral) **12**
5   a. Disco oral con dos filas de papilas marginales **6**
    b. Disco oral con una fila de papilas marginales **8**
6   a. Fórmula de filas de dientes 3–4/5–6; disco oral con pliegues laterales profundos;
        línea lateral café oscura a lo largo del cuerpo ....***Phrynohyas venulosa***
    b. Fórmula de filas de dientes 2/3; disco oral sin pliegues laterales profundos;
        sin línea lateral a lo largo del cuerpo **7**
7   a. Segunda fila anterior de dientes (A^2) con espacio liso ancho; punto
        claro por detrás del disco oral; cuerpo con pigmentación clara, sin pequeños
        puntos oscuros ....***Leptodactylus fragilis***
    b. A^2 con espacio liso angosto, difícil de ver; cuerpo densamente
        pigmentado; pigmentación pálida en espiráculo y áreas a los lados de
        los ojos ....***Leptodactylus melanonotus***
8   a. Papilas orales con espacio liso anterior, espacio liso posterior
        ausente; cuerpo crema pálido o blanco en preservante, rojo en vida
        debido a vascularización en la piel ....***Hyalinobatrachium fleischmanni***
    b. Papilas orales con espacio liso anterior y posterior presentes; cuerpo
        color café oscuro a negro **9**
9   a. Filas de dientes inferiores con longitud similar, siendo un poco más
        cortas que las filas superiores **10**
    b. Filas de dientes inferiores de longitud heterogénea, P^1 (primera fila posterior)
        con longitud similar a las filas superiores **11**
10 a. Fila de dientes A^2 (segunda fila anterior) con espacio liso medial que tiene
        un ancho aproximado al que ocuparían 22 dientes; superficie lateral de la
        musculatura de la cola uniformemente oscura (café); papilas orales
        submarginales (=inframarginales) presentes ....***Bufo luetkenii***
    b. Fila de dientes A^2 con espacio liso medial que tiene un ancho aproximado
        al que ocuparían cinco dientes; superficie lateral de la musculatura de la
        cola con pigmentación crema esparcida, papilas orales submarginales
        (=inframarginales) ausentes ....***Bufo valliceps***
11 a. Filas de dientes P^1 y P^2 con longitud heterogénea; fila de dientes A^2 con espacio liso

medial relativamente ancho; musculatura de la cola color crema .... ***Bufo coccifer***

b. Filas de dientes P^1 y P^2 con longitud similar, fila de dientes A^2 con
espacio liso medial relativamente angosto; musculatura de la cola color café
oscuro a negro, con una region angosta color crema ventralmente .... ***Bufo marinus***

12 a. Disco oral emarginado lateralmente (identación marginal) **13**

b. Disco oral no emarginado lateralmente **14**

13 a. Fila de dientes A^2 con segmentos laterales un poco más largos que el espacio medio;
musculatura de la cola relativamente angosta .... ***Physalaemus pustulosus***

b. Fila de dientes A^2 con segmentos laterales mucho más cortos que el espacio medio;
musculatura de la cola moderadamente robusta .... ***Rana forreri***

14 a. Entre 4–7 filas de dientes superiores; 4 filas de dientes inferiores;
manchas oscuras (café) en las aletas .... ***Rana maculata***

b. Entre 2–4 filas de dientes superiores; 3 ó 5–6 filas de dientes inferiores; sin manchas
oscuras (café) en las aletas **15**

15 a. Tres filas de dientes inferiores **17**

b. Cinco o seis filas de dientes inferiores **16**

16 a. Fórmula de filas de dientes 4/6, barra curva color crema-café en margen
posterior del cuerpo .... ***Ptychohyla euthysanota***

b. Fórmula de filas de dientes 2–3/5, barra crema-café en margen posterior
del cuerpo ausente .... ***Ptychohyla salvadorensis***

17 a. Papilas orales marginales del labio anterior sin espacio liso **20**

b. Papilas orales marginales del labio anterior con espacio liso medial **18**

18 a. Fila de dientes P^1 sin espacio liso medial .... ***Smilisca baudinii***

b. Fila de dientes P^1 con espacio liso medial angosto **19**

19 a. Ojos dispuestos lateralmente, fila de dientes A^2 con espacio liso ancho, cola con
segmentación muscular evidente .... ***Agalychnis moreletii***

b. Ojos dispuestos casi dorsalmente, fila de dientes A^2 con espacio liso ancho, cola con
segmentación muscular indistinta .... ***Scinax staufferi***

20 a. Fila de dientes A^2 sin espacio liso medial .... ***Plectrohyla psiloderma***

b. Fila de dientes A^2 con espacio liso medial angosto **21**

21 a. Pico (= queratostoma) con margen serrado no punteagudo; en vida,
iris café pálido .... ***Plectrohyla guatemalensis***

b. Pico (=queratostoma), con margen serrado punteagudo; en vida, iris bronce con
reticulación negra .... ***Plectrohyla sagorum***

Chapter 6
Class Reptilia

Reptiles are tetrapods that have adapted to life on land by evolving cornified scales, plates, or scutes on their bodies to prevent water loss. In contrast to amphibians that must live and breed in or near water, reptiles have amniotic eggs that allow them to reproduce far from sources of water (Chiszar & Smith 2003). Although the oldest-known reptiles (up to 270 mya) are not quite as ancient as the amphibians (up to 350 mya), the reptiles have evolved more species and occupy every corner of the globe except for the Arctic and Antarctic regions. Most reptiles are oviparous, but some groups are viviparous or ovoviviparous. In contrast to the amphibians, reptiles have invaded the marine environment, evolved venom-conducting fangs, and in some cases, are the top predators in their ecosystems (e.g., *Varanus komodoensis*). Major groups of reptiles include turtles, archosaurs (crocodilians and birds), and lepidosaurs (tuataras, amphisbaenians, lizards, and snakes). Although the phylogenetic positions of some reptile groups are well supported (e.g., *Sphenodon* is a basal lepidosaur), others remain contentious (e.g., phylogenetic position of turtles). Adults range in size from tiny geckos (< 30 mm) (Hedges & Thomas 2001) to long pythons and anacondas (ca. 10 m). Many new species of reptiles are still being described, but the most recent count lists approximately 7518 species of reptiles in 60 families (Zug et al. 2001, Baker 2003a, Britton 2003, Chiszar & Smith 2003, Pianka 2003a, Towns 2003).

Key to the Major Groups of Reptiles in El Salvador

1 a. Limbs absent .... **Serpentes**
   b. Limbs present **2**
2 a. Most of body enclosed in a bony shell .... **Testudines**
   b. Bony shell absent **3**
3 a. Thick, rectangular, upward pointing scales on the tail; massive jaws
     with socketed teeth .... **Crocodylia**
   b. Tails lacking thick, rectangular, upward pointing scales;
     jaws lacking socketed teeth .... **Sauria**

Clave para los Grupos Mayores de Reptiles en El Salvador

1 a. Extremidades ausentes .... **Serpentes**
   b. Extremidades presentes.. **2**
2 a. Mayor parte del cuerpo dentro de un caparazón óseo .... **Testudines**
   b. Caparazón óseo ausente... **3**
3 a. Cola con escamas gruesas, rectangulares, con puntas dirigidas hacia
     arriba formando serie de cretas; dientes incrustados en huecos de la maxila y
     mandíbula; maxila y mandíbula robustas .... **Crocodylia**
   b. Cola sin escamas gruesas, rectangulares, que forman crestas; maxila y
     mandíbula sin huecos para la incrustación de dientes .... **Sauria**

Order Crocodylia (Crocodilians)

The crocodilians are an ancient (240 mya) group of tetrapods that are closely related to birds. There are several groups of crocodilians, including alligators, crocodiles, caimans, and gharials. Crocodilians construct nest chambers in holes or in nests they form out of vegetation and mud; females protect the nest and young after they hatch. Crocodilians are found in tropical and subtropical areas of the New World, Africa (including Madagascar), Asia, and Australia. There are just 23 species of crocodilians in eight genera and three families (Britton 2003). Two families occur in El Salvador.

Key to the Crocodilians of El Salvador

1 a. A transverse preocular ridge present; no teeth of lower jaw visible
   when mouth is closed...*Caiman crocodilus*
   b. No transverse preocular ridge; 4th tooth on lower jaw visible when
   mouth is closed ....*Crocodylus acutus*

Clave para los Crocodrilos de El Salvador

1 a. Cresta transversal preocular presente; dientes de la mandíbula no visibles
   cuando la boca esta cerrada ....*Caiman crocodilus*
   b. Cresta transversal preocular ausente; 4to diente de la mandíbula visible
   cuando la boca esta cerrada ....*Crocodylus acutus*

Family Alligatoridae

This small family of crocodilians includes eight species in four genera distributed in China, southeastern United States, and from Mexico to central South America. These animals inhabit lowland freshwater habitats (Mertz 2003a). One genus occurs in El Salvador.

Genus *Caiman*

Three species are recognized in this genus (Mertz 2003a). These crocodilians are distributed from southern Mexico to western Ecuador and northern Argentina (Savage 2002). One species probably occurs in numerous freshwater habitats throughout El Salvador, but only one confirmed locality is currently known.

Caiman crocodilus (Linnaeus 1758)
(Caiman)
Plate 43, Map 35, Figure 17ab

1758 *Lacerta crocodilus* Linnaeus, Systema Naturae, ed. 10: 206; type locality: unknown.
Caiman crocodilus fuscus: Mertens 1952d,
Grenard 1991.
Caiman crocodilus: Villa et al. 1988, Köhler 2000, Dueñas et al. 2001, Köhler 2003b.
Caiman crocodilus chiapasius: King & Burke 1989.
Geographic distribution: From eastern Honduras along the Atlantic versant to northern Colombia, Venezuela, and the Guianas, through the Amazon basin to eastern Peru and central Brazil; from the Isthmus of Tehuantepec along the Pacific

Plate 43: *Caiman crocodilus* NICARAGUA: Chontales: Bartola (340 m). Photo: G. Köhler.

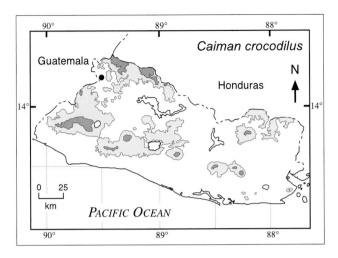

Map 35: Distribution of *Caiman crocodilus* in El Salvador.

Closed circles represent examined-specimen locality records; open squares are published locality records. Light shading indicates 600–1200 m elevation; dark shading indicates elevations ≥ 1200 m; large bodies of freshwater are outlined in bold, black lines.

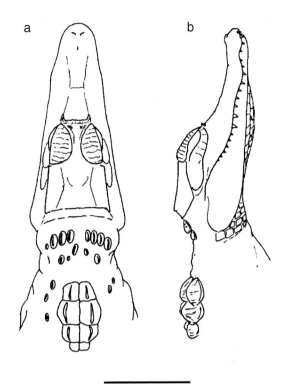

50 mm

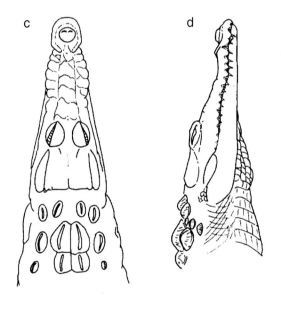

50 mm

Figure 17: Dorsal and lateral view of heads of juvenile a,b. *Caiman crocodilus* (SMF 8138); c,d. *Crocodylus acutus* (SMF 26339).

versant to southern Ecuador. Introduced to Florida, USA, eastern Puerto Rico, and Isla de la Juventud off Cuba (Savage 2002, Meshaka et al. 2004).

Ecological distribution: Marshes, lagoons, lakes, and mangroves between sea level and 450 m.

Description: A crocodilian (average adult size 1.5– 2 m total length) with a broad snout (length of snout about 1.5 times width at base); a transverse preocular ridge present; no teeth of lower jaw visible when mouth is closed.

Dorsal and lateral surfaces of head, body, and tail grayish brown or olive-brown with dark brown crossbands on body and tail; ventral surfaces cream or yellow.

Natual history: Savage (2002) noted this species is most active at night, although it will bask during the day. Juveniles eat arthropods, and adults tend to eat fish, frogs, and carrion. Breeding precedes the rainy season; females lay 15–40 eggs per clutch.

Conservation status: CITES: Appendix II.

Specimens examined: Santa Ana: Laguna de Güija, 450 m: SMF 42878.

Family Crocodylidae

This small family of crocodilians includes 14 species in three genera distributed from Mexico to northern South America in the New World, Africa and Madagascar, and Asia to northern Australia.

These animals inhabit a wide array of aquatic habitats (Whitaker & Whitaker 2003). One genus occurs in El Salvador.

Genus *Crocodylus*

Twelve species of this genus are distributed from southern Florida and Mexico to northern South America in the New World, Africa, Madagascar, Asia, Australia, and several islands in the vicinity of Fiji (Savage 2002). One species occurs in El Salvador.

Crocodylus acutus Cuvier 1807
(Cocodrilo)
Plate 44, Map 36, Figure 17cd

1807 *Crocodylus acutus* Cuvier, Ann. Mus. Hist. Nat., Paris, 10: 55; type locality: Santo Domingo.
Crocodylus acutus acutus: Mertens 1952d.
Crocodylus acutus: Villa et al. 1988, King & Burke 1989, Grenard 1991, Ernst et al. 1999, Köhler 2000, Dueñas et al. 2001, Köhler 2003b.
Geographic distribution: Southern Florida; Greater Antilles; from Tamaulipas, Mexico, to Colombia and northern Venezuela on the Atlantic versant; from Sinaloa, Mexico, to northern Peru on the Pacific versant (Savage 2002).
Ecological distribution: Marshes, lagoons, rivers, lakes, and mangroves between sea level and 450 m.
Description: A crocodilian (average adult size 2–3 m total length) with a narrow snout (length of snout about twice width at base); no transverse preocular ridge present; 4th teeth of lower jaw visible when mouth is closed.

Dorsal and lateral surfaces of head, body, and tail grayish brown or olive-brown with dark-brown crossbands on body and tail; ventral surfaces cream or yellow.
Natural history: Campbell (1998a) noted this species feeds mainly at night upon a wide array of vertebrate and invertebrate prey; females lay 30–70 eggs between March and May, which hatch 75–80 days later. Stafford & Meyer (2000) noted this species has occasionally been found swimming at sea some distance from the shore. Savage (2002) noted that large adults will attack humans in Costa Rica.
Conservation status: CITES: Appendix I; IUCN: Vulnerable (VU A1ac).
Specimens examined: <u>La Paz</u>: Laguna Limpia:

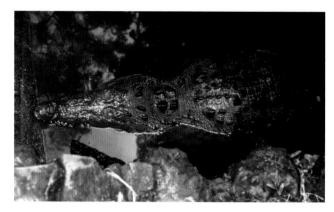

Plate 44: *Crocodylus acutus* EL SALVADOR: Usulután: Río Lempa. Zoo specimen. Photo: E. Greenbaum.

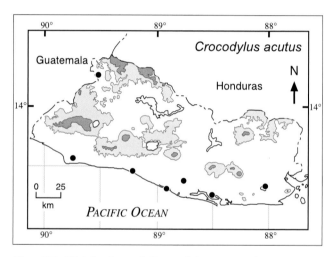

Map 36: Distribution of *Crocodylus acutus* in El Salvador.
Closed circles represent examined-specimen locality records; open squares are published locality records. Light shading indicates 600–1200 m elevation; dark shading indicates elevations ≥ 1200 m; large bodies of freshwater are outlined in bold, black lines.

SMF 42177 (*); Estero de Jaltepeque: SMF 51975, 57554. <u>San Miguel</u>: Laguna de Olomega, 61 m: MVZ 39906–07, 222426–27; Laguna de Jocotal: KU CT 11896. <u>Santa Ana</u>: Hacienda San Diego: SMF 42255, 42809; Laguna de Güija, 450 m: SMF 42808. <u>Sonsonate</u>: Río Ceniza near Los Damos: SMF 42221. <u>Usulután</u>: Estero de El Triunfo [probably refers to Bahía de Jiquilisco, near Puerto El Triunfo according to O. Komar pers. comm.]: SMF 42956. <u>Depto. unknown</u>: estero region, coast of El Salvador: SMF 42883 (*); no specific locality: SMF 60848, 69970 (*).

Order Testudines (Turtles)

The turtles are a distinct group of vertebrates that first appeared in the Triassic period (220 mya). Two major groups of turtles are recognized: suborder Pleurodira (side-necked turtles) and suborder Cryptodira (hidden-necked turtles). Distributed on every continent except Antarctica, there are just under 300 species of turtles in about 100 genera and 14 families (Baker 2003a). Five families occur in El Salvador.

Key to the Turtles of El Salvador

1 a. Each forelimb with two or fewer claws, but without separate digits (paddle-shaped) **2**
   b. Each forelimb with five claws and distinct digits **5**
2 a. Shell covered with a continuous layer of undivided skin .... ***Dermochelys coriacea***
   b. Shell covered with distinct horny scutes **3**
3 a. Four costal scutes present on each side; cervical scute not in contact
      with first costal scute **4**
   b. Five or more costal scutes present on each side; cervical scute in
      contact with first costal scute .... ***Lepidochelys olivacea***
4 a. One pair of prefrontals; beak not hawk-like; scutes of carapace
      non-imbricate .... ***Chelonia mydas***
   b. Two pairs of prefrontals; beak hawk-like; scutes of
      carapace imbricate .... ***Eretmochelys imbricata***
5 a. Front part of plastron moveable **6**
   b. Plastron solid, front part not moveable **7**
6 a. Plastron small, without closing carapace .... ***Staurotypus salvinii***
   b. Plastron large, closing carapace .... ***Kinosternon scorpioides***
7 a. Hind feet with little webbing; head with red stripes .... ***Rhinoclemmys pulcherrima***
   b. Hind feet with extensive webbing; head with yellow stripes .... ***Trachemys venusta***

Clave para las Tortugas de El Salvador

1 a. Dos o menos garras en cada extremidad anterior, dedos unidos **2**
   b. Cinco garras en cada extremidad anterior, dedos separados **5**
2 a. Caparazón cubierto con capas contínuas de piel .... ***Dermochelys coriacea***
   b. Caparazón cubierto con escudos córneos **3**
3 a. Cuatro escudos costales presentes en cada lado; escudo cervical separado
      del primer escudo costal **4**
   b. Cinco o más escudos costales presentes en cada lado; escudo cervical en
      contacto con el primer escudo costal .... ***Lepidochelys olivacea***
4 a. Un par de prefrontales; pico córneo sin forma curva; caparazón con
      escudos no imbricados .... ***Chelonia mydas***
   b. Dos pares de prefrontales; pico córneo con forma curva (aguileña);
      caparazón con escudos imbricados .... ***Eretmochelys imbricata***
5 a. Peto o plastron con parte frontal móvil **6**
   b. Peto o plastron sólido, parte frontal inmóvil **7**
6 a. Plastron pequeño, caparazón no se cierra .... ***Staurotypus salvinii***
   b. Plastron grande, caparazón se cierra .... ***Kinosternon scorpioides***
7 a. Dedos de extremidades posteriores con membranas basales; cabeza
      con líneas rojas .... ***Rhinoclemmys pulcherrima***
   b. Dedos de extremidades posteriores con membranas extensas;
      cabeza con líneas amarillas .... ***Trachemys venusta***

Family Cheloniidae

This small family of sea turtles includes six species in five genera distributed in tropical and temperate oceans across the world. Closely related to the leatherback turtles (Dermochelyidae), cheloniids are strictly marine (Iverson 2003a). Three genera occur in El Salvador.

Genus *Chelonia*

Commonly called green turtles, this genus includes one species that is present in all tropical and temperate seas (Iverson 2003a). As explained in the species account below, some sources recognize two species in this genus (e.g., Savage 2002).

Chelonia mydas (Linnaeus 1758)
(Tortuga Prieta)
Plate 45, Map 37

1758 *Testudo mydas* Linnaeus, Systema Naturae, ed. 10: 197; type locality: "insulas Pelagi: insulam Adscensionis"; restricted to "Insel Ascension," by Mertens & Müller (1928: Abh. Senck. Naturf. Ges, Frankfurt a.M., 41: 23).
Chelonia mydas: Mertens 1952d, Hirth 1980, Ernst & Barbour 1989, King & Burke 1989, Cornelius 1995, Köhler 2000, 2003b.
Chelonia agassizii: Villa et al. 1988, King & Burke 1989, Iverson 1992, Dueñas et al. 2001.
Chelonia mydas agassizii: Hasbún & Vásquez 1999.
Geographic distribution: Identical to genus *Chelonia*.
Ecological distribution: Sandy beaches (nesting females) and marine waters.
Description: A medium-sized sea turtle (average adult size 1000–1200 mm carapace length); head blunt (short snout: preorbital distance smaller than orbital length); carapace nearly oval; four costal scutes on each side; four inframarginals, none possessing pores; carapace scutes are juxtaposed; one pair of prefrontal scales; the cutting edge of the lower jaw is serrated; flippers usually with only one evident claw; in juveniles posterior margin of carapace serrated.

Dorsal and lateral surfaces of head, limbs, and tail are dark brown; the carapace is brown or olive-brown with dark brown wavy markings on scutes; ventral surfaces of head, limbs, shell, and tail are cream or yellow.
Taxonomic comments: The taxomomy of this

Plate 45: *Chelonia mydas* MEXICO: Chiapas: Paredon. Photo: J. L. Carr.

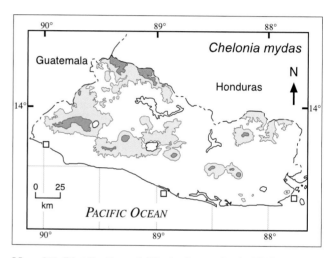

Map 37: Distribution of *Chelonia mydas* in El Salvador. Closed circles represent examined-specimen locality records; open squares are published locality records. Light shading indicates 600–1200 m elevation; dark shading indicates elevations ≥ 1200 m; large bodies of freshwater are outlined in bold, black lines.

species has been a point of debate for years. Some authors prefer to recognize the subspecies *Chelonia mydas agassizii* for the Eastern Pacific populations (Kamezaki & Matsui 1995, Hasbún & Vásquez 1999), others recognize *C. agassizii* as a distinct species (Pritchard 1999, Savage 2002), whereas others do not recognize the Pacific and Atlantic forms as distinct taxa (Ernst & Barbour 1989, Bowen & Karl 1999, Karl & Bowen 1999, Stafford & Meyer 2000). The criticism of morphological characters that purportedly distinguish *C. agassizii* and molecular evidence presented by Bowen & Karl (1999) effectively argued that the Atlantic and

Pacific populations of green turtles are conspecific, and we choose to uphold this decision here.

Natural history: Stafford & Meyer (2000) noted juveniles are carnivorous, but adults become omnivorous and feed upon eelgrass and marine algae. Savage (2002) reported peak nesting months are October–March, with occasional nesting at all times of the year. Clutch size varies from 67–107 eggs.

Conservation status: CITES: Appendix I; IUCN Red List: Endangered (EN A1bd).

Published locality records: <u>Ahuachapán</u>: Barra de Santiago beach (Hasbún & Vásquez 1999). <u>La Paz</u>: off the coast of La Herradura (Hasbún & Vásquez 1999). <u>La Unión</u>: Isla Conchaguita (Hasbún & Vásquez 1999).

Genus *Eretmochelys*

This monotypic genus is found in all tropical and subtropical seas and often enters cooler waters; nesting is restricted to tropical and subtropical areas (Savage 2002).

Eretmochelys imbricata (Linnaeus 1766)
(Tortuga Carey)
Plate 46, Map 38

1766 *Testudo imbricata* Linnaeus, Systema Naturae, ed. 12: 350; type locality: "Mari Americano, Asiatico."
Eretmochelys imbricata: Mertens 1952d, Villa et al. 1988, Ernst & Barbour 1989, King & Burke 1989, Iverson 1992, Cornelius 1995, Hasbún et al. 1998, Hasbún & Vásquez 1999, Köhler 2000, Dueñas et al. 2001, Hasbún 2002, Köhler 2003b.

Geographic distribution: Identical to genus.

Ecological distribution: Sandy beaches (nesting females) and marine waters.

Description: A medium-sized sea turtle (average adult size 900–1000 mm carapace length); head narrow with a narrow, elongated, hawk-like snout, decurved at the tip; carapace shield-shaped; posterior margin of carapace usually serrated (except in very old individuals); four costal scutes on each side; four inframarginals, none possessing pores; carapace scutes are distinctly imbricate in juveniles and subadults, whereas in adults overlapping becomes progressively less developed, until in very old individuals the scutes are juxtaposed; two pairs of prefrontal scales.

Dorsal and lateral surfaces of head, limbs, and tail are dark brown; the carapace is brown or olive-

Plate 46: *Eretmochelys imbricata* COLOMBIA: San Andrés y Providencía: Isla San Andrés. Photo: J. L. Carr.

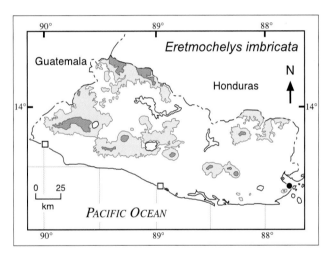

Map 38: Distribution of *Eretmochelys imbricata* in El Salvador.
Closed circles represent examined-specimen locality records; open squares are published locality records. Light shading indicates 600–1200 m elevation; dark shading indicates elevations ≥ 1200 m; large bodies of freshwater are outlined in bold, black lines.

brown with cream markings on scutes; ventral surfaces of head, limbs, shell, and tail are cream or yellow.

Natural history: Hasbún et al. (1998) reported a juvenile turtle collected in January by a group of fishermen using gill nets near Barra de Santiago estuary (Depto. Ahuachapán). Stafford & Meyer (2000) noted this omnivorous species feeds upon

mollusks, sponges, and other marine invertebrates. Savage (2002) noted that Atlantic populations of this species nest throughout the year and lay 53–206 eggs per clutch; renesting can occur every 12–15 days.
Conservation status: CITES: Appendix I; IUCN: Critically endangered (CR A1bd).
Specimens examined: <u>La Unión</u>: Golfo de Fonseca: SMF 42802.
Published locality records: <u>Ahuachapán</u>: Barra de Santiago beach (Hasbún & Vásquez 1999). <u>La Paz</u>: La Herradura beach (Hasbún & Vásquez 1999).

Genus *Lepidochelys*

This genus includes one wide-ranging species (*Lepidochelys olivacea*) and one with a restricted distribution in the Gulf of Mexico (*L. kempi;* Savage 2002). One species occurs in El Salvador.

Lepidochelys olivacea (Eschscholtz 1829)
(Tortuga Golfina)
Plate 47, Map 39

1829 *Chelonia olivacea* Eschscholtz, Zool. Atlas 1: 3; type locality: Manila Bay, Philippines.
Lepidochelys olivacea: Cornelius 1995, Ernst & Barbour 1989, King & Burke 1989, Iverson 1992, Hasbún & Melara 1994, Zug et al. 1998, Hasbún & Ramos 1999, Hasbún & Vásquez 1999, Köhler 2000, Dueñas et al. 2001, Köhler 2003b.
Geographic distribution: Warmer waters of the Indian, Pacific, and southern Atlantic oceans (Savage 2002).
Ecological distribution: Sandy beaches (nesting females) and marine waters.
Description: A relatively small sea turtle (average adult size 600–750 mm carapace length); carapace heart-shaped to nearly round, flattened dorsally; posterior margin of carapace only slightly serrated; five to seven vertebral scutes; five to nine costal scutes on each side; 13–14 marginal scutes; plastron with two longitudinal ridges; four inframarginals, each with a musk pore at the posterior edge; carapace scutes are juxtaposed; males have a well-developed claw on each front flipper (females without visible claws).

Dorsal and lateral surfaces of head, limbs, and tail are grayish brown; the carapace is grayish brown or olive-brown; ventral surfaces of head, limbs, shell, and tail are cream or yellow.
Natural history: Hasbún & Vásquez (1999) reported nesting of this species at Barra de

Plate 47: *Lepidochelys olivacea* EL SALVADOR: Usulután: Isla San Sebastián. Photo: ADESCOPP, courtesy of R. A. Vásquez.

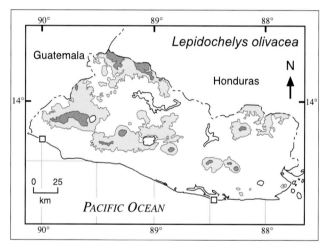

Map 39: Distribution of *Lepidochelys olivacea* in El Salvador.
Closed circles represent examined-specimen locality records; open squares are published locality records. Light shading indicates 600–1200 m elevation; dark shading indicates elevations ≥ 1200 m; large bodies of freshwater are outlined in bold, black lines.

Santiago, Depto. Ahuachapán and at Playa Hermosa, Isla San Sebastián, Depto. Usulután. According to these authors, the olive ridley is the most common sea turtle species in El Salvador and nests year round. However, nesting activity is concentrated during the rainy season between May and October, peaking in August and September. A clutch size of 24–143 eggs is reported for the population nesting in El Salvador (Hasbún & Vásquez 1999). Savage (2002) noted this species preys upon decapod crustaceans, echinoderms, mollusks, fish, and algae.

Conservation status: CITES: Appendix I; IUCN: Endangered (EN A1bd).

Published locality records: <u>Ahuachapán</u>: Barra de Santiago beach (Hasbún & Vásquez 1999). <u>Usulután</u>: Playa Hermosa, Isla San Sebastián (Hasbún & Vásquez 1999).

Family Dermochelyidae

This family includes one very large (244 cm, 867 kg) species of sea turtle that is distributed around the world's oceans (Iverson 2003b).

Genus *Dermochelys*

This monotypic genus is found in all tropical, subtropical, and temperate oceans (Savage 2002).

***Dermochelys coriacea* (Linnaeus 1766)**
(Tortuga Baule)
Plate 48, Map 40

1766 *Testudo coriacea* Linnaeus, Systema Naturae, ed. 12: 350; type locality: "maris Tyrrheni oram in agro Laurentiano."
Dermochelys coriacea: Pritchard 1980, Ernst & Barbour 1989, King & Burke 1989, Iverson 1992, Hasbún & Melara 1994, Cornelius 1995, Hasbún & Vásquez 1999, Köhler 2000, Dueñas et al. 2001, Köhler 2003b.

Geographic distribution: Identical to genus *Dermochelys*.

Ecological distribution: Sandy beaches (nesting females) and marine waters.

Description: The largest species of sea turtle (average adult size 1800–2200 mm carapace length) with an elongated, lyre-shaped carapace in dorsal view that tapers to a point posteriorly; the shell lacks keratinized scutes and is instead covered by a layer of leathery skin (small scales present only in hatchlings); seven longitudinal ridges on carapace, five longitudinal ridges on plastron; flippers without visible claws; the snout is blunt and non-projecting; a tooth-like cusp on each side of the upper jaw; patches of papillary projections arranged in rows on roof and floor of mouth, and in throat.

Dorsal and lateral surfaces of head, limbs, shell, and tail are dark brown to almost black, some individuals with dirty white or yellowish spots.

Natural history: Hasbún & Vásquez (1999) reported nesting of this species at Barra de

Plate 48: *Dermochelys coriacea* FRENCH GUIANA: Ya:lima:po-Awa:la beach. Photo: M. Godfrey.

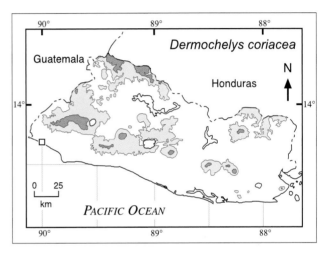

Map 40: Distribution of *Dermochelys coriacea* in El Salvador.
Closed circles represent examined-specimen locality records; open squares are published locality records. Light shading indicates 600–1200 m elevation; dark shading indicates elevations ≥ 1200 m; large bodies of freshwater are outlined in bold, black lines.

Santiago beach, Depto. Ahuachapán. According to these authors, the leatherback sea turtle nests sporadically in El Salvador in the dry months between November and February. Stafford & Meyer (2000) noted this species is omnivorous, but primarily feeds upon jellyfish. Savage (2002) reported this species lays 45–100 eggs per clutch, usually at night; renesting occurs 4–6 times per season at intervals of 7–11 days.

Conservation status: CITES: Appendix I; IUCN: Critically endangered (CR A1abd).

Published locality records: <u>Ahuachapán</u>: Barra de Santiago beach (Hasbún & Vásquez 1999).

Family Emydidae

Distributed in the lowland temperate regions of North and South America, North Africa, southern Turkey, the Middle East, and throughout mainland Europe to southern Russia, this family includes 10 genera (40 species) of semi-aquatic to fully terrestrial species of turtles (Baker 2003b, Stephens & Wiens 2003). Some recent publications on Central American herpetofauna treat geoemydid turtles (e.g., *Rhinoclemmys*) as a subfamily (Batagurinae) of the Emydidae (Campbell 1998a, Savage 2002). One genus occurs in El Salvador.

Genus *Trachemys*

Seidel (2002) recently divided the *Trachemys scripta* "superspecies" into 15 species, eight of which are polytypic. The genus is distributed from the northeastern United States through Central America on both versants to Argentina (Seidel 2002). One species occurs in El Salvador.

Trachemys venusta (Gray 1855)
(Jicotea del Pacífico)
Plate 49, Map 41

1855 *Emys venusta* Gray, Cat. Shield Rept. Brit. Mus. 1: 24; type locality: Honduras.
Pseudemys ornata: Mertens 1952d.
Pseudemys scripta grayi: Legler 1990.
Trachemys scripta: King & Burke 1989, Campbell 1998a, Köhler 2000, Dueñas et al. 2001, Köhler 2003b.
Trachemys scripta grayi: Iverson 1992.
Trachemys venusta grayi: Seidel 2002.
Geographic distribution: On the Atlantic versant from southern Veracruz, Mexico, to northern Colombia; on the Pacific versant from southern Oaxaca, Mexico, to western El Salvador (Legler 1990).
Ecological distribution: Freshwater habitats in dry forest and savanna between sea level and 200 m.
Description: A medium-sized turtle (carapace length 290 mm in Salvadoran specimen); the carapace is oval, only weakly keeled with a slightly serrated posterior rim; the toes are webbed.

The carapace is olive-brown with dark yellow, centered ocelli; head brown with yellow stripes; limbs have numerous narrow creamish stripes; plastron is usually yellow with a single dark brown

Plate 49: *Trachemys venusta* MEXICO: Chiapas: Estero Mafout, ca. 1.6 km S Cabeza de Toro. Juvenile. Photo: J. L. Carr.

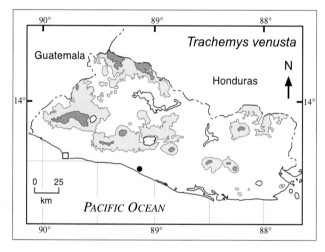

Map 41: Distribution of *Trachemys venusta* in El Salvador.
Closed circles represent examined-specimen locality records; open squares are published locality records. Light shading indicates 600–1200 m elevation; dark shading indicates elevations ≥ 1200 m; large bodies of freshwater are outlined in bold, black lines.

blotch on each scute.
Natural history: *Trachemys venusta* is a highly endangered freshwater turtle in El Salvador. Once abundant in the lower Río Lempa drainage, it has been heavily hunted to the verge of local extinction (F. Serrano, pers. comm.). Serrano recalls having seen several turtles 30 to 40 years ago, "sunning themselves on rocks and felled tree trunks that were semi-submerged at the river's edge. Ex-

tremely wary, they would plunge into the water when one was much closer than 50 m. *Trachemys venusta* was heavily coveted for its meat and the 'medicinal' properties of the same, being more valued than the *Rhinoclemmys* and *Kinosternon*." Mittermeier (1970) reported slider turtles offered for sale in markets in San Salvador. Legler (1990) noted this species flourishes in coastal lagoons. Campbell (1998a) noted that this species is common in freshwater habitats that contain abundant aquatic vegetation; these turtles will consume fruits, vegetation, fish, aquatic invertebrates, and carrion. Nesting occurs in the dry season from December–May; 5–22 eggs are laid per clutch.
Conservation status: IUCN: Lower risk/near threatened (LR/nt).
Specimens examined: <u>La Paz</u>: Laguna Limpia, ca Amatecampo: SMF 47850.
Published locality records: <u>Sonsonate</u>: just east of Acajutla, El Salvador.

Family Geoemydidae

Presumably based upon work by Yasukawa et al. (2001), Iverson (2003c) recognized this family to include 62 species (27 genera) of turtles formerly included in the family Bataguridae. Distributed from northern Mexico to Brazil and Ecuador in the New World, Europe and North Africa to southern China and the East Indies in the Old World. This family is closely related to tortoises in the family Testudinidae. One genus occurs in El Salvador.

Genus *Rhinoclemmys*

Yasukawa et al. (2001) hypothesized that this genus is polyphyletic, and future work might result in taxonomic changes to species currently included in this genus. Currently, nine species are recognized in a disjunct distribution from extreme southern Veracruz, Mexico, through the Yucatán Peninsula, and from northeastern Honduras to Colombia and Venezuela on the Atlantic versant. On the Pacific versant, the genus is known from southern Sonora, Mexico to northern Ecuador, and east and south from Ecuador and Venezuela to northeastern Brazil (J. L. Carr pers. comm., Savage 2002). One species occurs in El Salvador.

Rhinoclemmys pulcherrima (Gray 1855)
(Tortuga Pintada)
Plate 50, Map 42

Plate 50: *Rhinoclemmys pulcherrima* (SMF 81479) EL SALVADOR: Ahuachapán: Río Cuilapa bridge. Photo: M. Veselý.

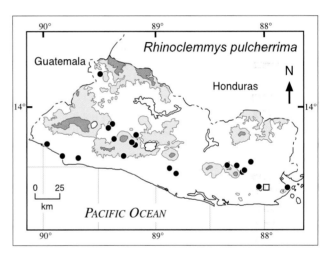

Map 42: Distribution of *Rhinoclemmys pulcherrima* in El Salvador.
Closed circles represent examined-specimen locality records; open squares are published locality records. Light shading indicates 600–1200 m elevation; dark shading indicates elevations ≥ 1200 m; large bodies of freshwater are outlined in bold, black lines.

1855 *Emys pulcherrimus* Gray, Cat. Shield Rept. Brit. Mus. 1: 25; type locality: Mexico.
Rhinoclemmys incisa: K. Schmidt 1928.
Geoemyda pulcherrima incisa: Mertens 1952d, Rand 1957.
Callopsis pulcherrima incisa: Ernst 1978.
Rhinoclemmys pulcherrima incisa: Ernst 1981, Hidalgo 1982c, Ernst & Barbour 1989, Iverson 1992.
Rhinoclemmys pulcherrima: Villa et al. 1988, King & Burke 1989, Köhler 2000, Dueñas et al. 2001, Köhler 2003b.

Geographic distribution: Disjunct and continuous populations on the Pacific versant from Sonora to Colima, Mexico, in Guerrero, and from eastern Oaxaca, Mexico, to central Costa Rica. Also in inland Atlantic drainages in southern Guatemala, Honduras, and Nicaragua (Savage 2002, J. L. Carr, pers. comm.).

Ecological distribution: Freshwater and terrestrial habitats in dry forest and savanna between sea level and 700 m.

Description: A medium-sized turtle (carapace length of largest specimen examined 172 mm); carapace relatively high-domed (usually widest and highest just behind the middle) with a medial keel; carapace surface rough, owing to growth annuli; the toes are webbed.

The carapace is brown with red or reddish brown ocelli; head olive with red lines and stripes; plastron is usually brownish yellow.

Natural history: M. Veselý (field notes) collected a specimen during the day as it crossed a road near a small river at the Río Cuilapa bridge, Depto. Ahuachapán in June. Mertens (1952d) noted that this turtle can be found far from water bodies and prefers humid habitats with dense vegetation in El Salvador. Rand (1957) collected an adult in scrub pasture (ca. 1.2 km away from permanent water) during a heavy rain in June at Instituto Tropical, Depto. San Salvador. Hidalgo (1982c) noted courtship and mating behavior occurs throughout the rainy season (May–October) in El Salvador. He described the courtship and mating behavior of this species in detail. A captive Guatemalan female laid four clutches of 3–5 eggs from September–December (Christensen 1975). Savage (2002) noted this diurnal, semiterrestrial species is omnivorous but prefers vegetation.

Specimens examined: Ahuachapán: on the road near Río Cuilapa bridge, 13°42.5′N, 89°57.5′W, 50 m: SMF 81479. La Libertad: Zaragoza, road San Salvador–La Libertad: SMF 43048; Hacienda Cuyagualo, 600 m: SMF 43164; Hacienda Talqualuya, N from San Juan Opico, 390 m: SMF 51978; Río Sucio: UU 11507. La Paz: Zacatecoluca: SMF 51974; 10 km SE Zacateco Luca: TCWC 22311. La Unión: La Unión: CAS-SU 11754. San Miguel: no specific locality: SMF 42197(*); Laguna de Olomega: SMF 42198–99; same locality at 61 m: MVZ 79099, 222417; Beneficio San Rafael near Quelepa: SMF 43050–52; San Miguel: SMF 44302; 17.5 km W San Miguel: LACM 61173; 9.7 km N, 11.3 km E San Miguel: TCWC 17367; San Miguel,

Río Antonio: TCWC 55016. Santa Ana: near Metapán: SMF 44301. San Salvador: Apopa: SMF 42200; San Salvador, Instituto Tropical de Investigaciones Científicas, 700 m: SMF 51972–73; San Salvador: SMF 68074; San Salvador, 670 m: FMNH 65021. Sonsonate: Acajutla: SMF 57546; 9.2 km SE Jct Hwys 12/2: TCWC 56879.

Published locality records: La Unión: Quebrada de Olomega, Cantón Olomega, 24 km SE San Miguel (Hidalgo 1982c).

Family Kinosternidae

This family includes 25 species (4 genera) of freshwater turtles that are distributed from southeastern Canada to central South America (Iverson 2003d). Two species occur in El Salvador.

Genus *Kinosternon*

This genus includes approximately 20 species of turtles that are distributed from southeastern Canada to Argentina (Savage 2002). One species occurs in El Salvador.

Kinosternon scorpioides (Linnaeus 1766)
(Pochitoque de Carilla Rojo)
Plate 51, Map 43

1766 *Testudo scorpioides* Linnaeus, Systema Naturae, ed. 12: 352; type locality: Surinam.
Kinosternon cruentatum cruentatum: Mertens 1952d, Rand 1957.
Kinosternon scorpioides: Villa et al. 1988, Ernst & Barbour 1989, King & Burke 1989, Iverson 1992, Campbell 1998a, Köhler 2000, Berry & Iverson 2001, Dueñas et al. 2001, Köhler 2003b, Leenders 2003.

Geographic distribution: Disjunct distribution from southern Tamaulipas and eastern Oaxaca, Mexico, through Central America to northern Peru and Brazil; an isolated population is present in southern Bolivia and northern Argentina (Savage 2002).

Ecological distribution: Freshwater habitats in dry forest and savanna between sea level and 1150 m.

Description: A medium-sized semiaquatic turtle (carapace length of largest specimen examined 152 mm); carapace elongated (widest behind the middle) and rather high-domed with three weak longitudinal keels; axillary and inguinal scutes usually in contact; the plastron bears two hinges that allow

Plate 51: *Kinosternon scorpioides* (KU 290017) EL SALVADOR: Cabañas: Bosque Cinquera (400 m). Photo: E. Greenbaum.

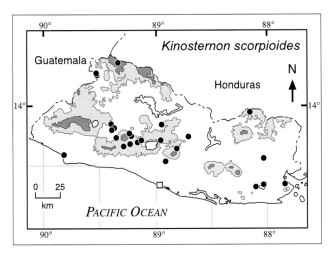

Map 43: Distribution of *Kinosternon scorpioides* in El Salvador.
Closed circles represent examined-specimen locality records; open squares are published locality records. Light shading indicates 600–1200 m elevation; dark shading indicates elevations ≥ 1200 m; large bodies of freshwater are outlined in bold, black lines.

movement of the anterior and posterior lobes; tail with a terminal spine; the snout is projecting with a hooked upper jaw; two barbels are present on the chin; the toes are webbed.

The carapace is brown; head brown, in life usually with orange blotches on lateral part of head; throat and ventral surfaces of neck dirty white with dark gray blotches.

Natural history: E. Greenbaum (field notes) collected an adult as it swam through a small stream in disturbed forest at night at Bosque Cinquera, Depto. Cabañas in August. A juvenile was collected from a flooded field adjacent to a road at night at Perquín, Depto. Morazán in August. Rand (1957) noted an individual in a shallow, temporary pond on the edge of a coffee plantation during the rainy season. Campbell (1998a) reported an omnivorous diet for this species; nesting occurs from March–May and 6–10 eggs are laid per clutch. Stafford & Meyer (2000) noted this species is mainly nocturnal; turtles trapped in evaporating water bodies may burrow underground and remain dormant until the rainy season.

Specimens examined: Ahuachapán: Río Paz: UF 116452 (*). Cabañas: Bosque Cinquera, 13°53.13´N, 88°57.36´W, 400 m: KU 290017. Cuscatlán: Cojutepeque: UU 7646. La Libertad: Sitio del Niño, Río Sucio: SMF 43132; Hacienda Cuyagualo, 600 m: SMF 42257; Nuevo San Salvador [= Santa Tecla]: SMF 43049, 43163, 70226; Laguna Zapotitán: SMF 51967; Hacienda Talqualuya, N from San Juan Opico, 390 m: SMF 51976–77; Guadalupe, 640 m: KU 291368. La Paz: La Herradura: SMF 42195; Hacienda Miraflores, road from San Salvador to Zacatecoluca, 100 m: SMF 51970. La Unión: Cantón Olomega, Laguna de Olomega: KU 183988–93; 1.6 km NNE La Unión turnoff at Sirama: UU 7675. Morazán: Montecristo Mine, NE San Miguel, 250 m: FMNH 65023, MVZ 78575; Perquín, 13°57.17´N, 88°10.01´W, 1150 m: KU 291352, MUHNES C–30–1390, C–30–1541–42. San Miguel: Laguna de Olomega: SMF 42192–93, 42196. San Salvador: San Antonio Abad, 3 km W San Salvador: SMF 43144; Villa Delgado, E San Salvador: SMF 43250; San Salvador, Instituto Tropical, 700 m: SMF 51968; Mejicanos, N from San Salvador: SMF 51969; San Salvador, 670 m: FMNH 65022; San Salvador, Río Acelhuate: LACM 105365. Santa Ana: Laguna de Metapán: SMF 51966; Lago de Güija (Delta del Angue): UU 7645. San Vicente: Laguna Ciega: SMF 42194, 51971; km 63, near Apastepeque, road San Salvador–San Miguel: SMF 50981. Sonsonate: Acajutla: SMF 61204.

Published locality records: La Paz: 6 km N Los Blancos (Rand 1957).

Genus *Staurotypus*

This genus includes two species of highly aggressive freshwater turtles that are distributed from Veracruz, Mexico, to western Honduras on the Atlantic versant, and Oaxaca, Mexico, to central El Salvador on the Pacific versant (Köhler 2003b). One species occurs in El Salvador.

Plate 52: *Staurotypus salvinii* (UTA R-52026) GUATE-MALA: Santa Rosa: Taxisco, Aldéa El Garitón. Photo: E. N. Smith.

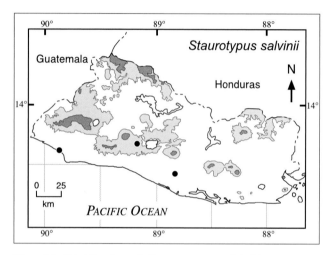

Map 44: Distribution of *Staurotypus salvinii* in El Salvador.
Closed circles represent examined-specimen locality records; open squares are published locality records. Light shading indicates 600–1200 m elevation; dark shading indicates elevations ≥ 1200 m; large bodies of freshwater are outlined in bold, black lines.

***Staurotypus salvinii* Gray 1864**
(Tortuga Chamarro)
Plate 52, Map 44

1864 *Staurotypus* (*Stauremys*) *salvinii* Gray, Proc. Zool. Soc. London 1864: 127; type locality: Huamuchil, Guatemala.
Staurotypus salvinii: Mertens 1952d, Villa et al.

1988, Ernst & Barbour 1989, King & Burke 1989, Iverson 1992, Köhler 2000, Dueñas et al. 2001, Köhler 2003b.
Staurotypus salvini: Dean & Bickham 1983.
Geographic distribution: From eastern Oaxaca and southern Chiapas, Mexico, through southern Guatemala along the Pacific versant to El Salvador (Köhler 2003b).
Ecological distribution: Freshwater habitats in dry forest and savanna between sea level and 700 m.
Description: A medium-sized freshwater turtle (carapace length of largest specimen 200 mm); the elongated, oval carapace bears three distinct longitudinal keels, the median keel extends from the posterior portion of the first vertebral scute to the seam between the 11th pair of marginals; the plastron is small and cross-shaped and bears a hinge that allows movement of the anterior lobe; the head is large with a projecting snout and a weak hook on the upper jaw; two barbels are present on the chin; the toes are webbed.

Dorsal surfaces of head, shell, limbs, and tail are dark gray; ventral surfaces of neck, limbs, and tail dirty white; plastron is dirty yellow.
Natural history: "In El Salvador, *Staurotypus salvinii* is mostly encountered in the freshwater and brackish swamps found at the high tide mark of, or just behind, the mangrove forests on the coast. This would seem to be the main reason for its radical drop in numbers, as most of these swamps have been drained, developed, filled with sediment or simply prevented from tidal movements by dikes. These turtles actually seem to move into the upper edges of mangroves during certain months of the year (to breed or to escape the dry season?), though in larger ponds they also seem to be quite sedentary" (F. Serrano pers. comm.). Mertens (1952d) noted that Salvadoran specimens of this turtle are very aggressive and can deliver serious bites.
Conservation status: IUCN: Lower risk/near threatened (LR/nt).
Specimens examined: <u>San Salvador</u>: San Salvador: SMF 42871. <u>San Vicente</u>: Río San Geronimo, midway between Zacatecoluca and Río Lempa, small tributary: UU 12134. <u>Sonsonate</u>: 1.6 km ESE Metalío: UU 6418.

Suborder Sauria (Lizards)

There are approximately 4450 species (ca. 1440 genera; 15 families) of lizards currently known from a wide array of habitats across the globe (excluding the Arctic and Antarctic regions). Together with snakes and amphisbaenians (worm-like reptiles), the lizards form the Order Squamata; tuataras (*Sphenodon)* are the sister group to the squamates (Pianka 2003a, Rest et al. 2003). Most lizards can be distinguished from snakes by the presence of four limbs, eyelids, and ear openings, but there are exceptions. Many lizards have fracture planes in their caudal vertebrae that allow them to autotomize their tails to escape predators. Lizards can be fossorial, terrestrial, semi-aquatic (freshwater or marine environments), or arboreal. Lizards range in size from tiny geckos (< 30 mm) (Hedges & Thomas 2001) to large varanids (3.0 m) that have been known to prey upon humans. Most lizards lay eggs, but nearly 20% of lizards are viviparous; some species are parthenogenetic (reproduction from virgin females; Zug et al. 2001, Pianka 2003a). There are eight families of lizards in El Salvador.

Key to the Lizards of El Salvador

1   a. Moveable eyelids absent **2**
     b. Moveable eyelids present **6**
2   a. Head covered with granular scales **3**
     b. Head covered by enlarged plates **5**
3   a. Digits without widened subdigital lamellae .... *Gonatodes albogularis*
     b. Digits with widened terminal subdigital lamellae **4**
4   a. Dilatation of subdigital lamellae restricted to two symmetrically
        enlarged terminal plates .... *Phyllodactylus tuberculosus*
     b. Dilatation of subdigital lamellae extends throughout most
        of digit .... *Hemidactylus frenatus*
5   a. Four fingers; gular fold absent; dorsum smooth .... *Gymnophthalmus speciosus*
     b. Five fingers; a distinct gular fold present; dorsum with
        distinct tubercles .... *Lepidophyma smithii*
6   a. Venter covered by large rectangular plates or with large, smooth imbricate,
        cycloid scales **7**
     b. Venter covered by small cycloid, granular, or rectangular scales **12**
7   a. Two or more pairs of scales between rostral and first unpaired scale on head;
        lateral body fold present or not **8**
     b. One or no pair of scales between rostral and first unpaired scale on head;
        no lateral body fold **10**
8   a. Lateral fold absent .... *Celestus atitlanensis*
     b. Lateral fold present **9**
9   a. No lateral fold between ear and forelimb; head widened
        and depressed .... *Abronia montecristoi*
     b. Lateral fold between ear and forelimb present; head not widened
        nor depressed .... *Mesaspis moreletii*
10 a. Dorsal pattern with no more than 5 longitudinal creamish
        stripes .... *Ameiva undulata*
     b. Dorsal pattern with 6–9 longitudinal creamish stripes **11**
11 a. Enlarged postantebrachial scales on forelimbs present;
        four supraoculars .... *Aspidoscelis motaguae*
     b. No enlarged postantebrachial scales on forelimbs;
        usually three supraoculars .... *Aspidoscelis deppii*
12 a. Head covered with granular scales **13**
     b. Head covered by enlarged plates **14**
13 a. Claws almost completely covered by a scaly sheath; first infralabial

        triangular; elongate rows of small scales behind internasals .... ***Coleonyx elegans***

    b. Claws not covered by a scaly sheath; first infralabial squarish; no rows of
       small scales behind internasals ....***Coleonyx mitratus***

14 a. Body covered by uniform cycloid scales; top of head with enlarged plates **15**

    b. Body not covered by uniform cycloid scales; top of head with slightly
       enlarged scales **17**

15 a. Supranasals absent; one frontoparietal.. ***Sphenomorphus assatus***

    b. Supranasals present; two frontoparietals **16**

16 a. Scales in temporal region conspicuously enlarged .... ***Mesoscincus managuae***

    b. Scales in temporal region same size as body scales .... ***Mabuya unimarginata***

17 a. Digits flat; subdigital lamellae smooth and widened; adult males with
       extensile gular fan **18**

    b. Digits compressed or cylindrical; subdigital lamellae keeled, not widened;
       gular fan present or absent **23**

18 a. A deep tube-like axillary pocket present; dorsal scales relatively enlarged,
       larger than ventral scales .... ***Norops tropidonotus***

    b. No deep tube-like axillary pocket; dorsal scales enlarged or not,
       but always smaller than ventral scales **19**

19 a. With laterals among which are scattered single or groups of enlarged scales;
       distinct enlarged postanal scales in males; six or fewer loreal rows; suboculars
       in contact with supralabials **20**

    b. Lateral scales homogeneous; postanal scales in males enlarged or not;
       loreal rows variable; suboculars in contact with supralabials or not **21**

20 a. Ventral scales smooth ....***Norops heteropholidotus***

    b. Ventrals strongly keeled and mucronate .... ***Norops crassulus***

21 a. Legs relatively short, when limb adpressed along side of body 4th toe
       reaches no further than ear opening; dewlap of adult males yellow with
       blue spot; maximum adult size 52 mm .... ***Norops sericeus***

    b. Legs relatively long, when limb adpressed along side of body 4th toe
       reaches between eye and nasal apertura; dewlap of adult males orange or red **22**

22 a. Ventral scales mucronate; dewlap of adult males brick red, darker centrally
       because of suffusion with black pigment; a small dewlap in some females;
       maximum SVL 85 mm in males, 78 mm in females .... ***Norops serranoi***

    b. Ventral scales usually not mucronate; dewlap of adult males flesh colored
       with a basal orange-yellow blotch; females without a dewlap; maximum
       SVL 44 mm in males, 45 mm in females ....***Norops macrophallus***

23 a. No femoral pores; head with a helmet, a vertical fin or a horizontal shelf,
       may be inconspicuous in females and juveniles.. **24**

    b. Femoral pores present; head without helmet, fin or shelf.. **25**

24 a. Toes of hind foot with fringes; no dewlap.. ***Basiliscus vitattus***

    b. Toes on hind foot without fringes; dewlap present .... ***Corytophanes percarinatus***

25 a. No gular fold and no dorsal crest present; small lizards (SVL < 100 mm)...................................... **26**

    b. A gular fold and a dorsal crest present; medium-sized to large lizards
       (SVL > 100 mm) **28**

26 a. Postfemoral pocket present .... ***Sceloporus variabilis***

    b. Postfemoral pocket absent **27**

27 a. Dorsolateral creamish stripes present; dorsal ground color brown to gray;
       3–7 femoral pores (one side); no colorful blotches on chest .... ***Sceloporus squamosus***

    b. No dorsolateral creamish stripes; in life malachite green in males
       or brown in females; 12–16 femoral pores (one side); males with blue
       blotches on chest ....***Sceloporus malachiticus***

28 a. Tail without heavy spines; orbit bordered below by an arc of five to

seven subequal scales; snout covered by large plate-like scales;
large rounded scale below ear opening .... *Iguana iguana*

    b. Tail with distinct spines; a single large, elongate subocular scale present;
snout covered by medium-sized scales; no large rounded scale below ear opening **29**

29 a. Tail very spinous and at maximum girth wider than high (width/height
ratio of 1.6–1.8); ratio of tail length/snout–vent length less than 1.6;
adult size 120–200 mm SVL .... *Ctenosaura flavidorsalis*

    b. Tail moderately spinous and at maximum girth more or less equal in
width and height (width/height ratio 0.9–1.1); ratio of tail length/snout–vent
length 1.6–2.1; adult size 250–350 mm SVL .... *Ctenosaura similis*

Clave para las Lagartijas de El Salvador

1 a. Párpado móvil ausente **2**
    b. Párpado móvil presente **6**
2 a. Cabeza cubierta con escamas granulares **3**
    b. Cabeza cubierta con escamas laminares grandes **5**
3 a. Dedos sin lamelas subdigitales ensanchadas .... *Gonatodes albogularis*
    b. Dedos con lamelas subdigitales terminales ensanchadas **4**
4 a. Ensanchamiento de lamelas subdigitales restringido a dos grandes placas
simétricas terminales .... *Phyllodactylus tuberculosus*
    b. Ensanchamiento de lamelas subdigitales presente a lo largo de la mayor
parte del dedo .... *Hemidactylus frenatus*
5 a. Manos con cuatro dedos; pliegue gular ausente;
dorso liso .... *Gymnophthalmus speciosus*
    b. Manos con cinco dedos; pliegue gular presente;
dorso con tubérculos .... *Lepidophyma smithii*
6 a. Vientre cubierto con placas rectangulares grandes o con grandes
escamas cicloideas lisas e imbricadas **7**
    b. Vientre cubierto con escamas cicloideas pequeñas, granulares o rectangulares **12**
7 a. Dos o más pares de escamas entre la rostral y la primera escama impar de la cabeza;
pliegue lateral del cuerpo presente o ausente **8**
    b. Un par de escamas o sin escamas entre la rostral y la primera escama
impar de la cabeza; pliegue lateral del cuerpo **10**
8 a. Cuerpo sin pliegue lateral .... *Celestus atitlanensis*
    b. Cuerpo con pliegue lateral **9**
9 a. Pliegue lateral entre el tímpano y el brazo ausente;
cabeza ensanchada y aplanada .... *Abronia montecristoi*
    b. Pliegue lateral entre el tímpano y el brazo presente;
cabeza no ensanchada ni aplanada .... *Mesaspis moreletii*
10 a. Patrón de coloración dorsal sin más de 5 líneas
longitudinales opacas .... *Ameiva undulata*
    b. Patrón de coloración dorsal con 6–9 líneas longitudinales opacas **11**
11 a. Escamas postantebraquiales agrandadas;
cuatro supraoculares .... *Aspidoscelis motaguae*
    b. Escamas postantebraquiales no agrandadas; normalemente,
tres supraoculares .... *Aspidoscelis deppii*
12 a. Cabeza cubierta con escamas granulares **13**
    b. Cabeza cubierta con escamas laminares grandes **14**
13 a. Uñas casi completamente cubiertas por una envoltura escamosa;
primera infralabial triangular; escamas pequeñas ubicadas detrás de
las internasales .... *Coleonyx elegans*

b. Uñas sin envoltura escamosa; primera infralabial cuadrada; sin escamas pequeñas detrás de las internasales .... ***Coleonyx mitratus***

14 a. Cuerpo uniformemente cubierto con escamas cicloideas; dorso de la cabeza con escamas laminares grandes **15**

b. Cuerpo no cubierto uniformemente con escamas cicloideas; dorso de la cabeza con escamas laminares ligeramente agrandadas **17**

15 a. Supranasales ausentes; una escama frontoparietal .... ***Sphenomorphus assatus***

b. Supranasales presentes; dos escamas frontoparietales **16**

16 a. Escamas de la region temporal agrandadas .... ***Mesoscincus managuae***

b. Escamas de la region temporal del mismo tamaño que escamas del cuerpo .... ***Mabuya unimarginata***

17 a. Dedos planos; lamelas subdigitales lisas y ensanchadas; machos adultos con saco gular extendible **18**

b. Dedos comprimidos o cilíndricos; lamelas subdigitales quilladas, no ensanchadas; saco gular presente o ausente **23**

18 a. Bolsillo axilar profundo, con forma tubular; escamas dorsales agrandadas, más grandes que las escamas ventrales .... ***Norops tropidonotus***

b. Bolsillo axilar ausente; escamas dorsales agrandadas o no agrandadas, pero siempre más pequeñas que las escamas ventrales **19**

19 a. Grupos dispersos de una o más escamas agrandadas en los flancos del cuerpo; en machos, escamas postanales grandes; seis o menos filas de escamas loreales; suboculares en contacto con supralabiales **20**

b. Escamas de los flancos del cuerpo homogéneas; en machos, escamas postanales agrandadas o no agrandadas; número variable de filas de escamas loreales; suboculares en contacto o separadas de supralabiales **21**

20 a. Escamas ventrales lisas .... ***Norops heteropholidotus***

b. Escamas ventrales quilladas y mucronadas .... ***Norops crassulus***

21 a. Piernas cortas, al juntarlas a los lados del cuerpo el dedo IV no pasa el nivel del tímpano; en machos adultos, saco gular amarillo con una mancha azul; longitud rostro–cloacal máxima 52 mm .... ***Norops sericeus***

b. Piernas largas, al juntarlas a los lados del cuerpo el dedo IV alcanza una posición entre el ojo y la apertura nasal; en machos adultos, saco gular anaranjado o rojo **22**

22 a. Escamas ventrales mucronadas; en machos adultos, saco gular rojo ladrillo, siendo más oscuro en el centro debido a pigmentación negra; saco gular pequeño en algunas hembras; longitud rostro–cloacal máxima 85 mm en machos, 78 mm en hembras .... ***Norops serranoi***

b. Escamas ventrales normalmente no mucronadas; en machos adultos, saco gular color carne con coloración amarillo-naranja en la base; hembras sin saco gular; longitud rostro–cloacal máxima 44 mm en machos, 45 mm en hembras .... ***Norops macrophallus***

23 a. Sin poros femorales; cabeza con un casco, aleta vertical o placa horizontal que puede ser inconspicua en hembras y juveniles **24**

b. Poros femorales presentes; cabeza sin casco, aleta o placa **25**

24 a. Dedos de las extremidades posteriores con pliegues laterales; saco gular ausente .... ***Basiliscus vitattus***

b. Dedos de las extremidades posteriores sin pliegues laterales; saco gular presente .... ***Corytophanes percarinatus***

25 a. Sin pliegue gular ni cresta dorsal; lagartijas pequeñas (LRC < 100 mm) **26**

b. Pliegue gular y cresta dorsal presentes; largartijas de tamaño medio a grande (LRC > 100 mm) **28**

26 a. Bolsillo postfemoral presente .... ***Sceloporus variabilis***

b. Bolsillo postfemoral ausente **27**

27 a. Dorso color gris a café con líneas dorsolaterales pálidas; 3–7 poros femorales
en cada lado; sin manchas de colores en el pecho .... *Sceloporus squamosus*

b. Líneas dorsolaterales ausentes; en vida, machos color verde malaquita y
hembras color café; 12–16 poros femorales en cada lado; machos con
manchas azules en el pecho .... *Sceloporus malachiticus*

28 a. Cola sin espinas pronunciadas; órbita ventralmente rodeada por un arco
de 5–7 escamas; hocico cubierto con escamas laminares grandes;
escama grande redondeada debajo del tímpano .... *Iguana iguana*

b. Cola con espinas pronunciadas; una escama subocular alargada presente;
hocico cubierto con escamas medianas; sin escama grande redondeada
debajo del tímpano **29**

29 a. Cola pronunciadamente espinosa; ancho máximo de la cola mayor a su altura
máxima (relación ancho/alto = 1.6–1.8); Longitud de la cola/Longitud rostro–cloacal
< 1.6; longitud rostro–cloacal 120–200 mm en adultos .... *Ctenosaura flavidorsalis*

b. Cola moderadamente espinosa; ancho máximo de la cola similar a su altura máxima
(relación ancho/alto = 0.9–1.1); Longitud de la cola/Longitud rostro–cloacal 1.6–2.1;
longitud rostro–cloacal 250–350 mm en adultos .... *Ctenosaura similis*

Family Anguidae

This family includes approximately 112 species (14 genera) distributed from southwestern Canada and the eastern United States to northern South America, eastern and southeastern South America, Europe to western Asia, and southeastern Asia (Gutberlet 2003). Many anguids are legless, but the three genera in El Salvador possess four limbs.

Genus *Abronia*

There are currently over 25 species of this genus, which are distributed from southern Tamaulipas, Mexico, to southern Honduras (Campbell & D. Frost 1993, Flores-Villela & Sánchez-H. 2003). One species is known in El Salvador. Campbell & D. Frost (1993:53) suggested the likelihood of extinct and unknown species of *Abronia* in El Salvador because of extensive deforestation of cloud forests.

Abronia montecristoi Hidalgo 1983
(Dragoncillo de Montecristo)
Plate 53, Map 45

1983 *Abronia montecristoi* Hidalgo, Occ. Pap. Mus. Nat. Hist. Univ. Kansas 105: 6; type locality: Cordillera de Alotepeque-Metapán, Hacienda Montecristo, 2250 m, Depto. Santa Ana, El Salvador.

Abronia montecristoi: Hidalgo 1983, Villa et al. 1988, Campbell & D. Frost 1993, Köhler 1996, 2000, Dueñas et al. 2001, Köhler 2003b.

Geographic distribution: Western and southwestern Honduras, and northwestern El Salvador (Köhler 2003b).

Ecological distribution: Cloud forest between 2150 and 2250 m.

Description: Largest Salvadoran specimen is 89.0 mm SVL; tail length/SVL 1.70–1.74; HL/SVL 0.22–0.24; HW/SVL 0.16–0.20; snout length/SVL 0.088–0.094; shank length/SVL 0.44–0.50; a single postmental scale; 7–8 supralabial scales to a point below center of eye (total number 10–11); occipital plate divided into 5 fragments; 4 primary temporal scales; 3–4 secondary temporal scales; 2–3 primary temporal scales contacting postocular scales; 14 longitudinal rows of dorsal scales; 30–31 transverse rows of dorsal scales; 12 longitudinal rows of

Plate 53: *Abronia montecristoi* HONDURAS: Copán: Quebrada Grande. Photo: J. R. McCranie.

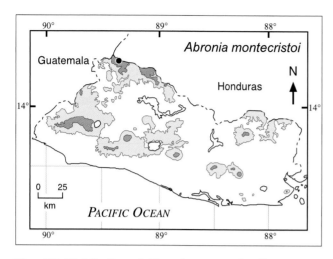

Map 45: Distribution of *Abronia montecristoi* in El Salvador.
Closed circles represent examined-specimen locality records; open squares are published locality records. Light shading indicates 600–1200 m elevation; dark shading indicates elevations ≥ 1200 m; large bodies of freshwater are outlined in bold, black lines.

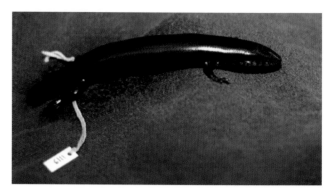

Plate 54: *Celestus atitlanensis* (KU 184048) EL SALVADOR: Ahuachapán: Parque Nacional El Imposible (800 m). Preserved specimen. Photo: E. Greenbaum.

ventral scales; 51–52 longitudinal rows of ventral scales; 19–22 lamellae under fourth toe.

In preservative, dorsal surface uniformly olive-brown, scales on head and neck scattered with numerous minute dark brown flecks, ventral surface creamy gray, small black spots on scales in gular region and anterior part of venter in one specimen (SMF 77368).
Natural history: Campbell & D. Frost (1993) suggested this species is restricted to cloud forest.
Conservation status: IUCN: Critically endangered (CR B1+2c).
Specimens examined: <u>Santa Ana</u>: Cordillera de Alotepeque-Metapán, Hacienda Montecristo, 2150–2250 m: KU 184046, SMF 68412, 77367–68.

Genus *Celestus*

This genus of viviparous skink-like lizards includes 28 species that are distributed from Veracruz, Mexico, to southeastern Costa Rica, Jamaica, Hispaniola, and Navassa Island (Savage 2002). One species occurs in El Salvador.

Celestus atitlanensis Smith 1950
(Salamanqueza de Atitlán)
Plate 54, Map 46

1950 *Celestus atitlanensis* Smith, in Smith & Taylor

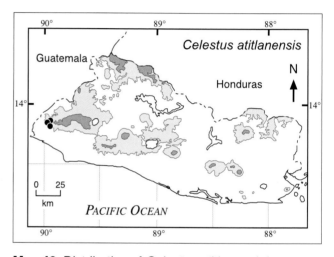

Map 46: Distribution of *Celestus atitlanensis* in El Salvador.
Closed circles represent examined-specimen locality records; open squares are published locality records. Light shading indicates 600–1200 m elevation; dark shading indicates elevations ≥ 1200 m; large bodies of freshwater are outlined in bold, black lines.

1950: Bull. U.S. Natl. Mus. 199: 195; type locality: Atitlán, Guatemala.
Diploglossus atitlanensis: Hidalgo 1982b, Campbell & Camarillo 1994.
Celestus bivittatus: Villa & Wilson 1988, Villa et al. 1988.
Celestus atitlanensis: Köhler 2000, Dueñas et al. 2001, Köhler 2003b, Leenders 2003.
Geographic distribution: From Guatemala along the Pacific versant to western El Salvador (Köhler 2003b).
Ecological distribution: Premontane evergreen

forest and subtropical humid forest between 720 and 800 m.

Description: A medium-sized lizard, largest Salvadoran specimen is 119.5 mm SVL; tail length/SVL 0.79–1.07; HL/SVL 0.148–0.149; HW/SVL 0.120–0.133; snout length/SVL 0.064–0.067; axilla–groin distance/SVL 0.58–0.60; shank length/SVL 0.089–0.090; no lateral prefrontal scales; 7 supralabial scales to the point below the center of eye; 4 pairs of chinshields; 31 scales around midbody; 74–77 dorsal scales between interparietal plate and level of posterior insertion of hind limbs; surface of dorsal scales finely striated, 23–30 striae on each scale; ventral-scale surfaces smooth.

Dorsal coloration of head and body tan in preserved specimens, two grayish brown dorsolateral stripes extending from snout to the tail followed laterally by darker bands with dark brown mottling extending from the eyes to the base of tail. Ventral surfaces creamish white.

Natural history: Hidalgo (1982b) reported an adult female with 12 large "ovarian eggs" that was collected while sunning itself on a tree trunk (*Lysiloma salvadorensis*) ca. 2.5 m above the ground at 0730 h at Finca El Imposible, Depto. Ahuachapán in October.

Specimens examined: <u>Ahuachapán</u>: Parque Nacional El Imposible, La Fincona, 13°50.8´N, 89°58.8´W, 720 m: SMF 79022; Finca San Benito: MUHNES 1044; 6 km NE San Francisco Menéndez, Finca El Imposible, 800 m: KU 184048.

Genus *Mesaspis*

This genus includes six montane species that have a disjunct distribution from Oaxaca, Mexico, to western Panama (Savage 2002, Köhler 2003b). One species occurs in El Salvador.

Mesaspis moreletii (Bocourt 1871)
(Dragoncito Liso de Montaña)
Plate 55, Map 47, Figures 18, 19a–c, 20a–c

1871 *Gerrhonotus moreletii* Bocourt, Bull. Nouv. Arch. Mus. Hist. Nat. Paris, 7: 102; type locality: Petén and pine forests of Alta Verapaz, Guatemala.
Gerrhonotus salvadorensis: K. Schmidt 1928.
Barisia moreleti salvadorensis: Tihen 1949, Rand 1957, Peters & Donoso-Barros 1970.
Mesaspis moreleti: Villa et al. 1988, Dueñas et al. 2001.
Gerrhonotus moreletii: Köhler 1996.

Plate 55: *Mesaspis moreletii* EL SALVADOR: Chalatenango: Cerro El Pital (ca. 2300 m). Photo: O. Komar.

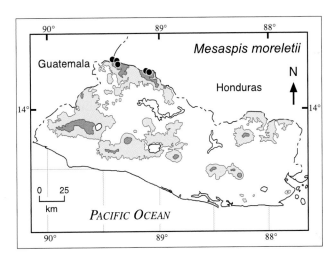

Map 47: Distribution of *Mesaspis moreletii* in El Salvador.
Closed circles represent examined-specimen locality records; open squares are published locality records. Light shading indicates 600–1200 m elevation; dark shading indicates elevations ≥ 1200 m; large bodies of freshwater are outlined in bold, black lines.

Mesaspis moreletii: Köhler 2000, Veselý & Köhler 2001, Köhler 2003b, Leenders & Watkins-Colwell 2004.

Geographic distribution: From southern Mexico to Honduras and probably northern Nicaragua (Köhler 2003b).

Ecological distribution: Pine-oak forest and cloud forest between 1800 and 2700 m.

Description: A lizard of a moderate size (SVL of largest specimen examined 96 mm); males slightly larger than females (maximum SVL 90 mm); tail

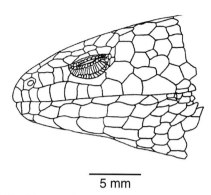

5 mm

Figure 18: *Mesaspis moreletii* (SMF 77377): Lateral view of head.

length/SVL 1.07–1.99; HL/SVL 0.17–0.22; HW/SVL 0.12–0.18; HL/HW 1.24–1.57; axilla–groin distance/SVL 0.44–0.58; shank length/SVL 0.09–0.11; lamellae beneath 4th toe 11–19; number of dorsal scales at midbody 18–22; number of dorsal scales in vertebral line to base of tail 47–55; number of ventral scales at midbody 10–12; number of supralabial scales 4–8; supralabial scales to point below the center of eye 4–7; number of infralabial scales 2–4; postmental scales 1–2; postnasals 1–3; prefrontal scales 0–2; secondary temporals contacting the lowermost primary temporal 0–2; posterior loreal scale usually touching supralabial scales (82.3%); anterior superciliary scale usually in contact with prefrontal (75.0%); frontonasal touching frontal (44.1%) or not (55.9%).

Well-defined dorsal longitudinal brown or olive-brown band, often with numerous irregular black blotches in adult males. Dorsal band bordered laterally by a thin interrupted yellowish line beginning at postoculars and extending at least to first third of body, followed laterally by black line in females. Lateral bands in males usually dark brown or blackish with pale yellowish green spots, in females and juveniles with 5–7 transverse pale yellow stripes bordered by black on the proximal part of body. Venter pale gray, in males often with black blotches laterally; an obscure whitish line extends from preocular across suboculars in some specimens. Sometimes series of dark brown dots forming a discontinuous middorsal line continuing onto tail (more distinct on regenerated parts of tail). Iris golden-orange in life.

Natural history: W. E. Duellman (field notes) encountered adults on or under logs at Cerro Montecristo, Depto. Santa Ana in February. O. Komar (field notes) encountered numerous indi-

viduals in leaf litter in or near cloud forest at Cerro El Pital, Depto. Chalatenango in May. M. Veselý (field notes) encountered several newborns in cloud forest at the top of Cerro Miramundo, Depto. Santa Ana in June. Mertens (1952d) reported this lizard around fallen logs in El Salvador. Rand (1957) observed individuals sunning themselves in a clearing near cloud forest among grass, moss, and leaf litter at Cerro Miramundo (2200 m), Depto. Santa Ana in February. Veselý & Köhler (2001) noted this species is live-bearing; nine dissected females contained 4–10 follicles and one female collected between April and May had eight well-developed embryos. Leenders & Watkins-Colwell (2004) noted the following stomach contents from Salvadoran specimens: large parasitic worms, Orthoptera, Coleoptera, larval lepidopterans, flies, and spiders. Sexually active males (as determined from strongly coiled and white vasa deferentia) were noted in late June.

Specimens examined: Chalatenango: Cerro El Pital, 14°23.82´N, 89°06.98´W, 2700 m: SMF 77956–58; Cerro El Pital at unknown elevation: KU 184377–81, YPM 12475; same locality at 2300 m: MUHNES C–30–1498; same locality at 2370 m: KU 291243–44, 291247; same locality at 2390 m: MUHNES C–30–1499–500; same locality at 2480 m: MUHNES C–30–1501, YPM 12482–84; E slope Los Esesmiles, Cerro El Pital, 2195 m: MVZ 40273–80, 40301; same locality at 2225 m: MVZ 40283–94, 40298–99, 40302; same locality at 2438 m: MVZ 40281–82, 40300; same locality at 2469 m: MVZ 40296; same locality at 2530 m: MVZ 40297; same locality at 2560 m: MVZ 40295; Los Esesmiles, Cerro El Pital, 1829–2438 m: FMNH 10956–57. Santa Ana: Parque Nacional Montecristo, the top of El Trifinio, Cerro Miramundo, 2350 m: SMF 79414; same locality at 2400 m: KU 67446–47; Hacienda Montecristo, Metapán mountains, 14°25´N, 89°22´W, 2150 m: SMF 44361–67, 77377–93, 52001–02, 57530, 77372–76; same locality at 2200 m: KU 62079–83, 62085–93, 67448–54, KU 184366–67, 184369–70; same locality at 2250 m: KU 184371–76; same locality at unknown elevation: UMMZ 117484–85, LACM 137219–24; Cerro Miramundo, 2200 m: FMNH 64971–72. San Salvador: San Salvador, Parque Saburo-Hirao: MUHNES 396–99, 400–03 (locality information erroneous).

Published locality records: Chalatenango: Cerro El Pital: YPM 12475, 12482–84 (Leenders & Watkins-Colwell 2004); Município San Ignacio, Cantón Las Pilas, Caserio El Centro, Cerro Las

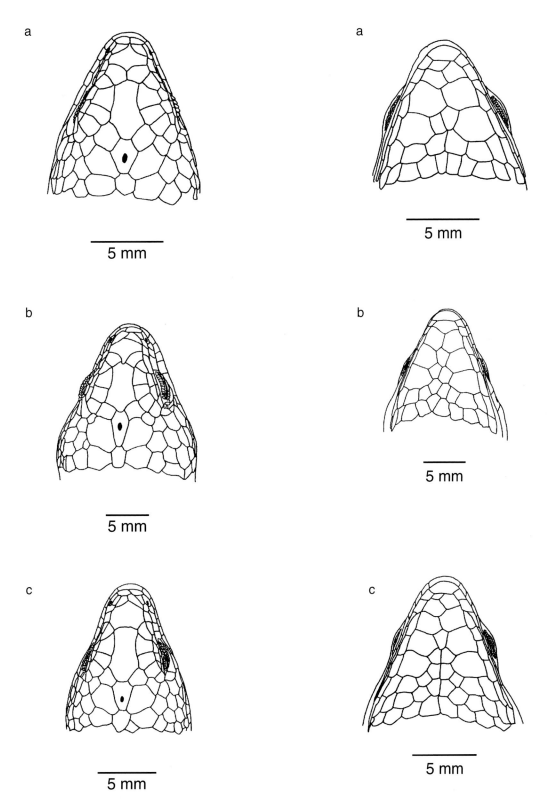

Figure 19: *Mesaspis moreletii:* Dorsal view of head, variation of prefrontal scales, a. SMF 77392, b. SMF 77372, c. SMF 77380.

Figure 20: *Mesaspis moreletii:* Ventral view of head, variation of postmental scales, a. SMF 77392, b. SMF 77377, c. SMF 77393.

Nubes, SE slope of Cerro El Pital (14.393°N, 89.105°W): YPM 12437 (Leenders & Watkins-Colwell 2004). Santa Ana: Município Metapán, Cantón Metapán, Parque Nacional Montecristo (14.401°N, 89.362°W) (Leenders & Watkins-Colwell 2004).

Family Eublepharidae

The six genera of this family are distributed from the southwestern United States to central Costa Rica in the New World, Africa, India to central Iraq, Japan and surrounding islands, and Thailand through Malaysia, Borneo, and Sanana Island (Savage 2002). All members of this family are terrestrial, nocturnal, and possess movable eyelids. Not all researchers recognize this family as a distinct group from the family Gekkonidae (e.g., Bauer 2003). One genus occurs in El Salvador.

Genus *Coleonyx*

The seven species of this genus have a disjunct distribution from the southwestern United States to western Mexico, the Chihuahua Desert, and Veracruz and Guerrero, Mexico, to Honduras (Atlantic versant) and western Costa Rica (Pacific versant; Savage 2002). Two species occur in El Salvador.

Coleonyx elegans Gray 1845
(Gueco Leopardo Yucateco)
Plate 56, Map 48, Figure 22ab

1845 *Coleonyx elegans* Gray, Ann. Mag. Nat. Hist. 16(1): 163; type locality: Belize, British Honduras.
Coleonyx elegans: Hidalgo 1981b, Villa et al. 1988, Köhler 2000, Dueñas et al. 2001, Köhler 2003b.
Geographic distribution: From Veracruz, Mexico, to northern Guatemala and Belize on the Atlantic versant; from southern Nayarit, Mexico, to western El Salvador on the Pacific versant (Köhler 2003b).
Ecological distribution: Dry forest around 470 m.
Description: A gecko of a moderate size, that is poorly documented from El Salvador. The only specimen reported from ElSalvador (Hidalgo 1981b) has the following characteristics: SVL 67 mm, tail length 57 mm; 7 supralabial scales; 6 infralabial scales; first infralabial scale triangular; 9 preanal pores in total; mental scale subtriangular; 7 scales bordering posterior margins of upper prenasal

Plate 56: *Coleonyx elegans* (KU 70052) MEXICO: Yucatan: Pisté (10 m). Photo: W. E. Duellman (KU CT 1744).

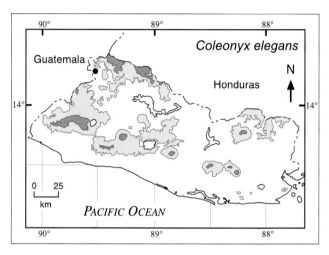

Map 48: Distribution of *Coleonyx elegans* in El Salvador.
Closed circles represent examined-specimen locality records; open squares are published locality records. Light shading indicates 600–1200 m elevation; dark shading indicates elevations ≥ 1200 m; large bodies of freshwater are outlined in bold, black lines.

scales between nostrils; claws of forefeet completely concealed by large terminal sheath scales, claws of hind feet with only the tips exposed. Three specimens of *C. elegans* (KU 55869, 144922, 157085) from El Petén, Guatemala, were included in the study to provide the following morphometric data: tail length/SVL 0.59–0.92; HL/SVL 0.21–0.22; HW/SVL 0.13–0.16; snout length/SVL 0.08–0.10; shank length/SVL 0.16–0.17.

Dorsal ground color cream; with four transverse narrow cream bands, each bordered anteriorly and posteriorly by broad dark brown bands on body and anterior part of tail; posterior part of tail having only dark brown rings; nape with V-shaped, cream band edged anteriorly and posteriorly by dark brown.

Natural history: Hidalgo (1981b) collected the single specimen at night in dry forest. Campbell (1998a) noted this nocturnal species eats small invertebrates; females can lay multiple clutches of eggs from February–August.

Specimens examined: <u>Santa Ana</u>: Metapán, zona entre Lagunas de Güija and San Diego: KU 183994.

Coleonyx mitratus (Peters 1863)
(Gueco Leopardo del Sur)
Plate 57, Map 49, Figure 21d, 22cd

1863 *Brachydactylus mitratus* Peters, Monats. Akad. Wiss., Berlin, 1863: 42; type locality: Panama. *Coleonyx mitratus*: K. Schmidt 1928, Klauber 1945, Mertens 1952d, Brongersma 1954b, Rand 1957, Peters & Donoso-Barros 1970, Villa et al. 1988, Köhler 2000, Dueñas et al. 2001, Köhler 2003b, Leenders 2003.

Geographic distribution: Northeastern Guatemala and northwestern Honduras on the Atlantic versant; from Guatemala to southwestern Costa Rica on the Pacific versant; possibly in Panama (Savage 2002).

Ecological distribution: Dry forest and savanna between sea level and 700 m.

Description: A gecko of a moderate size (SVL of largest specimen examined 73 mm); tail length/SVL 0.65–0.93; HL/SVL 0.21–0.23; HW/SVL 0.14–0.17; snout length/SVL 0.09–0.10; shank length/SVL 0.15–0.16; lamellae beneath 4th toe 14–17; mental scale large, with sides slightly convergent posteriorly, the posterior edge slightly convex to angular;

Plate 57: *Coleonyx mitratus* HONDURAS: Islas de la Bahía: Utila. Photo: G. Köhler.

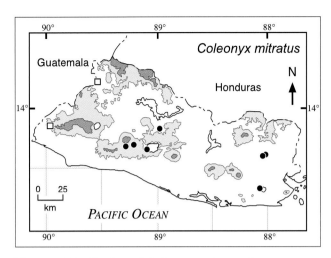

Map 49: Distribution of *Coleonyx mitratus* in El Salvador.

Closed circles represent examined-specimen locality records; open squares are published locality records. Light shading indicates 600–1200 m elevation; dark shading indicates elevations ≥ 1200 m; large bodies of freshwater are outlined in bold, black lines.

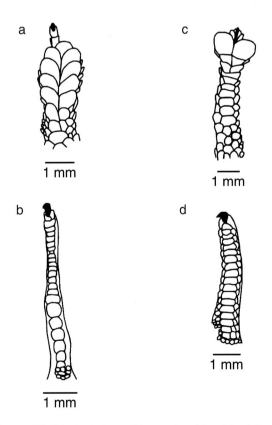

Figure 21: Ventral view of toes of a. *Hemidactylus frenatus* (SMF 80761); b. *Gonatodes albogularis* (SMF 77867); c. *Phyllodactylus tuberculosus* (SMF 79234); d. *Coleonyx mitratus* (SMF 81348).

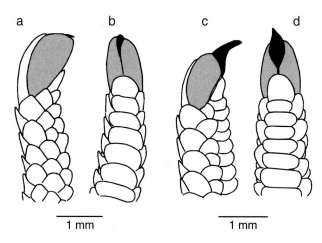

Figure 22: Ventral and lateral view of fingers of a,b. *Coleonyx elegans* (SMF 34398); c,d. *Coleonyx mitratus* (SMF 81348).

the first infralabial scales quadrangular; no longitudinal area of small scales behind nostril (present in *C. elegans*); terminal claws clearly visible, the sheath much smaller than in *C. elegans*.

Dorsal ground color creamy beige with five cream crossbars, first in nuchal region, last at level anterior to base of tail, 6–8 additional crossbars on tail and one across the snout; cream crossbars bordered anteriorly and posteriorly by black belts becoming narrower laterally, in middorsal region often fused forming dark middorsal band interrupted only by the cream crossbars mentioned above; black spots or mottling on lateral sides of head, body, and legs; ventral surface creamy yellow. **Natural history:** Cope (1879) reported finding this species in ant hills in Costa Rica. Mertens (1952d) collected a specimen in a house in Santa Tecla, Depto. La Libertad and reported another Salvadoran specimen found by a colleague on a trail at the base of a steep wall. Rand (1957) collected a specimen at night on a path of a brush-grown gully adjacent to a pasture at San Salvador, Depto. San Salvador in May. Savage (2002) noted this species is nocturnal and secretive. **Specimens examined:** Cuscatlán: Tenancingo, Copalchan: KU 183996. La Libertad: Nuevo San Salvador [= Santa Tecla]: SMF 42434. Morazán: Montecristo Mine, 213 m: MVZ 39911; Divisadero: FMNH 10939. San Miguel: Laguna de Olomega, 61 m: MVZ 39912–15. San Salvador: San Salvador, vicinity of Instituto Tropical de Investigaciones Científicas: SMF 44303, 51994–95; San Salvador, 670 m: FMNH 64966, SMF 81348; 3 km SE

Ilopango, Cantón Asino: KU 183997. **Published locality records**: Ahuachapán: Parque Nacional El Imposible (Leenders 2003). Santa Ana: Hacienda on the southeast bank of Lago de Güija, RMNH 9926 (Brongersma 1954b).

Family Gekkonidae

This large family includes approximately 800 species (ca. 70 genera) distributed on every continent across the world (excluding the Arctic and Antarctic regions). Many species have expanded lamellae, which allow them to climb sheer surfaces with ease (Savage 2002). Some researchers continue to include eublepharid geckos in this family (e.g., Bauer 2003). Three genera occur in El Salvador.

Genus *Gonatodes*

This genus of diurnal, scansorial lizards include just under 20 species, which are distributed from Chiapas, Mexico, through Central America and northern South America to northern Bolivia, Grand Cayman, Cuba, Jamaica, and Hispaniola (Savage 2002). One species occurs in El Salvador.

Gonatodes albogularis (Duméril & Bibron 1836)
(Gueco Cabeza Amarilla)
Plate 58, Map 50, Figure 21b

1836 *Gymnodactylus albogularis* Duméril & Bibron, Erp. Gén. 3: 415; type locality: Martínique.
Gymnodactylus fuscus: Bocourt 1873.
Gonatodes fuscus: K. Schmidt 1928, Ahl 1940, Mertens 1952d, Rand 1957.
Gonatodes concinnatus: Oeser 1933.
Gonatodes albogularis fuscus: Peters & Donoso-Barros 1970.
Gonatodes albogularis: Villa et al. 1988, Köhler 2000, Dueñas et al. 2001, Köhler 2003b, Leenders 2003, Leenders & Watkins-Colwell 2004.
Geographic distribution: From eastern Guatemala (Atlantic versant) and Chiapas, Mexico, (Pacific versant) to northwestern Colombia and western Venezuela; also in Cuba, Jamaica, Grand Cayman, and Hispaniola; introduced to southern Florida, USA (Savage 2002, Meshaka et al. 2004).
Ecological distribution: Dry forest and savanna between sea level and 1220 m; frequently encountered in or near human habitations.
Description: A relatively small gecko (SVL of

Plate 58: *Gonatodes albogularis* EL SALVADOR: San Salvador: San Salvador (670 m). Photo: G. Köhler.

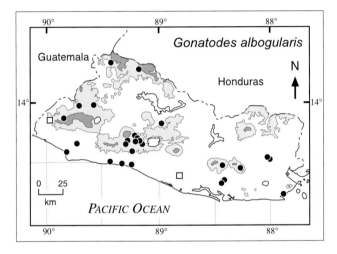

Map 50: Distribution of *Gonatodes albogularis* in El Salvador.

Closed circles represent examined-specimen locality records; open squares are published locality records. Light shading indicates 600–1200 m elevation; dark shading indicates elevations ≥ 1200 m; large bodies of freshwater are outlined in bold, black lines.

and tail black with numerous grayish granules intermixed through body and anterior 1/3 of tail; tip of tail grayish white; gular area cream, anterior half of belly with gray scales edged by black, posterior half with black scales except for lighter region between hind limbs; underside of limbs gray, underside of tail black.

Dorsal coloration in living males black with numerous scattered sky blue scales present also on base of tail, posterior tail black, white tip of tail; head bright yellow, in specimens from the Pacific coast reddish brown, posterior labials with blue coloration; gular area yellow with orange marks; anterior part of venter with darker reticulation, posterior part almost black except for white midventral stripe; ventral side of thighs, hind limbs, and tail creamy white. In females dorsal color grayish brown with numerous darker and lighter dots, usually forming 5–7 transverse rows continuing to the tail; ventral side pale white, chin and throat gray with median cream dividing line; gular region with scattered darker markings. Coloration of juvenile specimens similar to that of females.

Natural history: E. Greenbaum (field notes) recorded numerous individuals from the side of human habitations during the day from July–August throughout El Salvador. Mertens (1952d) noted that this lizard is very territorial (especially males) and is common on old houses and trees even within large Salvadoran cities. He observed them sitting outside their hiding places, exposed to direct sunlight. Rand (1957) collected four individuals around human habitations in San Salvador, Depto. San Salvador in March. Stafford & Meyer (2000) noted this species may inhabit tree bark in "semi-urban areas" and females lay a single egg. Savage (2002) noted this territorial species reproduces during the wet season on the Pacific versant.

Specimens examined: Ahuachapán: Finca Santa Leticia, 13°53´N, 89°47´W, 1224 m: MUHNES C–30–1407. Chalatenango: Ciudad La Palma: KU 184009. Cuscatlán: 0.5 km E Tenancingo: KU 184000. La Libertad: San Diego: ZMB 35651–52; Club Atami (near Playa El Palmarcito, Municipio Tamanique), 13´30.2´N, 89´25.0´W, 40 m: SMF 79020, 79338; Nuevo San Salvador [= Santa Tecla]: SMF 43157; W of La Libertad: SMF 42407; Huizucar: KU 183999; 10 km E La Libertad: KU 184001–08. La Unión: Hacienda del Cipres: MVZ 143988. Morazán: Montecristo Mine, 3 km W Divisadero: SMF 43137; same locality at 213 m:

largest specimen 43.7 mm [Leenders & Watkins-Colwell 2004]); tail length/SVL 0.98–1.53; HL/SVL 0.23–0.28; HW/SVL 0.15–0.20; snout length/SVL 0.09–0.12; shank length/SVL 0.15–0.20; lamellae beneath 4th toe 19–25; number of supralabial scales beneath the center of eye 5–6; dorsal scales granular, slightly larger laterally; mental scale large, two enlarged postmental scales.

Sexual dichromatism in adults well developed. In preservative, head of males grayish brown with scattered black scales, posterior labials and mouth angle bluish gray bordered by black scales; body

MVZ 40268, 40272; Divisadero: SMF 22511–12,
FMNH 10941, 10943, 10945–46, 10949, 10981. San
Miguel: San Miguel: SMF 42168–71; Volcán de San
Miguel, 740 m: KU 291278, MUHNES C–30–1493–
94. San Salvador: San Salvador, Colónia Modelo:
SMF 42167; San Salvador, Instituto Tropical de
Investigaciones Científicas: SMF 42172–75; San
Salvador, Hotel España: SMF 43100; San Salvador,
La Rabida: SMF 43080, 43138, 43178, 44306; San
Salvador, Villa Margarita: SMF 44307; San Salva-
dor: SMF 44308–09; San Salvador, 732 m: MVZ
40227, 40267, 40269–71, UMMZ 75878; San Salva-
dor, 700 m: FMNH 64967–68; San Salvador, Parque
Zoológico Nacional: KU 289808, 289835, 289889,
MUHNES C–30–1409, YPM 12474; Colónia Altos del
Cerro near slope of San Jacinto Mountain:
MUHNES C–30–1408; Nuevo San Salvador [= Santa
Tecla], Finca Santa María: CAS 147404; Colónia El
Refugio: KU 183998; Municipio Mejicanos, Cantón
Zacanil, 740 m: YPM 12473. Santa Ana:
Chalchuapa, Laguna Cuscachapa, 13°58.8´N,
89°40.5´W, 690 m: SMF 79337; Hacienda San José
near Metapán: SMF 44304–05; Santa Ana: KU
50626. Sonsonate: Hacienda San Antonio near
Sonsonate: SMF 42166, 42217, 42487–89; Acajutla:
CAS-SU 3524, 3526. Usulután: Santiago de María,
Hotel Villahermosa, 13°28.7´N, 88°28.0´W, 860 m:
SMF 79335–36; Santa María: MCZ 57091–92, 57097;
3.5 km E Usulután: KU 193011. Depto. unknown:
no specific locality: SMF 22508–09 (*).
Published locality records: Ahuachapán: Parque
Nacional El Imposible (Leenders 2003). La Paz:
Município Zacatecoluca, Finca La Esmeralda, 3 km
E Zacatecoluca (13.483°N, 88.850°W), 115 m: YPM
12345–47 (Leenders & Watkins-Colwell 2004). San
Salvador: Município Mejicanos, Cantón Zacamil,
Residencial Metrópolis Norte (13.85°N, 89.13°W),
740 m: YPM 12473 (Leenders & Watkins-Colwell
2004); Município San Salvador, Colonia Costa Rica,
Parque Zoológico Nacional (13.73°N, 89.09°W), 700
m: YPM 12474 (Leenders & Watkins-Colwell 2004).
Santa Ana: Parque Nacional Montecristo (Leenders
& Watkins-Colwell 2004).

Genus *Hemidactylus*

This genus includes approximately 75 species of
nocturnal geckos that are distributed from southern Europe, Africa, and southern Asia to Polynesia
and tropical and subtropical areas of the New World
(Savage 2002). One species has been introduced to
El Salvador.

Plate 59: *Hemidactylus frenatus* (SMF 79832) NICA-
RAGUA: Managua: Managua (100 m). Photo: G.
Köhler.

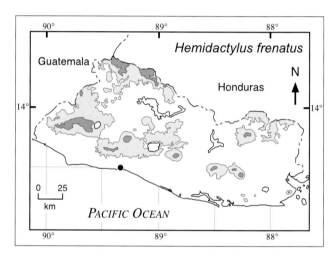

Map 51: Distribution of *Hemidactylus frenatus* in
El Salvador.
Closed circles represent examined-specimen locality records;
open squares are published locality records. Light shading
indicates 600–1200 m elevation; dark shading indicates elevations ≥ 1200 m; large bodies of freshwater are outlined in bold,
black lines.

Hemidactylus frenatus Duméril and Bibron 1836
(Gueco del Mediterraneo)
Plate 59, Map 51, Figure 21a

1836 *Hemidactylus frenatus* Duméril & Bibron,
Erp. Gén. 3: 366; type locality: many localities given
by Duméril & Bibron; restricted to Java by
Loveridge (1947: Bull. Mus. Comp. Zool. 98: 127).
Hemidactylus frenatus: Greenbaum 2002, Köhler
2003b.
Geographic distribution: East Africa, Madagas-
car, Seychelle Islands, Mediterranean region, India,

Asia including islands of the Pacific; probably introduced to northern Australia and several islands in the Papuan region, the New World in the United States (including Hawaii), Mexico, Belize, Guatemala, El Salvador, Honduras, and Nicaragua (Greenbaum 2002, Savage 2002, Meshaka et al. 2004).

Ecological distribution: Human habitations at low elevations.

Description: A gecko of a moderate size (SVL of single specimen examined 45.95 mm); tail length/ SVL 0.96; head widening behind eyes; HL/SVL 0.33; HW/SVL 0.19; snout length/SVL 0.12; axilla–groin distance/SVL 0.46; shank length/SVL 0.14; two postmental scales; number of scales bordering postmental scales 7; interorbital scales 32; number of scales across snout between third upper labials 29; scales bordering posterior edges of internasal scales 8; scales between nostril and eye 22; scales on dorsum and sides small, with 6 irregular, longitudinal rows of small, smooth tubercles; ventrals smooth and rounded; 36 transverse ventrals at midbody; 83 ventrals in a longitudinal row from the neck to the vent; venter of tail with enlarged median scales; tail with six longitudinal rows of smooth, rounded tubercles; 18 lamellae under 4th toe; 10 upper labials and 9 lower labials; nostrils bordered by the rostral, first labial and 3 small nasal scales.

Coloration of the preserved specimen is pale tan on the dorsum and cream on the venter. A faint black streak extends from the nostril through the eye to the flanks.

Natural history: Fitch (1970) noted this species reproduces year-round. Stafford & Meyer (2000) noted this nocturnal species often vocalizes, and sounds similar to the barking of a dog. Savage (2002) noted this species can be active during the day. Clutches of 1–2 eggs are laid by females.

Specimens examined: La Libertad: Hacienda Belmar ca. La Libertad: LACM 9375.

Genus *Phyllodactylus*

This genus of nocturnal lizards includes 45 species that are distributed from southern California, USA, through Central America to Chile (Savage 2002). One species occurs in El Salvador.

***Phyllodactylus tuberculosus* Wiegmann 1835**
(Gueco Tuberculoso)
Plate 60, Map 52, Figure 21c

Plate 60: *Phyllodactylus tuberculosus* EL SALVADOR: Ahuachapán: El Refugio (225 m). Photo: G. Köhler.

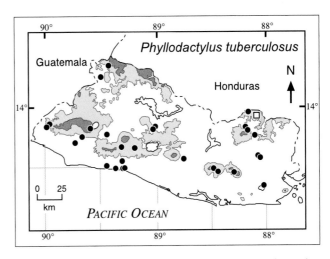

Map 52: Distribution of *Phyllodactylus tuberculosus* in El Salvador.
Closed circles represent examined-specimen locality records; open squares are published locality records. Light shading indicates 600–1200 m elevation; dark shading indicates elevations ≥ 1200 m; large bodies of freshwater are outlined in bold, black lines.

1835 *Phyllodactylus tuberculosus* Wiegmann, Nova Acta Acad. Leop.-Carol. 17(1): 241; type locality: California; restricted by Dixon (1960. Herpetologica 16: 4) to the village of California, Nicaragua.
Phyllodactylus tuberculosus: Bocourt 1873, K. Schmidt 1928, Dixon 1964, Villa et al. 1988, Köhler 2000, Dueñas et al. 2001, Köhler 2003b, Leenders 2003, Leenders & Watkins-Colwell 2004.
Phyllodactylus eduardofischeri: Mertens 1952d.
Phyllodactylus tuberculosus tuberculosus: Peters & Donoso-Barros 1970.

Geographic distribution: Central Guatemala and Belize on the Atlantic versant; from Sonora, Mexico, to central Costa Rica on the Pacific versant (Savage 2002).

Ecological distribution: Dry forest, pine-oak forest, and savanna between sea level and 1300 m.

Description: A gecko of a moderate size (SVL of largest specimen examined 70 mm); tail length/SVL 0.83–1.03; head widening behind eyes; HL/SVL 0.24–0.27; HW/SVL 0.19–0.22; snout length/SVL 0.10–0.11; axilla–groin distance/SVL 0.38–0.46; shank length/SVL 0.14–0.15; two postmental scales; number of scales bordering postmental scales 5–7; interorbital scales 15–20; number of scales across the snout between third labials 14–21; scales bordering the posterior edges of internasal scales 5–7; scales between nostril and eye 11–14; scales on dorsum and sides small, intermixed with large, trihedral, distinctly keeled tubercles, number of paravertebral tubercles 20–34, number of tubercles in distance from axilla to groin 15–22; transverse number of ventral scales 26–35; 53–67 ventral scales in longitudinal row from the neck to vent; lamellae beneath fourth toe 11–16; thighs and forearms covered with small granules intermixed with larger tubercles.

Dorsal coloration uniformly gray or grayish brown, in some specimens with distinct irregular dark brown blotches on dorsal surface; tail with crossbands; a dark brown stripe extending from nostril through eyes to the point above insertion of forelimb, indistinct in some specimens; ventral surfaces of head and body dirty white, those of tail orange in some specimens.

Natural history: E. Greenbaum (field notes) encountered adults and juveniles of this species in numerous human habitations at night throughout El Salvador from July–August. O. Komar (field notes) was given a juvenile collected in a bromeliad on a live pine trunk in pine-oak forest during the day at Perquín, Depto. Morazán in June. Mertens (1952d) noted that this crepuscular and nocturnal lizard lives in houses and on trees in El Salvador. Stafford & Meyer (2000) noted this nocturnal species has a vocalization that sounds like "a kiss." Savage (2002) noted this insectivorous species lays clutches of two eggs throughout the year. Leenders & Watkins-Colwell (2004) noted gravid females and sexually active males during the dry season in El Salvador; stomach contents of several individuals contained cockroaches, Diptera, Coleoptera, and small pebbles.

Specimens examined: Ahuachapán: Parque Nacional El Imposible, La Fincona, 13°50.8´N, 89°58.8´W, 720 m: KU 289758–63, MUHNES C–30–

1410–12, SMF 79234, 81306–09, 81315. Cuscatlán: 4 km NE Tenancingo: KU 184010–11; Tenancingo, Cantón Copalchan: KU 184012, 184015; 0.5 km E Tenancingo: KU 184013–14. La Libertad: Club Atami (near Playa El Palmarcito, Municipio Tamanique), 13°30.2´N, 89°25.0´W, 40 m: SMF 81302–05; W side of Río Chilama near La Libertad: SMF 43143, 43169; Nuevo San Salvador [= Santa Tecla]: SMF 42206; a waste water tube under the road San Salvador–La Libertad ca km 25, 60–100 m: SMF 52010–16; Parque Nacional Walter Deininger: MUHNES 676; Hacienda Zapotitán, 457 m: MVZ 39916–19; 10 km E La Libertad: KU 184016–45; 0.8 km N, 16.1 km W La Libertad: TCWC 17339. Morazán: Cerro Cacahuatique near Osicala, 1200 m: SMF 44313, 1310 m: MUHNES C–30–1510; Hacienda Talqualuya, N from Osicala, 1200 m: SMF 52003–09; Cacaopera: MUHNES 668–69; Montecristo Mine, 213 m: MVZ 39910; Divisadero: FMNH 10940; Perquín: MUHNES C–30–1512. San Miguel: Laguna de Olomega, 61 m: MVZ 39908–09; Volcán de San Miguel, 740 m: KU 291260–61, 291277, 291381–82, MUHNES C–30–1511, C–30–1513–14. San Salvador: San Salvador, Parque Zoológico Nacional: KU 289809. San Vicente: Cueva del Río Frio, Hacienda Purisima, N from Tecoluca, 300 m: SMF 52017–19. Santa Ana: Laguna de Güija: SMF 43310–11; Hacienda San José near Metapán: SMF 44312. Sonsonate: Sonsonate: SMF 42496; Izalco, finca of José Velado: USNM 523348; Bosque Las Lajas, 13°50.04´N, 89°33.56´W, 920 m: KU 289878–79. Usulután: Santiago de María, Hotel Villahermosa, 13°28.7´N, 88°28.0´W, 860 m: SMF 81300; Cerro del Tigre, 13°28.37´N, 88°26.21´W, 1100 m: KU 289857–60, MUHNES C–30–346–86.

Published locality records: Ahuachapán: Parque Nacional El Imposible: YPM 12320–21, 12340–44, 12421, 14015 (Leenders & Watkins-Colwell 2004). Morazán: Município Arambala, Cantón Cumaro, Río Sapo (13.959°N, 88.132°W), 1118 m: YPM 14013–14 (Leenders & Watkins-Colwell 2004). Sonsonate: Município Izalco, Cantón Las Lajas, Bosque Las Lajas (13.829°N, 89.567°W), 750–800 m: YPM 12322 (Leenders & Watkins-Colwell 2004).

Family Gymnophthalmidae

Formerly a part of the family Teiidae, lizards of the family Gymnophthalmidae (i.e., microteiids) currently include over 175 species (36 genera) distributed from southern Mexico to north-central

Argentina (east of the Andes) and several Caribbean islands (Fitzgerald 2003a). Presch (1983) suggested separating the so-called "microteiids" into a separate family (Gymnophthalmidae) from the "macroteiids" (Teiidae), a view that has not been universally accepted (Harris 1985, Myers & Donnelly 1996). However, numerous recent phylogenetic analyses and species descriptions recognize Gymnophthalmidae as a distinct family (e.g., Pellegrino et al. 2001, Fritts et al. 2002, Molina et al. 2002, Doan & Schargel 2003, Fitzgerald 2003a, Köhler 2003c), and we follow this classification here. One genus occurs in El Salvador.

Genus *Gymnophthalmus*

The eight species in this genus have only four fingers, no movable eyelids, and broad cycloid imbricate scales. The genus occurs from the Isthmus of Tehuantepec through Central America to northeastern Brazil, Trinidad and Tobago, and the Lesser Antilles to Guadeloupe (Savage 2002). One species occurs in El Salvador.

Gymnophthalmus speciosus (Hallowell 1861)
(Salamanqueza Cola Roja)
Plate 61, Map 53

1861 *Blepharictisis speciosa* Hallowell, Proc. Acad. Nat. Sci. Philad. 1860: 484; type locality: Nicaragua.
Gymnophthalmus sumichrasti: K. Schmidt 1928.
Gymnophthalmus speciosus birdi: Mertens 1952d, Rand 1957, Peters & Donoso-Barros 1970.
Gymnophthalmus speciosus: Villa et al. 1988, Köhler 1996, 2000, Dueñas et al. 2001, Köhler 2003b, Leenders & Watkins-Colwell 2004.
Geographic distribution: From northeastern Guatemala (Atlantic versant) and the Isthmus of Tehuantepec (Pacific versant) to Colombia, Venezuela, and Guyana (Savage 2002).
Ecological distribution: Dry forest and savanna between 480 and 1100 m.
Description: A small skink-like lizard (maximum SVL 43.7 mm [Leenders & Watkins-Colwell 2004]), tail length/SVL 1.00–1.18; HL/SVL 0.14–0.16; HW/SVL 0.11–0.13; snout length/SVL 0.05–0.06; shank length/SVL 0.08–0.10; lamellae beneath the 4th toe 12–13; 13 longitudinal scale rows around midbody; prefrontal contacting loreal or not (separated in 61%); number of supralabial scales to posterior margin of eye 4–5.

Plate 61: *Gymnophthalmus speciosus* (YPM 12440) EL SALVADOR: Ahuachapán: Parque Nacional El Imposible, ca. La Fincona (775 m). Photo: T. Leenders.

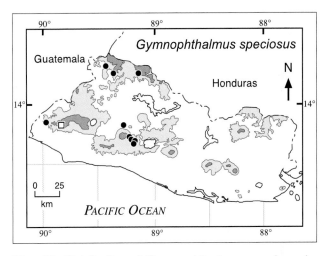

Map 53: Distribution of *Gymnophthalmus speciosus* in El Salvador.
Closed circles represent examined-specimen locality records; open squares are published locality records. Light shading indicates 600–1200 m elevation; dark shading indicates elevations ≥ 1200 m; large bodies of freshwater are outlined in bold, black lines.

Broad tan (with metallic reflection) longitudinal band (faded in older specimens) extending from tip of snout to base of tail, bordering on 1/3 of second dorsolateral scale row by brown coloration; tail pale brown; scales of ventral surface partly cream, partly dark gray, or grayish brown.
Natural history: K. Schmidt (1928) reported the remains of this species in the stomach of an *Oxybelis aeneus* (Serpentes: Colubridae) from San José del Sacaré (1097 m), Depto. Chalatenango in March. Rand (1957) collected a single individual during the day under debris at the bottom of a brush-grown gully in pasture at San Salvador,

Depto. San Salvador in May. Stafford & Meyer
(2000) noted this secretive, oviparous lizard is often
encountered under logs, debris, leaves, or in soil in
drier, semi-open habitats. Savage (2002) noted this
species is most active during midday and feeds upon
arthropods. Females lay 2–3 clutches of 1–4 eggs
each, and life expectancy is only one year. Leenders
& Watkins-Colwell (2004) noted this species on
roadsides and other sunny areas with sufficient
amounts of leaf litter in Depto. Ahuachapán, El
Salvador.

Specimens examined: Ahuachapán: Parque
Nacional El Imposible, La Fincona, 13°50.8´N,
89°58.8´W, 720 m: Plate 61. Chalatenango: San José
del Sacaré, 1097 m: FMNH 10965. La Libertad:
Quetzaltepeque: CAS 94255. Santa Ana: San Juan
Mine, 12.1 km SE Metapán, 488 m: MVZ 40361;
Metapán: KU 184346. San Salvador: San Antonio
near San Salvador: SMF 42932; Instituto Tropical
de Investigaciones Científicas, San Salvador, 700 m:
SMF 42161–64, 75809, 77237–39; San Salvador, 670
m: FMNH 64988, USNM 167212–13; San Salvador,
Colónia El Refugio: KU 184347.

Published locality records: Ahuachapán:
Município San Pedro Puxtla, Cantón La
Concepción, Cooperativa Concepción Miramar
(13.810°N, 89.807°W), 895 m: YPM 12441 (Leenders
& Watkins-Colwell 2004); Parque Nacional El
Imposible: YPM 12313, 12440, 12442 (Leenders &
Watkins-Colwell 2004).

Family Iguanidae

This large family of lizards includes approximately 900 species in 69 genera; the family is
distributed from southern Canada to southern
South America, Madagascar, and islands of
Polynesia (Mertz 2003b). The phylogenetic relationships and taxonomy of the pleurodont iguanians has
been subject to considerable controversy in recent
years. Therefore, some comments are appropriate
to justify our usage of the family name Iguanidae
for all pleurodont iguanians. For about a century
the concept of the family Iguanidae *sensu lato* as
proposed by Boulenger (1885) was followed by
essentially all herpetologists working on this group
until the late 1980s, when Etheridge & de Queiroz
(1988) demonstrated the existence of eight monophyletic groups within the family Iguanidae. These
groups were reclassified as eight families by D.
Frost & Etheridge (1989). The latter workers were
unable to find any evidence for the monophyly of all

pleurodont iguanians (the former family Iguanidae).
Initially, this new classification was strongly
criticized (Böhme 1990, Lazell 1992) and later
rejected on the basis of new molecular data (Macey
et al. 1997, Schulte et al. 1998). Most recently, D.
Frost et al. (2001) have presented a modified
classification in which they recognized the pleurodont iguanians as a monophyletic group, based on
the evidence provided by Macey et al. (1997). D.
Frost et al. (2001) proposed to maintain the sub-
groups as families and combine these in a higher
level taxon (Pleurodonta).

However, forthcoming work on this group of
lizards is likely to result in additional changes (e.g.,
the former Tropiduridae and Polychrotidae were
shown to be paraphyletic; see D. Frost et al. [2001]),
and there is a high probability that some of these
groups will change pending further studies. Because the current status of iguanian phylogenetics
is still contentious, we conserve the name
Iguanidae sensu Boulenger (1885) to combine all
pleurodont iguanians into a single family
(Iguanidae).

Genus *Basiliscus*

This genus includes four species with fleshy
crests on the head, especially in males. The genus
has a distrubtion from Jalisco and Tamaulipas,
Mexico, to central Ecuador and northwestern
Venezuela (Savage 2002). One species occurs in El
Salvador.

Basiliscus vittatus Wiegmann 1828
(Tenguereche)
Plate 62, Map 54

1828 *Basiliscus vittatus* Wiegmann, Isis von Oken
21: 373; type locality: Mexico.
Basiliscus vittatus: McLain 1899, K. Schmidt 1928,
Ahl 1940, Mertens 1952d, Brongersma 1954b, Rand
1957, Peters & Donoso-Barros 1970, Villa et al.
1988, Köhler 1996, 2000, Dueñas et al. 2001, Köhler
2003b, Leenders 2003, Leenders & Watkins-Colwell
2004.

Geographic distribution: From Jalisco and
southern Tamaulipas, Mexico, through Central
America to northwest Colombia exclusive of the
Pacific versant in southern Nicaragua, Costa Rica,
and western Panama; introduced to Florida, USA
(Savage 2002, Meshaka et al. 2004).

Ecological distribution: Dry forest and savanna

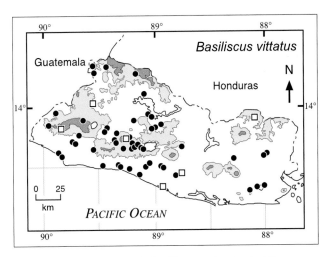

Map 54: Distribution of *Basiliscus vittatus* in El Salvador.
Closed circles represent examined-specimen locality records; open squares are published locality records. Light shading indicates 600–1200 m elevation; dark shading indicates elevations ≥ 1200 m; large bodies of freshwater are outlined in bold, black lines.

Plate 62: *Basiliscus vittatus* EL SALVADOR: Ahuachapán: El Refugio (225 m). Photo: G. Köhler.

(usually near freshwater) between sea level and 1300 m.

Description: A large lizard (SVL of largest specimen examined 140 mm) with a distinct dorsal crest and a triangular vertical head fin in males; tail length/SVL 2.54–2.97; HL/SVL 0.21–0.25; HW/SVL 0.14–0.17; snout length/SVL 0.09–0.11; distance between the tip of snout and the tip of head crest bone/SVL 0.43–0.47; shank length/SVL 0.29–0.41; 1–2 chin shields in contact with supralabials; ventral scales keeled; no preanal or femoral pores; the scales bordering the subdigital lamellae on hind feet are enlarged and form a fringe.

Dorsal and lateral surfaces of head and body grayish brown or olive-brown with two pale (yellow or dirty white) stripes; the upper stripe runs from posterior border of eye above ear opening to sacral region; the lower stripe runs from the nostrils below eye and ear opening over shoulder to flank region; tail grayish brown with indistinct dark brown crossbands; ventral surfaces of head and body pale brown.

Natural history: E. Greenbaum (field notes) recorded adults and juveniles of this species at numerous human-disturbed lowland habitats visited in the rainy season from July–August. Some individuals were collected from areas far from natural water sources. Mertens (1952d) noted that this lizard has a preference for gardens, fence posts, banana and coffee plantations, and house walls that are overgrown with vegetation. According to his observations, the flight distance is 6–8 m. This lizard is capable of rapid bipedal locomotion over water surfaces (Mertens 1952d). Brongersma (1954b) reported a female from Río Sauco near Santa Ana, Depto. Santa Ana with six developed eggs in her oviducts (19 × 11 mm). Rand (1957) noted a mating pair in March in El Salvador. Campbell (1998a) reported that this species feeds on insects and berries; females lay up to three clutches (3–8 eggs each) per season. Stafford & Meyer (2000) noted this species is mainly arboreal; breeding may occur year round. Savage (2002) added that this species will eat spiders, terrestrial crustaceans, and a wide array of plant material.

Specimens examined: Ahuachapán: El Refugio, vicinity of Mariposario of Francisco Serrano, 13°49.46′N, 89°59.98′W, 225 m: SMF 79327–28, 81285; 3.2 km NW Ahuachapán, 1067 m: MVZ 40087–92, 40099. Cabañas: Bosque Cinquera, 13°53.13′N, 88°57.36′W, 400 m: KU 289975, 289977,

289996, MUHNES C–30–1403, C–30–1405–06.
Chalatenango: San José del Sacaré, 1097 m: FMNH
10995; 44 km N San Salvador: KU 140035; 16.5 km
WNW Chalatenango: KU 184175–76. Cuscatlán:
Tenancingo, Copalchan: KU 184158; Tenancingo:
KU 184159; 2 km W Suchitoto: TCWC 23631–33;
2.9 km N Suchitoto: UU 11067. La Libertad: Playa
Las Flores: SMF 42107; La Joya near Ciudad Arce:
SMF 44332–33; Laguna de Chanmico: SMF 42446,
42624, UMMZ 117448, 119491; Los Chorros between
Colón and Nuevo San Salvador [= Santa Tecla]:
SMF 42435; Finca El Paraíso near Nuevo San
Salvador [= Santa Tecla]: SMF 42876, 42881, 43184;
W from La Libertad: SMF 42310, 42397; road San
Salvador–Sonsonate; turnoff to Talnique; 520 m:
SMF 52055; km 35 road San Salvador–Santa Ana;
490 m: SMF 52056; Hacienda Zapotitán, Río Sucio,
457 m: MVZ 40093–94; 16.1 km NW Nuevo San
Salvador [= Santa Tecla]: KU 43573–74; 14 km W
La Libertad: KU 62045; 6.9 km E La Libertad, 20
m: KU 85748; Hacienda Belmar, ca. La Libertad:
LACM 9373–74. La Paz: Miraflores near
Zacatecoluca: SMF 42121; km 31 road San Salva-
dor–Zacatecoluca: SMF 44338; road near
Amatecampo, 10 m: SMF 52061; 4 km W El Rosario
de La Paz, Río Jiboa: KU 62037–39; 3 km E San
Rafael Obrajuelo: KU 62040–44; La Zunganera: KU
184167. La Unión: Laguna de Olomega, Pueblo
Olomega: KU 184170. Morazán: Montecristo Mine,
213 m: MVZ 40075, 40078; 4.82 km NW
Montecristo Mine, 198 m: MVZ 40079–80; 1.6 km
SE Divisadero, 259 m: MVZ 40081. San Miguel:
Laguna de Olomega, 61 m: MVZ 40082–86, 40095–
98; San Pedro: MCZ 57063; E of Moncagua: MCZ
57088. San Salvador: San Antonio Abad near San
Salvador: SMF 42118; San Salvador, 65 Avenida Sur,
Casa Reich: SMF 42262, 42577, 42705; San Salva-
dor, Instituto Tropical de Investigaciones
Científicas: KU 62046–47, SMF 42120, 42999,
47207, 52057–60, 53574, 53684, 70246, 77369;
Puerta de la Laguna, San Salvador: ZMB 35645–48;
San Salvador: SMF 44334–37, ZMB 35661–66, MVZ
40076–77; San Salvador, 670 m: FMNH 64998–99;
San Salvador, Parque Saburo-Hirao: CAS 190157;
San Salvador, Parque Zoológico Nacional: KU
289821, 289887, MUHNES C–30–1404; Mejicanos:
KU 289886; 3 km SE Ilopango, Cantón Asino: KU
184160–65, 184169, 184173, 184179–82; 2.4 km SE
Ilopango: KU 184178; San Salvador, Río Acelhuate:
LACM 94008. San Vicente: Laguna de Apastepeque:
SMF 42380; same locality at 500 m: FMNH 64996.
Santa Ana: Laguna de Güija: SMF 42119; Finca Los

Tamagases, Cantón La Joya, 560 m: SMF 44331;
Finca El Milagro, 13°53.29′N, 89°37.17′W, 1300 m:
KU 289791–92; Entrance to Parque Nacional
Montecristo, 650 m: MUHNES C–30–1402.
Sonsonate: Hacienda San Antonio near Sonsonate:
SMF 42108–17, 42484; Metalio, W from Acajutla:
SMF 48080; Hacienda Chilata, 610 m: MVZ 40100;
Acajutla: CAS-SU 3528; Izalco: USNM 192605.
Published locality records: Ahuachapán: Parque
Nacional El Imposible: YPM 12432, 12434
(Leenders & Watkins-Colwell 2004); Município San
Pedro Puxtla, Cantón La Concepción, Cooperativa
Concepción Miramar (13.810°N, 89.807°W), 1100 m
(Leenders & Watkins-Colwell 2004). La Libertad:
Volcán San Salvador, "1917 Lava," 500–700 m (Rand
1957). La Paz: 6 km N Los Blancos (Rand 1957);
Município Zacatecoluca, Finca La Esmeralda, 3 km
E Zacatecoluca (13.483°N, 88.850°W), 115 m: YPM
12433 (Leenders & Watkins-Colwell 2004).
Morazán: Município Arambala, Cantón Cumaro, Río
Sapo (13.959°N, 88.132°W), 1118 m: YPM 13996–98
(Leenders & Watkins-Colwell 2004). San Salvador:
Laguna Ilopango, 400 m (Rand 1957). San Vicente:
Posa Los Tres Amates, a few km W of San Nicolás
Lempa: RMNH 9930 (Brongersma 1954b). Santa
Ana: Río Zarco (Río Sauco) near Santa Ana: RMNH
9929 (Brongersma 1954b); Parque Nacional
Montecristo, 800 m (Leenders & Watkins-Colwell
2004).

Genus *Corytophanes*

The three species of casque-headed lizards are
distributed from San Luis Potosí and Veracruz,
Mexico, (Atlantic versant) and Oaxaca, Mexico,
(Pacific versant) south to northwestern Colombia
(Savage 2002). One species occurs in El Salvador.

Corytophanes percarinatus Duméril 1856
(Tenguereche Bobo)
Plate 63, Map 55

1856 *Corytophanes percarinatus* Duméril, Arch.
Mus. Hist. Nat. Paris 8: 518; type locality:
Escuintla, Guatemala.
Corytophanes percarinatus: K. Schmidt 1928,
Mertens 1952d, Peters & Donoso-Barros 1970, Villa
et al. 1988, Köhler 2000, Dueñas et al. 2001, Köhler
2003b, Leenders 2003, Leenders & Watkins-Colwell
2004.
Geographic distribution: From the Isthmus of
Tehuantepec, Mexico, along the Pacific coast as far

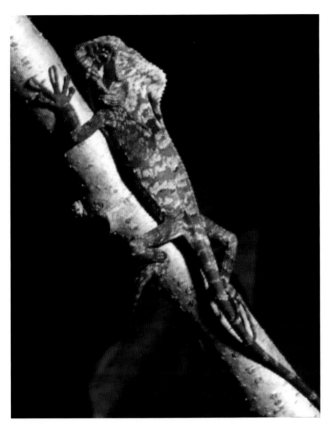

Plate 63: *Corytophanes percarinatus* (KU 289764) EL SALVADOR: Ahuachapán: Parque Nacional El Imposible, La Fincona (720 m). Photo: E. Greenbaum.

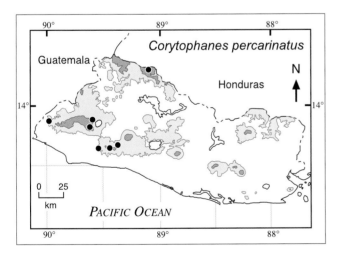

Map 55: Distribution of *Corytophanes percarinatus* in El Salvador.
Closed circles represent examined-specimen locality records; open squares are published locality records. Light shading indicates 600–1200 m elevation; dark shading indicates elevations ≥ 1200 m; large bodies of freshwater are outlined in bold, black lines.

as central El Salvador and into southwestern Honduras (Köhler 2003b).

Ecological distribution: Dry forest, premontane evergreen forest, subtropical humid forest, and pine-oak forest between 720 and 1900 m.

Description: A lizard of moderate size (SVL of largest specimen 103 mm [Leenders & Watkins-Colwell 2004]); tail length/SVL 1.89–2.38; HL/SVL 0.24–0.26; HW/SVL 0.17–0.19; snout length/SVL 0.09–0.11; distance between the tip of snout and the tip of head crest bone/SVL 0.43–0.47; shank length/ SVL 0.26–0.31; lamellae beneath 4th toe 22–25; supralabial scales beneath the center of eye 8–9; body covered with imbricate smooth scales mixed with scattered keeled scales, head scales keeled or rugose; tympanum large, oval; a laterally projecting spine-like scale above tympanum; supraorbital ridges slightly elevated; no preanal or femoral pores.

Dorsal color mainly brown or green with irregular darker and gray or grayish green crossbands extending laterally; frontal region brown with indistinct darker X-pattern; head gray or greenish gray with scattered darker scales, especially in region between eye and ear; gular region gray, grayish green or brownish; belly, ventral surfaces of limbs and tail gray or grayish brown with irregular lighter flecks; dorsal surfaces of legs and tail grayish brown with darker crossbars.

Natural history: E. Greenbaum (field notes) collected a juvenile 0.5 m from the ground on the side of a plant stem at Parque Nacional El Imposible, Depto. Ahuachapán in July at 0545 h; this individual was dark brown and asleep. An adult was collected at night as it slept in natural vegetation adjacent to a coffee finca at Finca La Giralda, Depto. La Libertad in August. M. Veselý (field notes) collected a specimen that was active during the day in ground vegetation surrounding a small pond within pine forest at Finca Los Andes, Depto. Santa Ana in June. Fitch (1970) noted this species is viviparous; births occur in late spring.

Specimens examined: Ahuachapán: Parque Nacional El Imposible, La Fincona, 13°50.8´N, 89°58.8´W, 720 m: KU 289764, 289769, MUHNES C–30–1391. Chalatenango: 11.4 km E La Palma, Cantón El Aguacatal: KU 184183–84. La Libertad: El Grito, hill above the Finca Los Angeles, 1500 m: SMF 42378; 1 km E from Finca Los Angeles, Cumbre: SMF 52870; Finca La Giralda, 13°39.34´N, 89°22.47´W, 1080 m: KU 289954. Santa Ana: Volcán de Santa Ana, Finca Los Andes, 13°52.1´N,

89°37.2´W, about 1900 m: SMF 81318. <u>Sonsonate</u>:
Hacienda Buena Vista, Cerro Verde (Mala Cara), E
of Volcán Izalco, 1200 m: SMF 44339; Hacienda
Chilata: FMNH 10986.
Published locality records: <u>Ahuachapán</u>: Parque
Nacional El Imposible, 720 m: YPM 12452
(Leenders & Watkins-Colwell 2004).

Genus *Ctenosaura*

The dozen species in this genus are distributed
from eastern Nicaragua to Panama (Atlantic
versant), and from Baja California and lowland
Mexico to Nicaragua on the Pacific versant (Savage
2002). Two species occur in El Salvador.

Ctenosaura flavidorsalis (Köhler & Klemmer 1994)

(Tanamáste)
Plate 64, Map 56

1994 *Ctenosaura flavidorsalis* Köhler & Klemmer,
Salamandra 30(3): 197; type locality: 1 km S La Paz,
14°16´N, 87°40´W, 750 m elevation, Depto. La Paz,
Honduras.
Enyaliosaurus quinquecarinatus: Hidalgo 1980a,
Gicca 1983.
Ctenosaura quinquecarinatus: Villa et al. 1988.
Ctenosaura flavidorsalis: Köhler 2000, Hasbún
2001, Hasbún et al. 2001, Savage 2002, Köhler
2003b, Leenders & Watkins-Colwell 2004.
Ctenosaura quinquecarinata: Dueñas et al. 2001.
Geographic distribution: Disjunct distribution
from eastern Guatemala to eastern El Salvador and
southwestern and south-central Honduras (Köhler
2003b).
Ecological distribution: Dry forest and savanna
between 100 and 1010 m.
Description: A small species of the genus (maximum SVL in males 160 mm, in females 130 mm);
tail length/SVL 1.30–1.64; HL/SVL 0.19–0.24; HW/
SVL 0.14–0.18; snout length/SVL 0.08–0.11; shank
length/SVL 0.18–0.24; usually 2–4 postmental
scales; 7–9 supralabial scales; 7–12 infralabial
scales; 1–2 scales between nasal and rostral scales;
1–2, occasionally 3, scales separating supraorbital
semicircles; 27–33 lamellae under fourth toe;
caudal whorls separated by 1 complete row of
intercalary scales throughout; 6–9 femoral pores on
each thigh; dorsal crest poorly developed in both
sexes, composed of 39–73 spines, interrupted at
posterior part of dorsum for 15–52 dorsal scale rows.

Plate 64: *Ctenosaura flavidorsalis* (YPM 13008) EL
SALVADOR: Morazán: Cantón Cumaro, Bailadero del
Diablo (1120 m). Photo: T. Leenders.

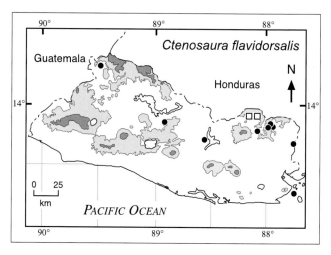

Map 56: Distribution of *Ctenosaura flavidorsalis* in El
Salvador.
Closed circles represent examined-specimen locality records;
open squares are published locality records. Light shading
indicates 600–1200 m elevation; dark shading indicates elevations ≥ 1200 m; large bodies of freshwater are outlined in bold,
black lines.

There is strong sexual dichromatism in *C.
flavidorsalis;* males are more colorful than females.
In males, there is yellow to orange-yellow coloration at the tip of the snout and vertebral region of
the dorsum and tail; the dorsal and lateral surfaces
of the head are otherwise grayish brown with
scattered pale brown mottling; the anterior part of
the chin is dirty white, its posterior portion yellow;
except for the medial portion (mostly yellow with
some scattered lime green mottling), the dorsum is
mostly grayish brown; flanks with dark grayish
brown stripes that extend onto venter; venter dirty
white with some yellow scales. Females are usually

less colorful than males although an orange-yellow rostrum and yellow middorsal region is present in some females. Otherwise they show different shades of brown. Juveniles have green blotches on the dorsal surface of the head and anterior half of the dorsum, and usually indistinct brownish crossbands on a grayish brown ground color.

Taxonomic comments: The Salvadoran populations of this species were referred to as *Ctenosaura quinquecarinata* by earlier authors (Hidalgo 1980a, Villa et al. 1988). Recently, Hasbún (2001) and Hasbún et al. (2001) demonstrated the Salvadoran populations to be conspecific with *C. flavidorsalis*.

Natural history: Hidalgo (1980a) noted Salvadoran animals were collected from under small flat rocks, slabs of limestone, and loose rock fences. Adults were noted to forage in trees. Leenders & Watkins-Colwell (2004) noted this species is common in sparsely populated, arid areas of Depto. Morazán, but it is hunted by local people.

Specimens examined: Cabañas: 3.4 km W Tejutepeque, Cantón La Joya: KU 184192–93. La Unión: 8 km E El Sauce, 100 m: MUHNES 30–1229; Isla Conchaguita: MUHNES C–390. Morazán: Corinto, La Cueva de Corinto, 863 m, 13°49.93´N, 87°57.59´W: MUHNES C–30–1223, SMF 79506; 1–2 km N La Cueva de Corinto: BMNH 2000.4, SMF 78507–09; Cerro El Aguacate, 13°48´N, 87°57.6´W, 1000–1010 m: BMNH 2000.5, MUHNES C–30–1224–25, C–30–1228, C–30–1230, SMF 79510–11, 79514–15; Cerro El Junco, 880–900 m: BMNH 2000.6–7, MUHNES C–30–1226–27, SMF 79512–13; Cacaopera, Río Torola, Cantón Calavera: MUHNES C–361. Santa Ana: Metapán, 1 km S Casas de Teja: MUHNES C–30–1232. San Vicente: 1 km W San Ildefonso, 210 m: MUHNES C–30–1231.

Published locality records: Morazán: Município Arambala, Cantón Cumaro, Bailadero del Diablo (13.931°N, 88.102°W), 696 m: YPM 13008 (Leenders & Watkins-Colwell 2004); Município Arambala, Cantón Cumaro, Río Sapo (13.959°N, 88.132°W): YPM 13007 (Leenders & Watkins-Colwell 2004).

***Ctenosaura similis* (Gray 1831)**
(Iguana Negra)
Plate 65, Map 57

1831 *Iguana (Ctenosaura) Similis* Gray, in Cuvier edit. Griffith, Anim. Kingd., London, 9: 38; type locality: unknown.
Ctenosaura completa: Bocourt 1874, K. Schmidt 1928, Ahl 1940.

Plate 65: *Ctenosaura similis* COSTA RICA: Guanacaste: Santa Rosa N. P., Playa Nancite (10 m). Photo: T. Leenders.

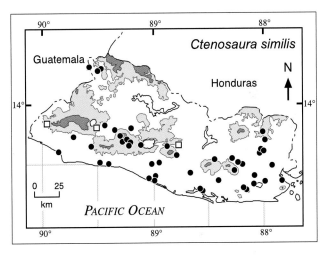

Map 57: Distribution of *Ctenosaura similis* in El Salvador.
Closed circles represent examined-specimen locality records; open squares are published locality records. Light shading indicates 600–1200 m elevation; dark shading indicates elevations ≥ 1200 m; large bodies of freshwater are outlined in bold, black lines.

Ctenosaura similis: Mertens 1952d, Rand 1957, Villa et al. 1988, Köhler 2000, Dueñas et al. 2001, Köhler 2003b, Leenders 2003, Leenders & Watkins-Colwell 2004.
Ctenosaura similis similis: Peters & Donoso-Barros 1970.

Geographic distribution: From the Isthmus of Tehuantepec along both versants to central Panama; also known from Islas San Andrés and Providencia, Colombia (Savage 2002). Introduced to Florida, USA (Meshaka et al. 2004).

Ecological distribution: Dry forest and savanna between sea level and 1320 m.

Description: A large species of the genus (maximum SVL in males 375 mm, in females 300 mm); tail length/SVL 1.63–2.14; HL/SVL 0.19–0.29; HW/SVL 0.14–0.18; snout length/SVL 0.08–0.11; shank length/SVL 0.17–0.27; usually 4 postmental scales (rarely 5 or 6); 11–15 supralabial scales; 10–15 infralabial scales; 2–3 scales between nasal and rostral scales; 2–3 scales separating supraorbital semicircles; 2–3 scales between interparietal plate and supraorbital semicircles; 30–39 lamellae under fourth toe; anterior 0–2 caudal whorls separated by 3 complete rows of intercalary scales, all other caudal whorls separated by 2 complete rows of intercalary scales; 4–10 femoral pores on each thigh; dorsal crest well developed in males, composed of 64–87 spines.

Head, body, and tail grayish brown with distinct dark brown dorsal crossbands on body and tail; crossbands on body are split medially in some specimens; flanks and limbs grayish brown with scattered pale brown round blotches. Juveniles are bright green with brown dorsal crossbands.

Natural history: Mertens (1952d) observed adults on large trees up to 12 m above the ground in El Salvador. Rand (1957) noted adults were common on stone fences and trunks of large trees in forests and human habitations; juveniles are more terrestrial than adults in El Salvador. This species is hunted for its meat in El Salvador. Campbell (1998a) noted this terrestrial species lives in ground burrows or hollow areas of trees, and can be active during the hottest times of the day. The diet includes vegetation, flowers, fruit, vertebrates, eggs, and arthropods. Breeding occurs in the dry season, 15–30 eggs are laid from March–May, and juveniles hatch in the rainy season. Savage (2002) commented about the complicated dominance hierarchy among males of this species. Sometimes communal nests are shared by multiple females. Leenders & Watkins-Colwell (2004) noted this species can be common near human habitations in El Salvador.

Specimens examined: La Libertad: road San Salvador–Nuevo San Salvador [= Santa Tecla]: SMF 42148; San Andrés, km 35 on road San Salvador–Santa Ana, 490 m: SMF 42150, 52062; Laguna de Chanmico: SMF 42447; W from La Libertad: SMF 42307–09, 42401–03; Volcán San Salvador "1917 Lava," 500 m: FMNH 64995; 14 km W La Libertad: KU 62049. La Paz: Los Blancos: SMF 42140; 6 km N Los Blancos: FMNH 64990–93; Puerto de Los Planes: SMF 42574–75 (*); 1 km E from La Palma,

100 m: SMF 52066; 4 km E Rosario de La Paz, Río Jiboa: KU 62048; El Pimental: KU 184185. La Unión: between Pueblo El Carmen and Laguna de Olomega: SMF 42138; La Unión: SMF 42154; M.A.G. Laboratory, 1 km S El Tamarindo: MVZ 143989. Morazán: Cantón San José near Jocoro: SMF 41244–45; Sociedad, 305–365 m: SMF 42152, 52086–87; road Sociedad–Corinto, 600–800 m: SMF 52088–89; Montecristo Mine: SMF 52090; Montecristo Mine, 213 m: MVZ 40103–05, 40112, 40116–17, 40303, 222442–43; 4.82 km W Montecristo Mine, 198 m: MVZ 40106–07; 1.6 km SE Divisadero, 259 m: MVZ 40119. San Miguel: Laguna de Olomega: SMF 42136; same locality at 61 m: MVZ 40108–10; Laguna de Aramuaca: SMF 42139; Carretera Panamericana in front of San Miguel, 250–400 m: 42142–43, 52071–72; San Miguel: SMF 42153; Hacienda San Pedro, SE from Usulután: SMF 52073; road Concepción Batres–San Miguel, 130 m: SMF 52074–82; km 131 road San Salvador–San Miguel: SMF 52083; San Pedro: MCZ 57083; Volcán de San Miguel, 740 m: KU 291383, 291389–90, MUHNES C–30–1491–92. San Salvador: Apopa: SMF 42141; San Salvador, 65 Avenida Sur: SMF 42256, 42500, 42576; San Salvador, Instituto Tropical de Investigaciones Científicas: SMF 42122–28, 42149, 43055, 52063–64; San Salvador: SMF 52065, ZMB 35656–57, 35667; 2.4 km SE Ilopango, Cantón Asino: KU 184186–88; 3 km SE Ilopango, Cantón Asino: KU 184189–90. San Vicente: Finca El Carmen, E part of Volcán San Vicente, 1319 m: SMF 44341; road San Vicente–Tecoluca, 420–450 m: SMF 52067–68. Santa Ana: Laguna de Güija: SMF 42151; Cerro de Cal, Metapán, 860 m: SMF 44340; Metapán, Volcán de San Diego crater: KU 184191. Sonsonate: beach near Acajutla: SMF 42129–31; Hacienda San Antonio near Sonsonate: SMF 42263; Hacienda Chilata, 610 m: MVZ 40120. Usulután: Puerto El Triunfo: SMF 42132–35, 42146–47; Hacienda La Carrera, near Puerto El Triunfo: SMF 42504–06; San Marcos Lempa, 130 m: SMF 52069; Hacienda San Pedro, Río San Miguel, 10 m: SMF 52070; near Batres: MCZ 57082; Usulután: CAS 94254. Depto. unknown: km 164 of Panamericana: SMF 52084–85 (*).

Published locality records: Ahuachapán: Parque Nacional El Imposible (Leenders 2003, Leenders & Watkins-Colwell 2004). San Miguel: Cantón El Volcán, N slope Volcán San Miguel, Finca Santa Isabel (13.468°N, 88.267°W), 800 m: YPM 12477 (Leenders & Watkins-Colwell 2004). San Vicente: Laguna Apastepeque, 500 m (Rand 1957).

Sonsonate: Município Izalco, Cantón Las Lajas, Bosque Las Lajas (13.829°N, 89.567°W), 750 m (Leenders & Watkins-Colwell 2004).

Genus *Iguana*

This genus includes two species that are widely distributed from Sinaloa and Veracruz, Mexico, through Central America to Paraguay and south-central Brazil, many of the Lesser Antilles, and several Caribbean islands (Savage 2002). One species occurs in El Salvador.

Iguana iguana (Linnaeus 1758)
(Iguana verde)
Plate 66, Map 58

1758 *Lacerta iguana* Linnaeus, Syst. Nat., Ed. 10, 1: 206; type locality: "Indiis;" restricted to the confluence of the Cottica River and the Perica Creek, Suriname by Hoogmoed (1973: Biogeographica 4: 1–419).
Iguana iguana rhinolopha: Ahl 1940, Mertens 1952d, Rand 1957, Peters & Donoso-Barros 1970.
Iguana iguana: Mitchell and Tully 1998, Villa et al. 1988, Köhler 2000, Dueñas et al. 2001, Nevarez et al. 2002, Köhler 2003b, Leenders 2003, Leenders & Watkins-Colwell 2004.
Geographic distribution: From Sinaloa and Veracruz, Mexico, through Central America (including the Lesser Antilles) to Bolivia, Paraguay and south-central Brazil (Atlantic versant) and Ecuador (Pacific versant); introduced to southern Florida, USA (Savage 2002, Meshaka et al. 2004).
Ecological distribution: Dry forest, premontane evergreen forest, and subtropical humid forest usually close to rivers and lakes (gallery forest) between sea level and 750 m; also in mangroves.
Description: A large species of lizard (SVL of largest specimen examined 515 mm); tail length/ SVL 2.50–3.09; HL/SVL 0.16–0.21; HW/SVL 0.11– 0.16; snout length/SVL 0.09–0.12; shank length/ SVL 0.22–0.27; dewlap large, with 8–12 spine-like scales; 3–5 postmental scales (rarely 2); 8–10 supralabial scales; 8–11 infralabial scales; 0–1, rarely 2, scales separating supraorbital semicircles; 0–1, rarely 2, scales between interparietal plate and supraorbital semicircles; 30–39 lamellae under fourth toe; 7–18 femoral pores on each thigh; dorsal crest well developed in both sexes, composed of 47– 56 spines; tail length/SVL 2.5–3.1.
The bright green color of juveniles gradually

Plate 66: *Iguana iguana* COSTA RICA: Heredia: Puerto Viejo Sarapiquí, Río Sarapiquí (30 m). Photo: T. Leenders.

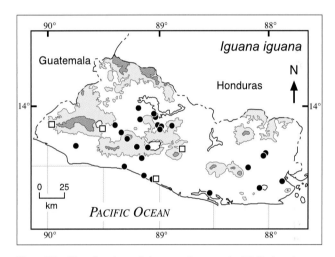

Map 58: Distribution of *Iguana iguana* in El Salvador. Closed circles represent examined-specimen locality records; open squares are published locality records. Light shading indicates 600–1200 m elevation; dark shading indicates elevations ≥ 1200 m; large bodies of freshwater are outlined in bold, black lines.

turns into olive to orange-brown in larger adults; females have the tendency to stay green up to a larger size (it also has been observed that *I. iguana* in mangroves tend to remain green even up to a very mature stage; F. Serrano pers. comm.); body pattern varies from having distinct oblique dark brown crossbars to almost unicolor green; tail with distinct dark brown crossbars. The adult coloration is variable, ranging from orange (which has led many local people to call these animals "garrobos dorados" [golden ctenosaurs]) to olive-brown or even gray and silvery gray.

Natural history: E. Greenbaum (field notes) observed an adult on a beach near mangroves during the day at Isla San Sebastián, Depto. Usulután in July. Adults were observed for sale on roadsides throughout El Salvador for meat. M. Veselý (field notes) observed juveniles on bushes near office buildings at Parque Zoológico Nacional, Depto. San Salvador in late June. Mertens (1952d) noted that the flight distance is about 10 m and that iguanas jumped from tree branches overhanging a river into the water in El Salvador. Rand (1957) noted juveniles of this species and *Ctenosaura similis* at the edge of a forest 6 km N Los Blancos, Depto. La Paz in May; both species are hunted for their meat in El Salvador. Rand (1968) reported communal nesting of this species in Panama. Campbell (1998a) noted this arboreal species eats vegetation, although juveniles will eat arthropods. Mating occurs from October–December, 15–60 eggs are laid from February–May, and juveniles hatch after approximately 90 days. Mitchell & Tully (1998) noted adult captive females (housed in open pens in El Salvador) deposit eggs in 50–60-cm deep nests from January to March, which hatch between March and June. Savage (2002) commented that iguanas are excellent swimmers and have been found in the open sea far from shore. A dominance hierarchy is in place for males, which are highly territorial in the breeding season.

Conservation status: CITES: Appendix II.

Specimens examined: Cabañas: Ilobasco: SMF 42157. Cuscatlán: 5 km E from Suchitoto: SMF 52092; Tenancingo, Cantón Huilihuishte: KU 184198; 3 km NE Tenancingo, Cantón Copalchan: KU 184200–01; Tenancingo, El Sitio de la Sánchez: KU 184205–07; 3 km NE Tenancingo, Río Quezalapa: KU 184213; 2.9 km N Suchitoto: UU 11088. La Libertad: Laguna de Chanmico, 480 m: SMF 42497, 42674; E side of Río Chilama near La Libertad: SMF 42616–17; San Andrés, km 35 road San Salvador–Santa Ana, 490 m: SMF 52091; Volcán San Salvador "1917 Lava": FMNH 65000–01. La Paz: Carretera near Olocuilta: SMF 42155; La Zunganera: KU 184199, 184202, 184209–10; El Pimental: KU 184208. La Unión: Hacienda San Cayetano: SMF 42158. Morazán: 4.82 km W Montecristo Mine, 198 m: MVZ 40113–14, 40118; Montecristo Mine, 244 m: MVZ 40115. San Miguel: San Miguel: SMF 42159, USNM 192596; Laguna de Olomega, 61 m: MVZ 40111, 40655. San Salvador: San Diego: ZMB 35649–50; 3 km SE Ilopango,

Cantón Asino: KU 184203–04, 184214. Sonsonate: Hacienda San Antonio near Sonsonate: SMF 42156. Usulután: Puerto El Triunfo: SMF 42160.

Published locality records: Ahuachapán: Parque Nacional El Imposible (Leenders 2003, Leenders & Watkins-Colwell 2004). La Paz: 6 km N Los Blancos (Rand 1957). San Vicente: Laguna Apastepeque, 500 m (Rand 1957). Sonsonate: Município Izalco, Cantón Las Lajas, Bosque Las Lajas (13.829°N, 89.567°W), 750 m: YPM 12451 (Leenders & Watkins-Colwell 2004).

Genus *Norops*

The anoles (*Anolis* sensu lato), with more than 300 valid species, represent the most diverse lizard genus, with an ever-increasing number of species. They are a conspicuous component of the fauna wherever they occur, and throughout their range it is common for several species of anoles to occur together. Macedonia (2001) noted that many species of anoles have females that possess a dorsal stripe or chevron pattern; this pattern may also be present in juveniles in both sexes. Savage (2002) listed 143 species of *Norops,* which are distributed from Mexico to Bolivia, Paraguay, and Brazil; some species occur on the islands of Jamaica, Cuba, the Bahamas, and Cayman Islands. Six species occur in El Salvador.

Despite the fact that anoles have been the focus of interest by herpetologists for more than a century, the phylogenetic relationships and taxonomy of this group of lizards remains subject to serious controversy in the recent literature. In the present work we follow the classification proposed by Guyer & Savage (1987, 1992) and Savage & Guyer (1989) in using the generic name *Norops* for the anole species of El Salvador. This decision reflects the strong support for the assertion that *Norops* represents a monophyletic lineage (*Norops* = the beta group of Etheridge [1959], species of which are characterized by autotomic caudal vertebrae with transverse processes that are directed anterolaterally; see figure 3A in Etheridge [1967]). However, the appropriateness of Guyer & Savage's (1987, 1992) other proposed genera (the alpha group of Etheridge [1959]) appears more uncertain. The anole classification of Guyer & Savage (1987) was heavily criticized by Cannatella & de Queiroz (1989) and by E. Williams (1989). However, a recent phylogenetic analysis of *Anolis* found support for the monophyly of *Norops* (Poe

2004). The latter author noted he is working on a classification of the anoles, which might result in taxonomic changes in the near future.

Norops crassulus (Cope 1864)
(Anolis Montano Vientre Aquillado)
Plate 67, Map 59, Figure 23ab

1864 *Anolis crassulus* Cope, Proc. Acad. nat. Sci. Philad. 1864: 173; type locality: Coban, Verapaz, Guatemala.
Anolis crassulus: Mertens 1952d.
Norops crassulus: Villa et al. 1988, Köhler 2000, Dueñas et al. 2001, Köhler 2003b, Leenders 2003.
Norops cf. *crassulus*: Leenders & Watkins-Colwell 2004.

Geographic distribution: Disjunct highlands from southern Mexico to central El Salvador (Köhler 2003b).

Ecological distribution: Cloud forest and pine-oak forest between 1300 and 2390 m.

Description: A medium-sized species of the genus (maximum SVL in males 50 mm, in females 51 mm); tail length/SVL 1.45–2.42; HL/SVL 0.25–0.29; HW/SVL 0.17–0.22; snout length/SVL 0.11–0.13; shank length/SVL 0.19–0.25; ventral scales distinctly keeled, mucronate; 10–23 rows of medial dorsal scales distinctly enlarged; flank scales heterogeneous, enlarged, keeled scales scattered among smaller granular laterals; 0–1 scales separating supraorbital semicircles; 1–3 scales between interparietal plate and supraorbital semicircles; 4–6 rows of loreal scales; suboculars and supralabials usually in contact, rarely separated by one scale row; 5–8 supralabial scales to a point below center of eye; 21–27 lamellae under phalanges II to IV of fourth toe; distinctly enlarged postanal scales in males; no deep tube-like axillary pocket; tail length/SVL 1.8–2.4; shank length/SVL 0.19–0.25.

Head, body, and tail grayish brown; male dewlap red with white or cream scales. Some females have a white vertebral stripe flanked by a tan stripe. Leenders & Watkins-Colwell (2004) noted this species has sexual dimorphism in dewlap color; males have an orange dewlap with cream gorgetal and marginal scales, whereas females have a relatively smaller yellow dewlap with cream gorgetal scales.

Natural history: E. Greenbaum (field notes) recorded one individual from leaves of a coffee plant at Finca El Milagro, Depto. Santa Ana in July. M. Veselý (field notes) caught several specimens from

Plate 67: *Norops crassulus* (KU 289793) EL SALVADOR: Santa Ana: Finca El Milagro (1300 m). Photo: E. Greenbaum.

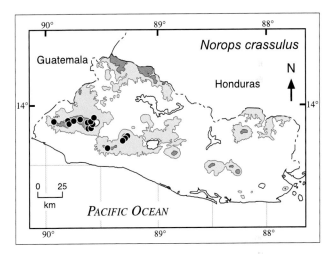

Map 59: Distribution of *Norops crassulus* in El Salvador.
Closed circles represent examined-specimen locality records; open squares are published locality records. Light shading indicates 600–1200 m elevation; dark shading indicates elevations ≥ 1200 m; large bodies of freshwater are outlined in bold, black lines.

leaves of a liana covering a bush (30 cm to 2 m above ground) at Cerro Verde, Depto. Santa Ana in May. Fitch (1970) noted Guatemalan females with large eggs in May.

Specimens examined: <u>Ahuachapán</u>: Apaneca, Laguna de Las Ranas, 1750 m: SMF 44314, MUHNES 432; Parque Nacional El Imposible, footpath to Tacuba: MUHNES 1083; Cerro Campana: MUHNES 1071; Cerro de Apaneca, 1524 m: MVZ 40027; Apaneca, 1463 m: MVZ 40028–29. <u>La Libertad</u>: Boquerón, 1850 m: SMF 42183; Finca Los Angeles, Cumbre 1400 m: SMF 43159–60. <u>San</u>

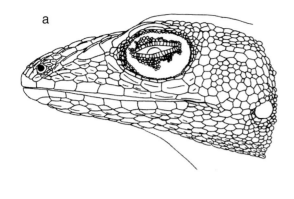

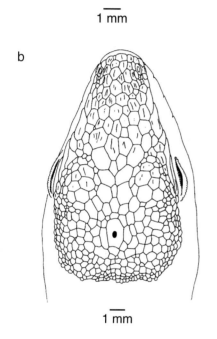

Figure 23: *Norops crassulus* (SMF 78100): a. lateral view of head, b. dorsal view of head.

Salvador: W of El Picacho, top of Volcán San Salvador, 1965 m: SMF 44316; El Picacho: MUHNES 1121, 1123. Santa Ana: Cerro Verde: CAS 94800; Cerro Verde, 13°49.6´N, 89°37.3´W, 1900 m: MUHNES 629; top of Cerro Verde: SMF 78094 (1900 m elevation), 78095–97, 78104 (1910 m elevation); Cerro Verde, on the way to Volcán, 1920 m: SMF 78098; wood on the W part of Volcán Santa Ana near Finca Buenos Aires, 1600–1700 m: SMF 44315; Turicentro Cerro Verde, 1800–2000 m: CAS 147403; Volcán Santa Ana, Los Andes, near the forester's house: SMF 78099, 78100–03; Volcán Santa Ana: MUHNES 637; same locality at 2000 m: KU 184088; same locality southern direction, 2000

m: KU 184051–82; Cerro El Aguila, 1676 m: MVZ 39928, 40014–24; same locality at 1798 m: MVZ 40014; same locality at 1829 m: MVZ 39927, 39995–98; Finca El Milagro, 13°53.29´N, 89°37.17´W, 1300 m: KU 289793, MUHNES C–30–1395. Sonsonate: Cerro de Los Naranjos, 1829 m: MVZ 40000; same locality at 1555 m: MVZ 40025–26; 1.6 km E Cerro de Los Naranjos, 1798 m: MVZ 40007–13; same locality at 1768 m: MVZ 40121.

Published locality records: Santa Ana: Município Santa Ana, Cantón Los Flores, Parque Nacional Los Andes and Volcán Santa Ana (13.869°N, 89.620°W), 1715–2390 m: YPM 14025–41 (Leenders & Watkins-Colwell 2004).

Norops heteropholidotus (Mertens 1952)
(Anolis Montano Vientre Liso)
Plate 68, Map 60, Figure 24ab

1952 *Anolis heteropholidotus* Mertens, Zool. Anz. 148: 89; type locality: Hacienda Los Planes, Cerro Miramundo, 2000 m, Depto. Santa Ana, El Salvador.
Anolis heteropholidotus: Mertens 1952a, d, Rand 1957, Peters & Donoso-Barros 1970.
Norops heteropholidotus: Köhler 1996, Köhler & McCranie 1998, Köhler 2000, Dueñas et al. 2001, Köhler 2003b, Leenders & Watkins-Colwell 2003c, 2004.

Geographic distribution: Highlands of north-western El Salvador and southwestern Honduras (Köhler 2003b).

Ecological distribution: Cloud forest and pine-oak forest between 1500 and 2480 m.

Description: A medium-sized species of the genus (maximum SVL in males 51 mm, in females 59 mm); tail length/SVL 1.48–2.67; HL/SVL 0.23–0.30; HW/SVL 0.15–0.20; snout length/SVL 0.10–0.14; shank length/SVL 0.21–0.29; ventral scales smooth; medial dorsal scales distinctly enlarged with vertebral rows largest; flank scales heterogeneous, enlarged keeled scales scattered among smaller granular laterals; 0–2 scales separating supraorbital semicircles; 1–3 scales between interparietal plate and supraorbital semicircles; 4–6 rows of loreal scales; suboculars and supralabials in contact; 5–8 supralabial scales to a point below center of eye; 22–33 lamellae under phalanges II to IV of fourth toe; distinctly enlarged postanal scales in males; no deep tube-like axillary pocket; tail length/SVL 2.0–2.5; shank length/SVL 0.24–0.29.

Head, body, and tail grayish brown; male dewlap red-orange with white or cream scales.

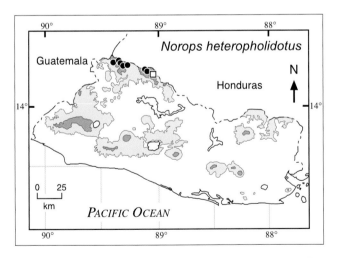

Plate 68: *Norops heteropholidotus* EL SALVADOR: Chalatenango: Cerro El Pital (2380 m). Photo: O. Komar.

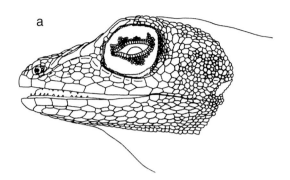

a

1 mm

b

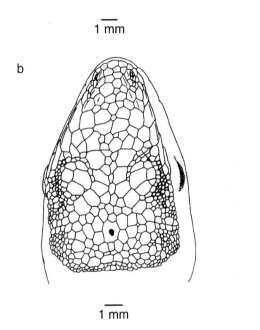

1 mm

Map 60: Distribution of *Norops heteropholidotus* in El Salvador.

Closed circles represent examined-specimen locality records; open squares are published locality records. Light shading indicates 600–1200 m elevation; dark shading indicates elevations ≥ 1200 m; large bodies of freshwater are outlined in bold, black lines.

Figure 24: *Norops heteropholidotus* (SMF 77155): a. lateral view of head, b. dorsal view of head.

Leenders & Watkins-Colwell (2003c) reported male dewlap color as strawberry red, and female dewlap color as orange-yellow at Cerro Las Nubes, Depto. Chalatenango. Some females have a white verte-bral stripe. Leenders & Watkins-Colwell (2004) reported a female with an orange dewlap and cream gorgetal and marginal scales from Parque Nacional Montecristo (Depto. Santa Ana).

Natural history: W. E. Duellman (field notes) collected several adults on bushes in cloud forest at Cerro Montecristo, Depto. Santa Ana in February. O. Komar (field notes) recorded several adults on or near small, rotted tree trunks in disturbed cloud forest during the day at Cerro El Pital, Depto. Chalatenango in May. M. Veselý (field notes) collected specimens from a fallen tree in cloud

forest at Cerro Miramundo (2200 m), Depto. Santa
Ana in June. Mertens (1952d) collected this species
on a small bush 30 cm above the ground at the edge
of cloud forest in El Salvador. Rand (1957) collected
three specimens as they sunned themselves on low
branches along a trail near the edge of a clearing in
cloud forest at Cerro Miramundo (2200 m), Depto.
Santa Ana in March. Leenders & Watkins-Colwell
(2003c) observed over two dozen specimens in cloud
forest during the day at Cerro Las Nubes, Depto.
Chalatenango in December; gorgetal color of males
changed from slate gray (before 1000 h) to white
(some with gray speckling) after 1000 h.

Specimens examined: Chalatenango: Los
Esesmiles, Cerro El Pital, 1829 m: MVZ 39969;
same locality at 2225 m: MVZ 39920–21, 39953–68,
39972–73; same locality at 1524–1829 m: MVZ
39952, 39970; Las Palmas, Metapán Mt: KU
193012–22; Cerro El Pital, 2350 m: KU 291250–58,
MUHNES C–30–1502–08; same locality at 2480 m:
YPM 12479. Santa Ana: Parque Nacional
Montecristo, on the road to El Trifinio, Cerro
Miramundo, 2150 m: SMF 78031, 79051, 79088;
near Hacienda Los Planes, Metapán mountains,
2000 m: SMF 43041, MUHNES 1126, 1170–72;
Hacienda Montecristo, Metapán mountains, 2150–
2200 m: SMF 42191, 44394, 51979, 51990, 77141–47,
77149–58, 77160–63, UMMZ 117647, KU 62027–34,
66867–75; El Trifinio, Cerro Miramundo, near
parking place: MUHNES 1124–25, 1127, 1131–35;
Parque Nacional Montecristo: MUHNES 351, 732–
35, 1136, 1164–65; Cerro Miramundo, 2000 m:
FMNH 65019; Cerro Miramundo, 2200 m: FMNH
65017.

Published locality records: Chalatenango: Cerro
El Pital: YPM 12479 (Leenders & Watkins-Colwell
2004); Cerro Las Nubes, 14°23.3´N, 89°6.2´W, 2090
m: YPM 12379–85, 12422–23 (Leenders & Watkins-
Colwell 2003c, 2004). Santa Ana: Municípío
Metapán, Cantón Metapán, Parque Nacional
Montecristo (14.401°N, 89.362°W), up to 2480 m:
YPM 14033, 14042–52, 14054–57 (Leenders &
Watkins-Colwell 2004).

***Norops macrophallus* (Werner 1917)**
(Anolis Común)
Plate 69, Map 61, Figure 25ab

1917 *Anolis macrophallus* Werner, Mitt. Zool. Mus.
Hamburg 34: 31; type locality: "S. José de Guatemala" (= Puerto San José, Depto. Escuintla, Guatemala).

Plate 69: *Norops macrophallus* EL SALVADOR:
Ahuachapán: El Refugio (225 m). Photo: G. Köhler.

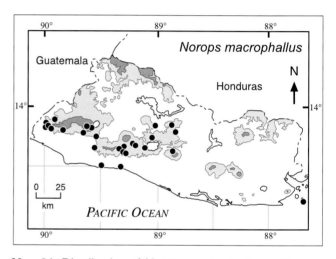

Map 61: Distribution of *Norops macrophallus* in El
Salvador.
Closed circles represent examined-specimen locality records;
open squares are published locality records. Light shading
indicates 600–1200 m elevation; dark shading indicates elevations ≥ 1200 m; large bodies of freshwater are outlined in bold,
black lines.

Anolis biontatus: K. Schmidt 1928.
Anolis cupreus: K. Schmidt 1928, Ahl 1940, Mertens
1952d, Peters & Donoso-Barros 1970, Fitch et al.
1972.
Norops cupreus: Villa et al. 1988, Dueñas et al. 2001.
Norops macrophallus: Köhler & Kreutz 1999,
Köhler 2000, 2003b, Leenders 2003, Leenders &
Watkins-Colwell 2004.

Geographic distribution: From southeastern
Guatemala along the Pacific versant to central El
Salvador (Köhler 2003b).

Ecological distribution: Dry forest, premontane
evergreen forest, and sub-tropical humid forest
between sea level and 1320 m.

a

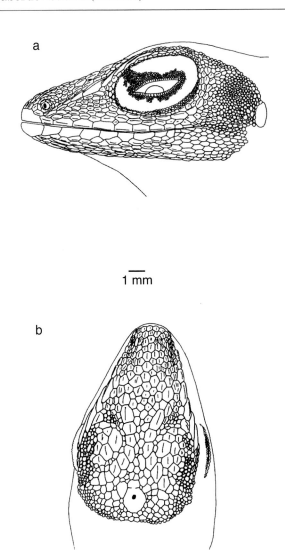

1 mm

b

1 mm

Figure 25: *Norops macrophallus* (SMF 79039): a. lateral view of head, b. dorsal view of head.

Description: A medium-sized species of the genus (maximum SVL in males 50 mm [Leenders & Watkins-Colwell 2004], in females 45 mm); tail length/SVL 1.71–2.05; HL/SVL 0.23–0.33; HW/SVL 0.14–0.22; snout length/SVL 0.12–0.19; shank length/SVL 0.23–0.34; ventral scales distinctly keeled but usually not mucronate; 2–4 rows of medial dorsal scales slightly enlarged; flank scales homogeneous; 1–2 scales separating supraorbital semicircles; 2–3 scales between interparietal plate and supraorbital semicircles; 5–8 rows of loreal scales; suboculars and supralabials separated by one scale row; 6–8 supralabial scales to a point below center of eye; 28–34 lamellae under phalan-

ges II to IV of fourth toe; no enlarged postanal scales; no deep tube-like axillary pocket; tail length/ SVL 1.7–2.1; shank length/SVL 0.25–0.32. Head, body, and tail grayish brown; male dewlap flesh colored with a basal orange-yellow blotch.

Natural history: E. Greenbaum (field notes) recorded this species in subtropical humid forest during the day at Parque Nacional El Imposible, Depto. Ahuachapán in July. Another specimen was collected on a coffee plant in the early morning at Finca Concepción Miramar, Depto. Ahuachapán in August. Mertens (1952d) noted that this lizard prefers shady microhabitats in El Salvador. Fitch (1970) noted gravid females from Costa Rica in June, July, and August. Leenders & Watkins-Colwell (2004) noted this species will hunt for invertebrate prey on or near the ground during the day, but sleep on the tops of leaves (sometimes several meters above the ground) at night in El Salvador.

Specimens examined: Ahuachapán: Finca Concepción Miramar, 13°48.46´N, 89°48.03´W, 920 m: KU 289918, 289945–46, 290060, MUHNES C–30–1397; Parque Nacional El Imposible, La Fincona, 13°50.80´N, 89°58.80´W, 720 m: SMF 79031–32, 79038, 79044, MUHNES 882, 1117, KU 289766, 289768, MUHNES C–30–1401; Parque Nacional El Imposible, Distrito San Benito, El Caschal, 500 m: SMF 79040, same locality near Río Guayapa 480 m: KU 289836; Distrito San Benito, Piedra Sellada, 520 m: SMF 79036–37; El Refugio, vicinity of Mariposario of Francisco Serrano, 13°49.46´N, 89°59.98´W, 225 m: SMF 79039, 79041–42; Parque Nacional El Imposible: MUHNES 111, 874–75, 909B, 1058–59; Finca San Benito: MUHNES 430, 433–34, 1038, 1047; Parque Nacional El Imposible, Zona de las Escaleras, Montaña del Bálsamo: MUHNES 315–318 (*); Finca Las Delicias, 13°52´N, 89°53´W, 1200 m: KU 290055–56; Finca Los Tres Hermanos, 13°52´N, 89°53´W, 1200 m: KU 290057; Finca Santa Luisa, 13°52´N, 89°53´W, 900 m: KU 290058, MUHNES C–30–1399. Cabañas: Ilobasco: SMF 51983. Cuscatlán: Finca near San Martín, 700 m: SMF 42303–05, 42376–77; 0.5 km NE Tenancingo, Santa Rita: KU 184049–50. La Libertad: Club Atami (near Playa El Palmarcito, Municipio Tamanique), 13°30.20´N; 89°25.00´W, 40 m: SMF 79030; Hacienda Miramar near Zaragoza: SMF 42180–81; Finca Los Cedros, about 1000 m: SMF 42894; La Bomba, Finca Los Naranjos near Nuevo San Salvador [= Santa Tecla], about 900 m: SMF 42882; Finca El Paraíso near Nuevo San

Salvador [= Santa Tecla]: SMF 42590, 42713, 43146, 43158, 45025, 45402–03; Río San Antonio, 2 km E La Libertad: SMF 43113. La Unión: Isla Meanguerita, Golfo de Fonseca: MUHNES 429. San Salvador: San Salvador, Barranco 65 Avenida Sur: SMF 42603; San Salvador, Instituto Tropical de Investigaciones Científicas: SMF 42179, 51982, 51991; 2.4 km SE Ilopango, Cantón Asino: KU 184090–96; San Salvador, CAMRS: USNM 167203–05. San Vicente: E part of Volcán San Vicente, Finca El Carmen, 1319 m: SMF 44321, 51984–85. Sonsonate: Finca La Joya, km 48 on road San Salvador–Sonsonate, 600 m: SMF 44317–20; Hacienda Chilata, 610 m: MVZ 39922–26, 39930–38, 39999, 40033, 40036–38, 40040–46, FMNH 10992–94; Bosque Las Lajas, 13°50.04′N, 89°33.56′W, 920 m: KU 289865, MUHNES C–30–1396, C–30–1398; Finca Nuevos Horizontes, 13°47′N, 89°37′W, 920 m: KU 290059, MUHNES C–30–1400.

Published locality records: Ahuachapán: Município San Pedro Puxtla, Cantón La Concepción, Cooperative Concepción Miramar (13.810°N, 89.807°W), 950 m: YPM 12332, 12401, 12410, 12414, 12416–17, 12419 (Leenders & Watkins-Colwell 2004); Parque Nacional El Imposible: YPM 12329, 12339, 12400, 12402, 12407–08, 12412, 12415, 12420, 12424, 12993–98 (Leenders & Watkins-Colwell 2004). Sonsonate: Município Izalco, Cantón Las Lajas, Bosque Las Lajas (13.829°N, 89.567°W), 750 m: YPM 12338–39, 12404–06, 12409, 12411, 12418 (Leenders & Watkins-Colwell 2004); Município Izalco, Cantón Cruz Grande, Finca Nuevos Horizontes (13.821°N, 89.653°W), 1150 m: YPM 12328, 12330–31, 12333–37, 12403, 12413 (Leenders & Watkins-Colwell 2004).

Norops sericeus (Hallowell 1856)
(Anolis Punto Azul)
Plate 70, Map 62, Figure 26ab

1856 *Anolis sericeus* Hallowell, Proc. Acad. Nat. Sci. Philad. 1856: 227; type locality: Jalapa, Veracruz, Mexico.
Anolis binotatus: Bocourt 1873, Ahl 1940.
Anolis sallaei: K. Schmidt 1928.
Anolis salleei: Oeser 1933.
Anolis sericeus: Mertens 1952d, Brongersma 1954b, Rand 1957, Peters & Donoso-Barros 1970, Lee 1980, 1983.
Norops sericeus: Villa et al. 1988, Köhler 2000, Dueñas et al. 2001, Köhler 2003b, Leenders 2003, Leenders & Watkins-Colwell 2004.

Plate 70: *Norops sericeus* EL SALVADOR: Ahuachapán: El Refugio (225 m). Photo: G. Köhler.

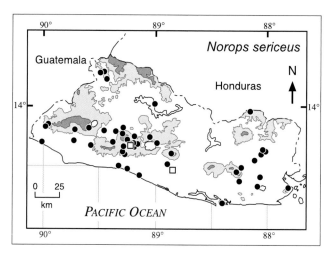

Map 62: Distribution of *Norops sericeus* in El Salvador.
Closed circles represent examined-specimen locality records; open squares are published locality records. Light shading indicates 600–1200 m elevation; dark shading indicates elevations ≥ 1200 m; large bodies of freshwater are outlined in bold, black lines.

Geographic distribution: From Tamaulipas, Mexico, to northeastern Costa Rica on the Atlantic versant, and from the Isthmus of Tehuantepec to western Costa Rica on the Pacific versant (Savage 2002).

Ecological distribution: Dry forest, pine-oak forest, and savanna between sea level and 1150 m.

Description: A medium-sized species of the genus (maximum SVL in males 47 mm, in females 44.5 mm); tail length/SVL 1.57–2.33; HL/SVL 0.23–0.28; HW/SVL 0.14–0.17; snout length/SVL 0.10–0.13; shank length/SVL 0.20–0.26; ventral scales dis-

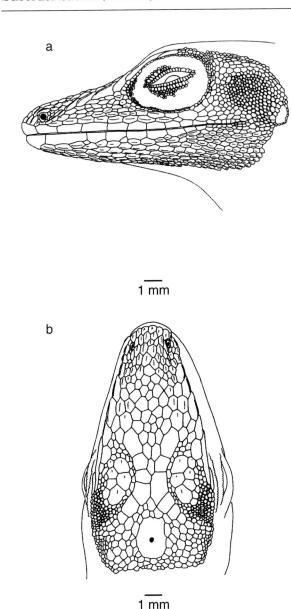

a

1 mm

b

1 mm

Figure 26: *Norops sericeus* (SMF 79235): a. lateral view of head, b. dorsal view of head.

tinctly keeled, mucronate; 16–24 rows of medial, dorsal scales distinctly enlarged; flank scales homogeneous; 0–1 scales separating supraorbital semicircles; 1–3 scales between interparietal plate and supraorbital semicircles; 5–7 rows of loreal scales; suboculars and supralabials usually in contact, rarely separated by one scale row; 6–8 supralabial scales to a point below center of eye; 21–26 lamellae under phalanges II–IV of fourth toe; no enlarged postanal scales; no deep tube-like axillary pocket; tail length/SVL 1.6–2.3; shank length/SVL 0.20–0.26. Head, body, and tail grayish

brown; females often with a distinct creamish middorsal stripe; male dewlap yellow or orange-yellow with a central blue blotch.

Natural history: E. Greenbaum (field notes) collected this species around human habitations during the day at Bosque Las Lajas, Depto. Sonsonate in July; another adult was collected 2–3 m above ground in a tree at Isla San Sebastián, Depto. Usulután in July. O. Komar (field notes) collected an adult male from a pine tree during the day in pine-oak forest at Perquín, Depto. Morazán in June. Mertens (1952d) observed several juveniles in mid-August. Rand (1957) noted this species from the ground, low bushes, and vine mats in brush-grown gullies in San Salvador, Depto. San Salvador. Campbell (1998a) noted females lay multiple clutches of a single egg over the course of the rainy season. Stafford & Meyer (2000) noted this semiar-boreal species is common in open areas in forests or near forest edges; they frequently inhabit bushes or lower branches of trees. Savage (2002) commented that Pacific versant populations of this species have a breeding period from April–September.

Specimens examined: Ahuachapán: Finca Concepción Miramar, 13°48.46´N, 89°48.03´W, 920 m: KU 290054; El Refugio, vicinity of Mariposario of Francisco Serrano, 13°49.46´N, 89°59.98´W, 225 m: SMF 79235–38; Parque Nacional El Imposible: MUHNES 912; Finca San Benito: MUHNES 1046, Río Guajapa: MUHNES 1063 (*); Barra de Santiago: KU 184130. Cuscatlán: Finca near San Martín, about 700 m: SMF 42512–13; El Playón Cujiapa: MUHNES 603; Colima Dry Forest, 14°03´N, 89°08´W, 420 m: MUHNES C–30–1392. La Libertad: Laguna de Chanmico, 480 m: SMF 42443–45, 42481, 42625; Quetzaltepeque: CAS 94796; Finca Mirasol, 900 m: SMF 42702; Los Chorros, between Nuevo San Salvador [= Santa Tecla] and Colón: SMF 42448; Finca El Paraíso, Santa Tecla: SMF 42374 (egg), 42619, 42712, 42800, 42868; Nuevo San Salvador [= Santa Tecla]: SMF 43140–42; W of La Libertad (E side Río Chilama): SMF 42405–06; Río San Antonio, 2 km E La Libertad: SMF 43093–99, 43185, 44391; Río San Antonio: SMF 45140; La Libertad: MUHNES 786; Laguna de Zapotitán, 457 m: MVZ 40047; Volcán San Salvador, "1917 Lava," 500 m: FMNH 65016; 1.8 km NE Quetzaltepeque: KU 184131. La Paz: Zacatecoluca: MUHNES 722; La Zunganera: KU 184132–33. La Unión: Punta Gorda near La Unión: SMF 43139. Morazán: Loma Tendida: MUHNES 605–09, 631–32, 634–36, 638, 640, 642, 646 (*); 3 km W of Divisadero: SMF

42994; Montecristo Mine, 213 m: MVZ 39939–45, 39950–51, 39975–80, 39982–84; 1.6 km SE Divisadero, 259 m: MVZ 40030; Divisadero: FMNH 10982, 10950–55; Perquín: KU 291351. San Miguel: San Miguel: SMF 42948; Laguna Aramuaca: SMF 44329–30; Cantón El Colorado: MUHNES 604; Laguna de Olomega, 61 m: MVZ 39946–49, 39986–91, 39993–94, 40031; Volcán de San Miguel: MCZ 57062; San Pedro: MCZ 57079. San Salvador: San Salvador, 65 Avenida Sur, Casa Reich: SMF 42216; San Salvador, Colónia America Nr. 3, Villa Margarita: SMF 42306; San Salvador, vicinity of Instituto Tropical de Investigaciones Científicas: KU 62035–36, SMF 44323–28, 51980–81 (700 m elevation); "environs from San Salvador": SMF 51748–49; Colónia Altos del Cerro near slope of San Jacinto Mountain: MUHNES C–30–1393; near Ateos N of San Salvador: MCZ 54964; San Salvador, near airport: CAS 144032–35; 1.6 km NW San Salvador: KU 42263. San Vicente: crater of Volcán de San Vicente: SMF 46813. Santa Ana: San Juan Mine, 12.1 km SE Metapán, 488 m: MVZ 40001–06, 40032; Hacienda San José: KU 67102, 6 km S Metapán: KU 184137; 6 km S Metapán, Cantón Las Piedras: KU 184134; Metapán, San Diego: MUHNES 1191–92. Sonsonate: Hacienda San Antonio, near Sonsonate: SMF 42490–93; Hacienda Chilata, 610 m: MVZ 40034–35, 40039; Bosque Las Lajas, 13°50.04´N, 89°33.56´W, 920 m: KU 289885. Usulután: Isla San Sebastián, 13°10.01´N, 88°24.49´W, 20 m: KU 289917. Depto. unknown: no specific locality: SMF 77164 (*).

Published locality records: Ahuachapán: Parque Nacional El Imposible: YPM 12391 (Leenders & Watkins-Colwell 2004). La Paz: Município Zacatecoluca, Finca La Esmeralda, 3 km E Zacatecoluca (13.483°N, 88.850°W), 115 m: YPM 12390, 12392–98 (Leenders & Watkins-Colwell 2004). San Salvador: Instituto Tropical de Investigaciones Científicas, San Salvador: RMNH 9928 (Brongersma 1954b).

Norops serranoi Köhler 1999
(Anolis de Serrano)
Plate 71, Map 63, Figure 27ab

1999 *Norops serranoi* Köhler, Salamandra 35(1): 39; type locality: Mariposario of Francisco Serrano, (13°49.46´N, 89°59.98´W), 225 m, Depto. Ahuachapán, El Salvador.
Anolis biporcatus: Oeser 1933, Ahl 1940.
Anolis lemurinus bourgeaei: Mertens 1952d,

Plate 71: *Norops serranoi* EL SALVADOR: Ahuachapán: El Refugio (225 m). Photo: G. Köhler.

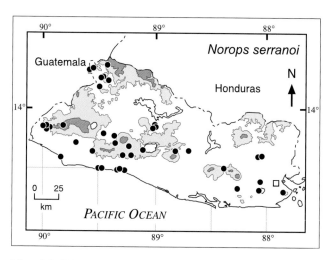

Map 63: Distribution of *Norops serranoi* in El Salvador. Closed circles represent examined-specimen locality records; open squares are published locality records. Light shading indicates 600–1200 m elevation; dark shading indicates elevations ≥ 1200 m; large bodies of freshwater are outlined in bold, black lines.

Brongersma 1954b, Rand 1957.
Anolis lemurinus lemurinus: Peters & Donoso-Barros 1970.
Norops lemurinus: Villa et al. 1988, Köhler 1996, Dueñas et al. 2001.
Norops serranoi: Köhler 1999, 2000, 2003b, Leenders 2003, Leenders & Watkins-Colwell 2004.
Geographic distribution: From Chiapas, Mexico, along the Pacific versant to eastern El Salvador (Köhler 2003b).
Ecological distribution: Dry forest, premontane evergreen forest, and subtropical humid forest between sea level and 820 m.

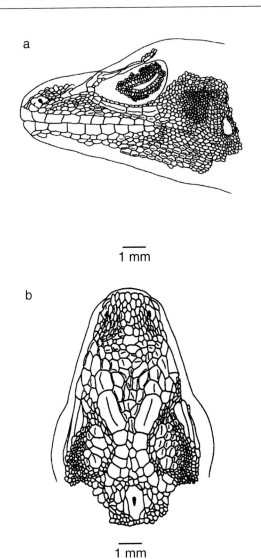

a

1 mm

b

1 mm

Figure 27: *Norops serranoi* (SMF 78834): a. lateral view of head, b. dorsal view of head.

Description: A large-sized species (maximum SVL in males 85 mm, in females 78 mm); tail length/ SVL 1.86–2.24; HL/SVL 0.25–0.27; HW/SVL 0.14–0.19; snout length/SVL 0.10–0.13; shank length/ SVL 0.26–0.30; ventral scales distinctly keeled, mucronate; 2 rows of medial dorsal scales slightly enlarged; flank scales homogeneous; 0–3 scales separating supraorbital semicircles; 2–6 scales between interparietal plate and supraorbital semicircles; 6–8 rows of loreal scales; suboculars and supralabials usually separated by one scale row, occasionally in contact; 6–8 supralabial scales to a point below center of eye; 25–31 lamellae under phalanges II–IV of fourth toe; no enlarged postanal scales; no deep tube-like axillary pocket; tail length/

SVL 1.8–2.4; shank length/SVL 0.25–0.31.

Head, body, and tail grayish brown to yellowish; male dewlap brick red, darker centrally because of suffusion with black pigment.

Natural history: G. Köhler (field notes) observed several individuals of this species sitting head-down on trunks of trees 100–150 cm above the ground in Parque Nacional El Imposible, Depto. Ahuachapán. O. Komar (field notes) recorded several adults in leaf litter next to a river during the day at Guadalupe, Depto. La Libertad in June. M. Veselý (field notes) caught an active adult sitting on a bush under a street light in the evening at Club Atami, Depto. La Libertad in May. Mertens (1952d) noted that this lizard prefers shady microhabitats. Rand (1957) collected an individual sitting on a log on the wooded side of a deep gully at Barranco del Sisimico, Depto. San Vicente in March. Fitch (1970) noted gravid females from Guatemala in May and June. Leenders & Watkins-Colwell (2004) noted juveniles in October, but only adults between December and February. One specimen's stomach contents included a large caterpillar of an arctiid moth.

Specimens examined: <u>Ahuachapán</u>: Parque Nacional El Imposible, Zona de las Escaleras, Montaña del Bálsamo: MUHNES 319; El Refugio, vicinity of Mariposario of Francisco Serrano, 13°49.46´N, 89°59.98´W, 225 m: SMF 78834–38, 78840; Parque Nacional El Imposible, Finca San Benito: MUHNES 1036, 1041; Parque Nacional El Imposible, near Podrero, La Timbona: MUHNES 1057; Parque Nacional El Imposible: MUHNES 909A, 910, 828; "cueva de cal abajo del paseo de Los Imposibles": MUHNES 350; Laguna Verde de Metapán, 13°53´N, 89°47´W, 500 m: MUHNES C–30–1394; Parque Nacional El Imposible, 13°50.50´N, 89°58.51´W, 720 m: KU 290053; Barra de Santiago: KU 184098. <u>Cuscatlán</u>: 4 km NE Tenancingo: KU 184099; 3 km E Tenancingo: KU 184106–07; Tenancingo, Copalchan: KU 184100. <u>La Libertad</u>: Club Atami (near Playa El Palmarcito, Municipio Tamanique), 10 km W La Libertad: SMF 78839; E La Libertad: SMF 77165; 7 km E La Libertad, Cantón San Diego: KU 184101–05; Cueva Hedionda, 5 km E La Libertad, on the road to San Diego: SMF 77136; Finca El Paraíso, Nuevo San Salvador [= Santa Tecla]: SMF 42997, 43145; Los Chorros, road from San Salvador to Santa Ana, near Colón, 716 m: SMF 77137; Río San Antonio, 2 km E La Libertad: SMF 43088–90; Hacienda Zapotitán, 457 m: MVZ 40067–69, 40101; Laguna de Chanmico: UMMZ 117629; 30.4 km W La Paz-San Salvador border on CA-2: KU 193024; Guadalupe, 640 m: KU 291367, MUHNES C–30–1509. Morazán: Loma Tendida: MUHNES 630, 643–44 (*); Cantón Colorado: MUHNES 633 (*); 4.8 km W Montecristo Mine, 198 m: MVZ 39981; Montecristo Mine, 213 m: MVZ 40074. San Miguel: Laguna de Aramuaca: SMF 42187; Laguna de Olomega, 61 m: MVZ 39985, 39992, 40048–60. San Salvador: San Salvador: MVZ 40070; 3 km SE Ilopango, Cantón Asino: KU 184097, 184116–17, 184124–28; 2.4 km SE Ilopango, Cantón Asino: KU 184129. Santa Ana: Laguna de Güija: SMF 44322; Hacienda San José, 800 m: SMF 43046; San Juan Mine, 12.1 km SE Metapán, 488 m: MVZ 40061–62; La Barra, 14°18´N, 89°34´W, 480 m: KU 289972; Metapán: KU 184118; Metapán, Volcán de San Diego crater: KU 184119–21; 7 km E Metapán: KU 184122–23. San Vicente: forest at km 80 on road San Salvador–San Miguel, 110 m: SMF 77139–40; Barranco del Sismico near San Vicente, 350 m: FMNH 65020. Sonsonate: Acajutla: SMF 43741; Hacienda San Antonio, 13°42´N, 89°45´W, 220 m: SMF 42188–89; Hacienda Chilata, 5 km S San Julián: SMF 77138; same locality at 610 m: MVZ 40064–66.

Published locality records: Ahuachapán: Parque Nacional El Imposible, 260–800 m: YPM 12324–26, 12447–50, 12990–91 (Leenders & Watkins-Colwell 2004). La Unión: highway W of La Unión, km 180–181 E: RMNH 9955 (Brongersma 1954b).

Norops tropidonotus (Peters 1863)
(Anolis Grande de Selva)
Plate 72, Map 64, Figure 28ab

1863 *Anolis tropidonotus* Peters, Monats. Akad. Wiss. Berlin 1863: 135; type locality: Huanusco, Veracruz, Mexico.
Norops tropidonotus: Köhler 2000, Dueñas et al. 2001, Köhler 2003b.
Geographic distribution: Lowlands of Pacific slopes of Oaxaca, Mexico, and Atlantic slope of Veracruz, Mexico, to Honduras and Nicaragua (Köhler 2003b).
Ecological distribution: Pine-oak forest (in El Salvador known only from a single specimen without elevational data).
Description: (based mostly on specimens from southwestern Honduras because only one specimen is known from El Salvador): A medium-sized species of the genus (maximum SVL in males 56 mm, in females 55 mm); tail length/SVL 1.50–1.98; HL/SVL 0.25–0.30; HW/SVL 0.15–0.20; shank length/SVL

Plate 72: *Norops tropidonotus* HONDURAS: Atlantida: Pico Bonito (120 m). Photo: G. Köhler.

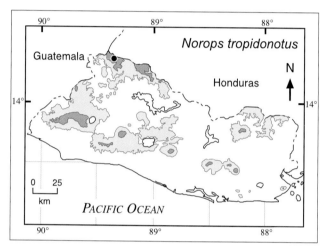

Map 64: Distribution of *Norops tropidonotus* in El Salvador.
Closed circles represent examined-specimen locality records; open squares are published locality records. Light shading indicates 600–1200 m elevation; dark shading indicates elevations ≥ 1200 m; large bodies of freshwater are outlined in bold, black lines.

0.26–0.33; ventral scales distinctly keeled, mucronate; 9–11 rows of medial dorsal scales distinctly enlarged (larger than ventral scales); flank scales homogeneous; 1–3 scales separating supraorbital semicircles; 2–3 scales between interparietal plate and supraorbital semicircles; 5–6, rarely 7, rows of loreal scales; usually 1 scale row between suboculars and supralabials, rarely in contact; 5–6 supralabial scales to a point below center of eye; 22–28 lamellae under phalanges II–IV of fourth toe; no enlarged postanal scales; a deep tube-like axillary pocket present; tail length/SVL 1.5–1.8; shank length/SVL 0.26–0.30.

Head, body, and tail grayish brown; male dewlap red-orange with an oblique dark streak.

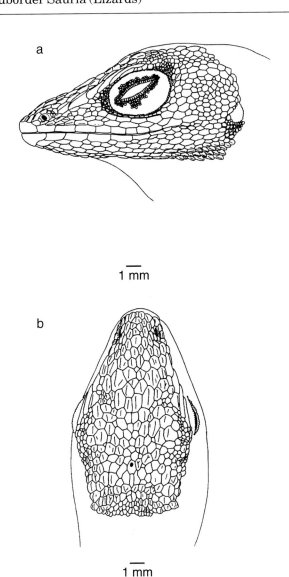

1 mm

1 mm

Figure 28: *Norops tropidonotus* (SMF 78710): a. lateral view of head, b. dorsal view of head.

Natural history: This anole can be found on the ground and on low vegetation (G. Köhler field notes). Campbell (1998a) noted this species does not bask often; females lay multiple clutches of a single egg over the course of the rainy season.
Specimens examined: <u>Santa Ana</u>: Montecristo, Majada Vieja: MUHNES 731.

Genus *Sceloporus*

This genus includes approximately 80 species that are distributed from the United States south through Central America to western Panama (Savage 2002). Three species occur in El Salvador.

Sceloporus malachiticus Cope 1864
(Lagartija Espinosa Verde)
Plate 73, Map 65

1864 *Sceloporus malachiticus* Cope, Proc. Acad. Nat. Sci. Philad. 1864: 178; type locality: "Arriba" [see comment under *Bufo coccifer*], Costa Rica.
Sceloporus malachiticus: K. Schmidt 1928, Peters & Donoso-Barros 1970, Villa et al. 1988, F. Schmidt et al. 1999, Köhler 1996, 2000, Dueñas et al. 2001, Köhler 2003b, Leenders & Watkins-Colwell 2004.
Sceloporus formosus malachiticus: Smith 1939.
Sceloporus acanthinus: K. Schmidt 1928, Ahl 1940.
Sceloporus malachiticus malachiticus: Mertens 1952d, Brongersma 1954b, Rand 1957.
Sceloporus acanthinus acanthinus: Peters & Donoso-Barros 1970.
Sceloporus acanthinus lunaei: Peters & Donoso-Barros 1970.
Sceloporus acanthinus-like: Stuart 1971.
Geographic distribution: From western Honduras to western Panama (Savage 2002).
Ecological distribution: Dry forest, cloud forest, and pine-oak forest between 500 and 2480 m, rarely as low as 200 m.
Description: A medium-sized species of the genus (maximum SVL in males 98.2 mm [Leenders & Watkins-Colwell 2004], in females 94 mm) with a robust body; tail length/SVL 0.75–1.34; HL/SVL 0.20–0.26; HW/SVL 0.14–0.21; snout length/SVL 0.08–0.10; shank length/SVL 0.18–0.23; usually a single canthal scale; 3–5 internasal scales; 9–19 lorilabial scales; 1–2 scales between subocular and supralabial scales; 5–7 supralabial scales; 5–8 infralabial scales; 28–37 dorsal scales between interparietal plate and level of posterior insertion of hind limbs; 28–41 scales around midbody; 12–17 femoral pores on each side; 18–25 lamellae under fourth toe; distinctly enlarged postanal scales in males; tail length/SVL 0.8–1.3; shank length/SVL 0.18–0.23.

The dorsal surfaces of the head and body of adult male *Sceloporus malachiticus* are bright green, whereas the lateral neck and the complete tail are turquoise blue; a black nuchal collar is separated dorsomedially by 7–12 green scales; an orange yellow blotch is usually present on the throat; two large blue blotches on the chest are medially bordered by black. Females and juveniles are less colorful than adult males and show many diffuse dark brown blotches on a pale grayish brown ground color on the dorsal surfaces of the

Plate 73: *Sceloporus malachiticus* EL SALVADOR: San Vicente: Finca El Carmen, Volcán de San Vicente (1319 m). Photo: M. Veselý.

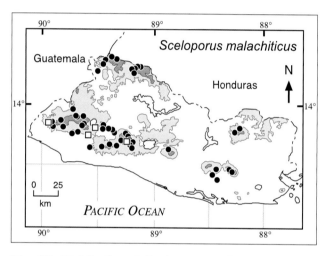

Map 65: Distribution of *Sceloporus malachiticus* in El Salvador.
Closed circles represent examined-specimen locality records; open squares are published locality records. Light shading indicates 600–1200 m elevation; dark shading indicates elevations ≥ 1200 m; large bodies of freshwater are outlined in bold, black lines.

head, body, and tail; the ventral surfaces are pale cream.

Taxonomic comments: The taxonomy of this species in El Salvador may be subject to major revisions in the near future. Smith et al. (2001) stated that *S. acanthinus* ranges into El Salvador, whereas Köhler & Heimes (2002), partly based on advice by E. Smith (pers. comm.), referred all malachite *Sceloporus* in El Salvador to *S. malachiticus*, and we have used the latter name herein.

Natual history: E. Greenbaum (field notes) recorded this species at nearly every human-disturbed habitat visited in the rainy season from July–August; individuals were observed crawling on

human habitations during sunny days. W. E. Duellman (field notes) collected an adult on a tree in cloud forest at Cerro Montecristo, Depto. Santa Ana in February. Mertens (1952d) noted this species on trees, fence posts, and on the roofs of houses in El Salvador. Usually a single male would inhabit a tree, which it would defend from rivals. Rand (1957) also reported territorial behavior in Salvadoran animals. F. Schmidt et al. (1999) noted juveniles in January, April, October, and November in El Salvador. Savage (2002) commented that the diet consists of arthropods. This species is territorial and viviparous; breeding is seasonal (rainy season) at low to mid-elevations and year-round at high elevations.

Specimens examined: <u>Ahuachapán</u>: Finca Concepción Miramar, 13°48.46′N, 89°48.03′W, 920 m: KU 289933; Cerro de Apaneca, 1067 m: MVZ 40172; 1524 m: MVZ 40168–71; Finca Las Delicias, 13°52′N, 89°53′W, 1200 m: KU 290065–66, MUHNES C–30–1385; Finca La Esperanza, 13°49′N, 89°52′W, 1000 m: MUHNES C–30–1382; Finca Santa Luisa, 13°49′N, 89°52′W, 900 m: MUHNES C–30–1383. <u>Chalatenango</u>: Los Esesmiles, Cerro El Pital, 2195 m: MVZ 40131; same locality at 2225 m: MVZ 40123–24, 40140–51; same locality at 2438 m: 40130, 40132–39; same locality at 1829–2438 m: FMNH 10958–62; San José del Sacaré, 1097 m: FMNH 10970–71; 2.7 km SE La Palma, Río Numapa: KU 184222; 6 km ENE La Palma, Cantón Los Pozos, 1500 m: KU 184224; Cerro El Pital, 2180 m: MUHNES C–30–1515–16, MUHNES C–30–1518, KU 291249; same locality at 2480 m: YPM 12481. <u>La Libertad</u>: Finca El Paraíso near Nuevo San Salvador [= Santa Tecla]: SMF 42205, 42237–41, 42889–90, 43151, 46927; Laguna Chanmico: SMF 42442, 42478–80; Chanmico: SMF 46883; San Andrés, km 35 on the road from San Salvador–Santa Ana, 490 m: SMF 75725–26, 75848–49; the highest peak above Finca Los Angeles, 1600 m: SMF 42893; Nuevo San Salvador [= Santa Tecla]: SMF 43154–56; Finca La Peña, 900 m: SMF 43167 (*); Ciudad Arce: SMF 43172; Hacienda Zapotitán, Río Sucio, 457 m: MVZ 40173–77; Nueva San Salvador, 1300 m: KU 184223; Finca La Giralda, 13°39.34′N, 89°22.47′W, 1080 m: KU 289948, 289965. <u>Morazán</u>: W slope Mt. Cacahuatique, 1341 m: MVZ 40125; N slope Mt. Cacahuatique, 1150 m: KU 291393; same locality at 1311 m: MVZ 40189; same locality at 1341 m: MVZ 4019193; same locality at 1360 m: MUHNES C–30–1517; same locality at 1375 m: KU 291314; same locality at

1402 m: MVZ 40190. San Miguel: Volcán de San Miguel, 13°26.2′N, 88°16.2′W, 1600 m: SMF 78354–56; Volcán San Miguel, 1800 m: SMF 42075; same locality at 740 m: YPM 12480; same locality at 1670 m: YPM 12472. San Salvador: San Salvador, CAMRS: USNM 167206–08, 521723; Los Planes de Renderos near San Salvador: SMF 42073–74; San Salvador, Instituto Tropical de Investigaciones Científicas, ca. 700 m: KU 62050–59, SMF 42077–81, 43173–74, 44343–45, 47836–42, 48249, 49689, 49830, 54329, 55781, 58487–89, 59555, 75729–31, 75853, 77395, UMMZ 117459; Barranco near 65 Avenida Sur: SMF 42264–65, 42892; San Salvador: ZMB 35674–83; same locality at 750 m: FMNH 65013; same locality at 670 m: FMNH 65002–05; Mejicanos: KU 289841; San Salvador, Parque Balboa: UMMZ 123018; 1.6 km NW San Salvador: KU 42001. San Vicente: Finca El Carmen, Volcán de San Vicente, 1319 m: SMF 75850, 78357–58, 78360. Santa Ana: Hacienda San Diego, NW of San Salvador: SMF 42510–11; Chalchuapa, Laguna Cuscachapa, 13°58.8′N, 89°40.5′W, 690 m: SMF 78359; Cerro Verde, 13°49.5′N, 89°37.4′W, 1940 m: SMF 78353; Hacienda San José near Metapán: SMF 42076, 77396, UMMZ 117461; Metapán: KU 184215; Hacienda Los Planes, 1830 m: SMF 43029–30; Hacienda Montecristo, NE from Metapán mountains, 2150–2200 m: SMF 44342, 75727–28, 75854–56, 77394, 77397–98, KU 62060–62, 67265–69, UMMZ 117460; same locality at 1650 m: MUHNES C–30–1389; Cerro del Aguila, 1676 m: MVZ 40178–80; Finca El Milagro, 13°53.29′N, 89°37.17′W, 1300 m: KU 289780, 289787–89, 289790, 289797, MUHNES C–30–1386–88. Sonsonate: 1.6 km NE Cerro de Los Naranjos, 1585 m: MVZ 40128, 40182–84; same locality at 1646 m: MVZ 40186–88; same locality at 1768 m: MVZ 40181; same locality at 1829 m: MVZ 40185; Hacienda San Antonio: SMF 42072; Hacienda Chilata, 5 km S San Julián, 700 m: SMF 75847, 610 m: MVZ 40122, 40126–27, 40160–67, 40257–64, FMNH 10991; Cráter del Volcán de Izalco: KU 184217; Izalco: USNM 192598, 521721–22. Border of Santa Ana and Sonsonate: Hacienda Las Brumas, Cerro Verde: SMF 75846 (2000 m), 75851–52 (1800 m). Usulután: Cerro del Tigre, 13°28.37′N, 88°26.21′W, 1100 m: KU 289856; Volcán de Usulután: KU 184216; 3.5 km E Usulután: KU 193025.

Published locality records: Ahuachapán: Parque Nacional El Imposible: YPM 12350, 12356–57 (Leenders 2003, Leenders & Watkins-Colwell 2004); Município San Pedro Puxtla, Cantón La

Concepción, Cooperativa Concepción Miramar (13.810°N, 89.807°W), 950 m: YPM 12306–10, 12349, 12353, 12355, 12359–60 (Leenders & Watkins-Colwell 2004). Chalatenango: Cerro El Pital, 2480 m: YPM 12481 (Leenders & Watkins-Colwell 2004). San Miguel: Cantón El Volcán, N slope Volcán San Miguel, Finca Santa Isabel (13.468°N, 88.267°W), 800 m: YPM 12472, 12480 (Leenders & Watkins-Colwell 2004). San Salvador: Instituto Tropical de Investigaciones Científicas, San Salvador: RMNH 9931–32 (Brongersma 1954b); San Salvador: YPM 12361 (Leenders & Watkins-Colwell 2004). Sonsonate: Município Izalco, Cantón Las Lajas, Bosque Las Lajas (13.829°N, 89.567°W), 750 m: YPM 12351, 12354 (Leenders & Watkins-Colwell 2004); Município Izalco, Cantón Cruz Grande, Finca Nuevos Horizontes (13.821°N, 89.653°W), 1250 m: YPM 12352 (Leenders & Watkins-Colwell 2004).

Sceloporus squamosus Bocourt 1874
(Lagartija Espinosa Delgada)
Plate 74, Map 66

1874 *Sceloporus squamosus* Bocourt, Miss. Sci. Mex., Rept.: 212; type locality: Guatemala, Antigua, 1500 m; and embayment of Río Nagualate, Guatemala.
Sceloporus fulvus: Bocourt 1874, McLain 1899, K. Schmidt 1928.
Sceloporus squamosus: Smith 1939, Mertens 1952d, Brongersma 1954b, Rand 1957, Peters & Donoso-Barros 1970, Villa et al. 1988, Köhler et al. 1998, Köhler 2000, Dueñas et al. 2001, Köhler 2003b, Leenders 2003, Leenders & Watkins-Colwell 2004.

Geographic distribution: From western Chiapas, Mexico, along the Pacific versant to northwestern Costa Rica; dry valleys on Atlantic versant of Guatemala and Honduras (Savage 2002, Köhler 2003b).

Ecological distribution: Dry forest, premontane evergreen forest, subtropical humid forest, savanna, and pine-oak forest between sea level and 1500 m.

Description: A small species of the genus (maximum SVL in males 58 mm, in females 59 mm) with a slender body; tail length/SVL 1.65–2.46; HL/SVL 0.21–0.27; HW/SVL 0.15–0.20; shank length/SVL 0.22–0.29; usually a single canthal scale; 4–6 postrostral scales; 3–7 lorilabial scales; 1 scale between subocular and supralabial scales; 4–6 supralabial scales; 29–37 dorsal scales between interparietal plate and a level of posterior insertion

Plate 74: *Sceloporus squamosus* EL SALVADOR: Ahuachapán: El Refugio (225 m). Photo: G. Köhler.

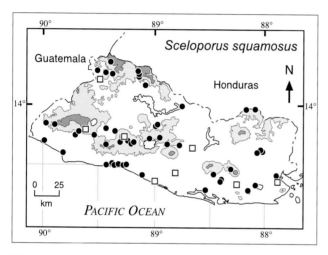

Map 66: Distribution of *Sceloporus squamosus* in El Salvador.

Closed circles represent examined-specimen locality records; open squares are published locality records. Light shading indicates 600–1200 m elevation; dark shading indicates elevations ≥ 1200 m; large bodies of freshwater are outlined in bold, black lines.

of hind limbs; 35–43 scales around midbody; 3–7 femoral pores on each side; 19–26 lamellae under fourth toe; distinctly enlarged postanal scales in about 41% of males; tail length/SVL 1.7–2.5; shank length/SVL 0.22–0.29.

Dorsum grayish brown or walnut-brown with a series of 7–9 dark brown chevrons; a dorsolateral creamish longitudinal stripe begins at level of tympanum and disappears at base of tail; the flanks are usually darker than the dorsal surfaces and show numerous creamish spots; ventral surfaces of head and body are uniformly cream to pale brown; there are no colorful blotches on the chest in males.

Natural history: O. Komar (field notes) recorded

several adults in pine-oak forest during the day at Perquín, Depto. Morazán in June. Mertens (1952d) noted that this lizard is commonly observed on fence posts and tree trunks exposed to full sunlight in El Salvador, usually not higher than 1 m above the ground. Rand (1957) noted this "strictly terrestrial" species is common in grassy pastures and scrub-grown gullies in and around San Salvador, Depto. San Salvador. Savage (2002) commented that this species is diurnal and mainly terrestrial. Leenders & Watkins-Colwell (2004) noted numerous juveniles from November through February in El Salvador.

Specimens examined: Ahuachapán: El Refugio, vicinity of Mariposario of Francisco Serrano, 13°49.46′N, 89°59.98′W, 225 m: SMF 79241–42; Parque Nacional El Imposible, La Fincona, 13°50.8′N, 89°58.8′W, 720 m: SMF 77919–20, KU 289765, MUHNES C–30–1361; Finca Santa Luisa, 13°49′N, 89°52′W, 900 m: KU 290062; Barra de Santiago: KU 184225. Cabañas: 8.9 km W Sensuntepeque, 457 m: MVZ 40256. Chalatenango: La Chorrera: SMF 42086; La Palma: SMF 42091–93; Hacienda El Morito, 2.3 km E desvío to Dulce Nombre de María on road from San Salvador–Chalatenango: SMF 43351–52; near La Palma, 14°17.1′N, 89°08.2′W: SMF 77914; San José del Sacaré, 1097 m: FMNH 10967–69; 3.5 km S La Palma: KU 184250–52. Cuscatlán: Cerro de las Pavas, Municipio Cojutepeque: SMF 42087; Tenancingo, Copalchan: KU 184229; 2 km E Tenancingo, Copalchan: KU 184230–31; 4 km E Tenancingo: KU 184232, 184234–35; Tenancingo, Cantón Huilihuishte: KU 184233. La Libertad: Playa de las Flores: SMF 42088–90 (*); Finca Los Cedros: SMF 42379, 42908–20, 43133–36; W Río Chilama at La Libertad: SMF 42404, 42891; Laguna de Chanmico: SMF 42441, 42622–23, 42476–77; Río San Antonio, 2 km E La Libertad: SMF 43081–86, 43149; El Grito, Finca Los Angeles, Cumbre de Jayaque, 1510 m: SMF 44350; La Libertad: SMF 47080; 4 km E La Libertad: SMF 52042–43; near La Libertad, 13°30.2′N, 89°25.0′W: SMF 77915; Hacienda Zapotitán, Río Sucio, 457 m: MVZ 40265–66; 4.2 km W Nuevo San Salvador [= Santa Tecla]: KU 62064; 6 km W La Libertad, 91 m N of point where it crosses Carretera Litoral: AMNH 81810. La Paz: La Zunganera: KU 184236–47. La Unión: km 194 on Carretera Roosevelt, N La Unión: SMF 42954. Morazán: Morazán mountains, road to Honduras, 13°58.5′N, 88°07.8′W: SMF 77916–17; Montecristo Mine, 213 m: MVZ 40207–17, 40221–25, 40228–30,

40240–41; 4.8 km W Montecristo Mine, 198 m: MVZ 40218–20; Divisadero, 198 m: MVZ 40226; Gigante Mine near Divisadero: FMNH 10985; Perquín: KU 290026–29, 291340–41, 291360–61, MUHNES C–30–1521, C–30–1527. San Miguel: NW slope Volcán San Miguel, 540 m: SMF 42947, MCZ 57072; San Pedro: MCZ 57068; Laguna de Olomega, 61 m: MVZ 40233–36, 40238, 40242–47. San Salvador: Instituto Tropical de Investigaciones Científicas: SMF 42082–83, KU 62063; Apulo at Lago de Ilopango: SMF 43148; San Salvador, near Airport: CAS 144031; San Salvador, 700 m: FMNH 65006–07; same locality at 670 m: FMNH 65008–09; San Salvador, CAMRS: USNM 167209. Santa Ana: above Hacienda San José: SMF 42464–65; San Juan Mine, 12.1 km SE Metapán, 488 m: MVZ 40248–55; 6 km S Metapán: KU 184248–49, 184253; Municipio de Metapán, ca. Laguna Güija, 450 m: YPM 12471. San Vicente: above Barranca del Sisimico, road from San Salvador–Río Lempa (bridge): SMF 42942–43; Volcán San Vicente, road from Tepetitán to El Carmen, near Tepetitán, 13°57.7′N, 88°50.4′W: SMF 77918. Sonsonate: Hacienda San Antonio near Sonsonate: SMF 42084–85, 42258, 42486, 42502–03, 42934; Hacienda Cuyan-Cuya at Izalco, 380 m: SMF 43001; Finca La Joya at km 48 on road from San Salvador–Sonsonate, 587 m: SMF 44347–49; Acajutla: SMF 52054, CAS-SU 3525, 3529. Usulután: El Triunfo: SMF 42094; Santa María: MCZ 57074–75; Volcán de Usulután: KU 184226, 184228; 3.5 km E Usulután: KU 193026–29.

Published locality records: Ahuachapán: Parque Nacional El Imposible: YPM 12368, 12370–71, 12373–77 (Leenders & Watkins-Colwell 2004). La Libertad: Volcán San Salvador, "1917 Lava," 500–700 m (Rand 1957); Río Conchalío, on bank near the crossing with the coastal road, W of La Libertad: RMNH 9936 (Brongersma 1954b). La Paz: 6 km N Los Blancos (Rand 1957); Município Zacatecoluca, Finca La Esmeralda, 3 km E Zacatecoluca (13.483°N, 88.850°W), 115 m: YPM 12372, 12378 (Leenders & Watkins-Colwell 2004). La Unión: along highway W of La Unión, km 180–181 E: RMNH 9937 (Brongersma 1954b). San Miguel: Laguna Aramuaca: RMNH 9938 (Brongersma 1954b). Santa Ana: Município Metapán, E side Volcán San Diego, Area Protegida San Diego y La Barra (14.262°N, 89.470°W), 450 m: YPM 12471 (Leenders & Watkins-Colwell 2004). San Vicente: eastern part of virgin forest S of Pan American Hwy at km 80–81 E: RMNH 9934 (*) (Brongersma 1954b). Sonsonate: Município Izalco, Cantón Cruz

Grande, Finca Nuevos Horizontes (13.821°N, 89.653°W), 1250 m: YPM 12315–19, 12369 (Leenders & Watkins-Colwell 2004).

Sceloporus variabilis Wiegmann 1834
(Lagartija Espinosa Panza Rosada)
Plate 75, Map 67

1834 *Sc[eloporus] variabilis* Wiegmann, Herpetol. Mex.: 51; type locality: Mexico.
Sceloporus variabilis: K. Schmidt 1928, Villa et al. 1988, Köhler 2000, Dueñas et al. 2001, Köhler 2003b.
Sceloporus variabilis olloporus: Smith 1937, 1939, Mertens 1952d, Brongersma 1954b, Rand 1957, Peters & Donoso-Barros 1970, Smith et al. 1993.
Sceloporus variabilis variabilis: Mather & Sites 1985.

Geographic distribution: From southern Texas, USA, to Nicaragua (exclusive of Yucatán Peninsula) on the Atlantic versant; from Oaxaca, Mexico, to northwestern Costa Rica on the Pacific versant (Savage 2002).

Ecological distribution: Dry forest, pine-oak forest, and savanna between sea level and 1600 m.

Description: A medium-sized species of the genus (maximum SVL in males 71.1 mm [Leenders & Watkins-Colwell 2004], in females 62 mm) with a stout body; tail length/SVL 1.18–1.70; HL/SVL 0.22–0.24; HW/SVL 0.17–0.20; shank length/SVL 0.24–0.28; usually 2 canthal scales; 4–7 postrostral scales; 5–12 lorilabial scales; 1 scale between subocular and supralabial scales; 4–6 supralabial scales; 50–60 dorsal scales between interparietal plate and level of posterior insertion of hind limbs; 50–75 scales around midbody; 9–11 femoral pores on each side; 19–24 lamellae under fourth toe; distinctly enlarged postanal scales in about 80% of the males; tail length/SVL 1.4–1.7; shank length/SVL 0.21–0.28.

On a grayish brown or walnut-brown ground color a series of 9–11 pairs of dark brown paramedian blotches on the dorsum, bordered by cream dorsolateral longitudinal stripes that begin at level of eye and disappear on base of tail; usually a vertebral pale cream stripe is indicated; the flanks are usually uniform brown in females, but interrupted by numerous pale cream flecks in males; adult males have pink ventral blotches that are bordered by black; in females the lateral neck region is usually orange-red. Rand (1957) noted smaller individuals have a bright red tail.

Plate 75: *Sceloporus variabilis* MEXICO: Chiapas: Cañon de Sumidero. Photo: G. Köhler.

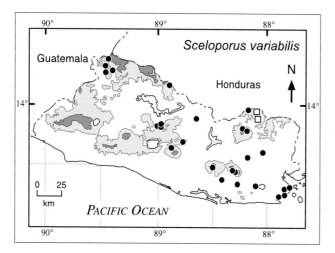

Map 67: Distribution of *Sceloporus variabilis* in El Salvador.
Closed circles represent examined-specimen locality records; open squares are published locality records. Light shading indicates 600–1200 m elevation; dark shading indicates elevations ≥ 1200 m; large bodies of freshwater are outlined in bold, black lines.

Natural history: E. Greenbaum (field notes) collected this species during the day in pine-oak forest at Perquín, Depto. Morazán in August; M. Veselý collected specimens from this same locality in May; O. Komar (field notes) collected adults and juveniles in the same locality in June. Mertens (1952d) noted that this lizard is commonly observed on natural walls, rocks, and fallen logs, rarely on fences and tree trunks, but always exposed to full sunlight in El Salvador. Rand (1957) commented this species was common in the rocky floor and heavily wooded sides of a steep gully at Barranco del Sisimico, Depto. San Vicente in March. Stafford & Meyer (2000) noted females lay eggs in loose soil at the end of the dry season or beginning of the wet season. Savage (2002) noted this diurnal species preys upon arthropods; females lay multiple

clutches of 1–5 eggs, mostly in the rainy season.
Specimens examined: <u>Cabañas</u>: Sensuntepeque, 838 m: MVZ 40205–06. <u>Chalatenango</u>: Carrizal, Río Sumpul: SMF 43150. <u>Cuscatlán</u>: Tenancingo, Río Tizapa: KU 184255, 184257–60; Tenancingo, Río Quezalapa: KU 184261; 2.8 km NE Tenancingo, Río Quezalapa: KU 184264–65; 3 km E Tenancingo, Río Quezalapa: KU 184266. <u>La Unión</u>: Punta Gorda near La Unión: SMF 42949–53, 43111–12; Volcán Conchagua, 13°16.9´N, 87°50.9´W, 1000 m: SMF 81287–88; El Cacao, 13°14.4´N, 87°51.6´W, 30 m: SMF 81289–90; Hacienda del Cipres, La Billal, Carretera Litoral, km 180: MVZ 143990–92. <u>Morazán</u>: about 5 km NE of Perquín, 13°58.5´N, 88°07.8´W, 1000 m: SMF 81291–92; Perquín: MUHNES 1217; Perquín, 13°57.17´N, 88°10.01´W, 1150 m: KU 290014–15, 290026–29, 291336–37, 291342–45, MUHNES C–30–1362–65, C–30–1520, C–30–1528–29; E slope Mt. Cacahuatique, 1280 m: MVZ 40194; N slope Mt. Cacahuatique, 1311 m: MVZ 40196; same locality at 1372 m: MVZ 40198; same locality at 1402 m: MVZ 40195, 40197, 40232; 1.6 km SE Divisadero, 259 m: MVZ 40231. <u>San Miguel</u>: Volcán de San Miguel, 13°26.2´N, 88°16.2´W, 1600 m: MCZ 57077–78, SMF 81312; Volcán de San Miguel, 720 m: KU 291279–80, 291284; Volcán de San Miguel, 740 m: KU 291386, MUHNES C–30–1525–26; same locality at 1450 m: KU 291386, 291391, MUHNES C–30–1519, C–30–1522–23; Laguna de Aramvaca: SMF 42096, 44356; Laguna El Jocotal, lava field behind Borbollón village: 70 m: SMF 44354–55; Laguna de Olomega, 61 m: MVZ 40199–204, 40237, 40239; 10 km NNE San Miguel, San Antonio Chávez: KU 184254, 184256, 184267. <u>Santa Ana</u>: above Hacienda San José, 7 km N of Metapán: SMF 42453–54; 6 km S Metapán: KU 184268; 7 km SE Metapán: KU 184269. <u>San Vicente</u>: km 67.5 road San Salvador–Lempa; above Barranca del Sisimico, 480 m: SMF 42994; Finca El Carmen, E part of Volcán San Vicente, 1319 m: SMF 44353, 81293–94. <u>Usulután</u>: Santa María: MCZ 57076.
Published locality records: <u>Morazán</u>: Município Arambala, Cantón Cumaro, Río Sapo (13.959°N, 88.132°W): YPM 7231 (Leenders & Watkins-Colwell 2004); Município Arambala, Cantón Cumaro, Río Negro (13.977°N, 88.129°W): YPM 14012 (Leenders & Watkins-Colwell 2004). <u>San Salvador</u>: San Salvador, 670 m (Rand 1957). Because *Sceloporus squamosus* is common in San Salvador and there are no proximate records for *S. variabilis*, this sight record is most likely erroneous and it is not mapped.

Family Scincidae

This nearly cosmopolitan family of lizards includes approximately 1400 species (ca. 126 genera) on every continent (absent from high latitudes) except Antarctica. This family has colonized the New World only a few times and is relatively poor in species richness (ca. 45 species) compared to the Old World. Like geckos, skinks have the ability to autotomize their tails to escape predators (Pianka 2003b). There are three genera in El Salvador.

Genus *Mabuya*

As currently defined, this genus includes approximately 85 species that are found in the New World, Africa (including Madagascar), and Asia (Savage 2002). However, a recent study suggested that this genus is not monophyletic, and the 15 species of New World *Mabuya* might be restricted to their own genus in future taxonomic changes (Honda et al. 2003). One species occurs in El Salvador.

Mabuya unimarginata Cope 1862
(Salamanqueza Vivípara)
Plate 76, Map 68

1862 *Mabuia unimarginata* Cope, Proc. Acad. Nat. Sci. Philad. 1862: 187; type locality: Panama.
Mabuya agilis: K. Schmidt 1928.
Mabuya mabouya mabouya: Ahl 1940, Brongersma 1954b.
Mabuya mabuya: Mertens 1952d.
Mabuya brachypodus: Taylor 1956.
Mabuya mabouya alliacea: Peters & Donoso-Barros 1970.
Mabuya unimarginata: Villa et al. 1988, Köhler 2000, Dueñas et al. 2001, Köhler 2003b, Leenders 2003, Leenders & Watkins-Colwell 2004.
Geographic distribution: From Colima and Veracruz, Mexico, to Panama (Savage 2002).
Ecological distribution: Dry forest, premontane evergreen forest, subtropical humid forest, savanna, and pine-oak forest between sea level and 1390 m.
Description: A large skink (SVL of largest specimen examined 83 mm); tail length/SVL 1.31–1.97; HL/SVL 0.16–0.21; HW/SVL 0.12–0.17; snout length/SVL 0.05–0.09; axilla–groin distance/SVL 0.48–0.58; limbs strong, well developed; shank

Plate 76: *Mabuya unimarginata* EL SALVADOR: Ahuachapán: El Refugio (225 m). Photo: G. Köhler.

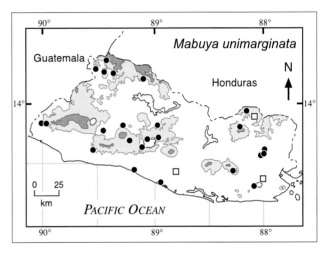

Map 68: Distribution of *Mabuya unimarginata* in El Salvador.
Closed circles represent examined-specimen locality records; open squares are published locality records. Light shading indicates 600–1200 m elevation; dark shading indicates elevations ≥ 1200 m; large bodies of freshwater are outlined in bold, black lines.

length/SVL 0.11–0.12; forelimb length/SVL 0.07–0.09; hind limb length/SVL 0.25–0.33; lamellae beneath 4th toe 12–18; body scales smooth; number of scale rows at midbody 30–34; number of scales from parietals to above vent 50–60; ventral scales in axilla–vent distance 32–38; eyelids movable, lower eyelid with transparent disc.

Dorsal ground color brown, sometimes spotted with black posteriorly and on base of tail; a broad dark brown lateral stripe extending from nostril to base of tail, bordered laterally by cream line beginning on tip of snout and extending through ear opening to groin; chin and sides of body brownish black for a width of 1–3 scales, then becoming lighter and fusing with pale cream or yellowish coloration on ventral side of head, body, tail, and legs; upper surface of legs brown with scattered lighter and black spots. Some of the MVZ specimens have a cream line just above the brown stripe that is 1–2 scales thick.

Natural history: E. Greenbaum (field notes) encountered an individual of this species that was sunning itself in a clearing at Parque Nacional El Imposible, Depto. Ahuachapán in July. O. Komar (field notes) collected several individuals in pine-oak forest at Perquín, Depto. Morazán in June. Another individual was collected in a coffee plantation during the day at Volcán de San Miguel, Depto. San Miguel in July. M. Veselý collected specimens at El Refugio, Depto. Ahuachapán in June. Mertens (1952d) noted that this lizard is found on fence posts, rock walls, and around human habitations in El Salvador. Stafford & Meyer (2000) noted this species is common around human-disturbed habitats, but will climb tree trunks in natural habitats. Savage (2002) noted this species feeds upon arthropods. Breeding occurs in the middle of the rainy season, and 4–6 live young are born at a time.

Specimens examined: Ahuachapán: El Refugio, vicinity of Mariposario of Francisco Serrano, 13°49.46´N, 89°59.98´W, 225 m: SMF 79021, 79023–26, 81342; Parque Nacional El Imposible, San Benito, near Río Guayapa 740 m: KU 289839. Chalatenango: Hacienda El Morito, road San Salvador–Chalatenango, 2.3 km E after the turnoff to Dulce Nombre de María: SMF 44390. Cuscatlán: Cojutepeque, 700 m: MUHNES C–30–1218, Tenancingo, La Laguneta at El Puente: KU 184348. La Libertad: Hacienda Zapotitán, Río Sucio, 457 m: MVZ 40393; 1.8 km NE Quetzaltepeque, Cantón Platanillos: KU 184350. La Paz: Fluker Farm, desvío a La Herradura: MUHNES C–30–1349; La Zunganera: KU 184351–55. Morazán: Montecristo Mine, 213 m: MVZ 40387, 40394; 4.8 km W Montecristo Mine, 198 m: MVZ 40388; N slope Mt. Cacahuatique, 1372 m: MVZ 40395; same locality at 1390 m: MUHNES C–30–1497; Divisadero: FMNH 10972; Perquín: KU 291346, MUHNES C–30–1495–96. San Miguel: Laguna de Olomega, 61 m: MVZ 40389; Volcán de San Miguel, 800 m: YPM 12470; Volcán de San Miguel, 900 m: KU 291283. San Salvador: Apulo, Lago de Ilopango: SMF 42416; San Diego: ZMB 35660; San Salvador: UMMZ 117649; 3 km SE Ilopango, Cantón Asino: KU 184349, 184356–63. Santa Ana: Laguna de Güija: SMF 44389; Hacienda San José, 7 km N of Metapán: SMF 43131; San Juan Mine, 12.1 km SE Metapán, 488 m: MVZ 40390; 6 km S Metapán: KU 184364. Sonsonate: Hacienda Chilata, 610 m: MVZ 40391–92.

Published locality records: Ahuachapán: Parque Nacional El Imposible: YPM 12311, 12444–46. La Paz: Munícipio Zacatecoluca, Finca La Esmeralda, 3 km E Zacatecoluca (13.483°N, 88.850°W), 115 m: YPM 12443 (Leenders & Watkins-Colwell 2004). La Unión: 5 km N of Olomega: RMNH 9947 (Brongersma 1954b). Morazán: Munícipio Arambala, Cantón Cumaro, Río Sapo (13.959°N, 88.132°W): YPM 14002 (Leenders & Watkins-Colwell 2004). San Miguel: Cantón El Volcán, N slope Volcán San Miguel, Finca Santa Isabel (13.468°N, 88.267°W), 800 m: YPM 12470 (Leenders & Watkins-Colwell 2004).

Genus *Mesoscincus*

Based on a phylogenetic analysis of taxa that were traditionally grouped under the generic name *Eumeces*, Griffith et al. (2000) provided evidence that this assemblage was not a natural grouping. Consequently, they split *Eumeces* (*sensu lato*) into several genera. According to this new classification, one Central American species (*E. sumichrasti*) remains in the genus *Eumeces* whereas two other species (*Mesoscincus managuae* and *M. schwartzei*) are assigned to a new genus. The two members of the genus *Mesoscincus* are distributed from the Yucatán Peninsula and Tabasco, Mexico, to northwestern Costa Rica (Köhler 2003b). Only *M. managuae* occurs in El Salvador.

Mesoscincus managuae (Dunn 1933)
(Salamanqueza de Managua)
Plate 77, Map 69

1933 *Eumeces managuae* Dunn, Proc. Biol. Soc. Washington 46: 67; type locality: "campo de aviación," Managua, Nicaragua.
Eumeces managuae: Reeder 1990.
Mesoscincus managuae: Greenbaum et al. 2002a, Köhler 2003b, Leenders 2003.
Geographic distribution: From western El Salvador and southern Honduras to northwestern Costa Rica (Greenbaum et al. 2002a, Savage 2002, Köhler 2003b).
Ecological distribution: Dry forest between sea level and 750 m.
Description: A large skink, largest specimen from El Salvador has SVL 120 mm (Leenders & Watkins-Colwell 2004); morphometric data available for one specimen: tail length/SVL 1.58; HL/SVL 0.16; HW/SVL 0.11; snout length/SVL 0.07; axilla–groin

Plate 77: *Mesoscincus managuae* EL SALVADOR: Ahuachapán: Parque Nacional El Imposible, San Benito (750 m). Photo: T. Leenders.

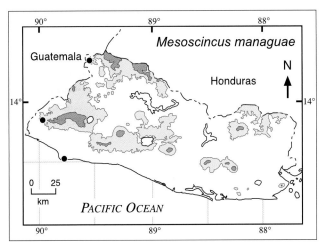

Map 69: Distribution of *Mesoscincus managuae* in El Salvador.
Closed circles represent examined-specimen locality records; open squares are published locality records. Light shading indicates 600–1200 m elevation; dark shading indicates elevations ≥ 1200 m; large bodies of freshwater are outlined in bold, black lines.

distance/SVL 0.58; limbs well developed; shank length/SVL 0.09; forelimb length/SVL 0.20; hind limb length/SVL 0.28; lamellae beneath 4th toe 12; body scales smooth; vertebral dorsal scale row enlarged, about 2–3 times wider than adjacent scales; number of scale rows around midbody 17; number of dorsal scales from parietals to above vent 65; ventral scales in axilla–vent distance 40; eyelids movable, no transparent disc in lower eyelid.

Dorsal ground color brown, six well-defined black longitudinal stripes present on dorsum and sides of body; two dorsal stripes on the row of enlarged medial scales; dorsolateral stripes thinner than those on top of dorsum; lateral stripes turning lighter ventrally and grading into pale cream coloration of venter. Head scales with black spots on their posterior portions; chin and throat scales pale yellow; dorsal and lateral black longitudinal stripes on tail fusing posteriorly; two thinner stripes present on ventral side of tail, which is otherwise pale cream.

Natural history: Cruz et al. (1979) collected an adult female under some rocks in a disturbed area near dry forest in Honduras in February. Greenbaum et al. (2002a) reported an adult from under a log in dry forest at N side of Lago Güija, Depto. Santa Ana in September.

Specimens examined: <u>Ahuachapán</u>: Parque Nacional El Imposible, San Benito 750 m: Plate 77. <u>Santa Ana</u>: N side of Lago Güija, Cantón Tecomapa, Metapán, San Diego y La Barra, 14°18.5'N, 89°32'W, 425 m: YPM 12468 (coordinates not in error as suggested by Leenders & Watkins-Colwell 2004). <u>Sonsonate</u>: Mariculture Station El Zope, ca. 2 km W Playa Los Cóbanos, 13°32'N, 89°49'W, 5 m: KU CT 11862.

Genus *Sphenomorphus*

Over 100 species are currently included in this genus, which occurs from Mexico to Panama in the New World, and Pakistan through southeast Asia and the Australo-Papuan region (Savage 2002). One species occurs in El Salvador.

Sphenomorphus assatus (Cope 1864)
(Salamanqueza del Bosque)
Plate 78, Map 70

1864 *Lampropholis assatus* Cope, Proc. Acad. Nat. Sci. Philad. 1864: 179; type locality: Volcán Izalco, El Salvador.
Leiolopisma assatum: K. Schmidt 1928.
Lygosoma assatum: Ahl 1940.
Leiolopisma assatum cherriei: Stuart 1940.
Lygosoma assatum assatum: Stuart 1940, Mertens 1952d, Rand 1957.
Leiolopisma assatum assatum: Smith 1946, Peters & Donoso-Barros 1970.
Sphenomorphus assatum: Villa et al. 1988.
Sphenomorphus assatus: Köhler 2000, Dueñas et al. 2001, Köhler 2003b, Leenders 2003, Leenders & Watkins-Colwell 2004.

Plate 78: *Sphenomorphus assatus* HONDURAS: Intibucá: Santa Lucía (370 m). Photo: G. Köhler.

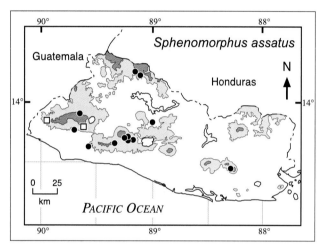

Map 70: Distribution of *Sphenomorphus assatus* in El Salvador.
Closed circles represent examined-specimen locality records; open squares are published locality records. Light shading indicates 600–1200 m elevation; dark shading indicates elevations ≥ 1200 m; large bodies of freshwater are outlined in bold, black lines.

Geographic distribution: From Colima, Mexico, along the Pacific versant to eastern El Salvador and southern Honduras (Köhler 2003b).

Ecological distribution: Dry forest, premontane evergreen forest, subtropical humid forest, savanna, and pine-oak forest between sea level and 1300 m.

Description: A skink of a small size (SVL of largest specimen 52.5 mm [Leenders & Watkins-Colwell 2004); TL/SVL 1.39–1.75; HL/SVL 0.15–0.19; HW/SVL 0.11–0.13; axilla–groin distance/SVL 0.48–0.58; limbs moderately developed, forelimb length/SVL 0.17–0.22; hind limb length/SVL 0.26–0.33; forelimb length + hind limb length/axilla–groin distance 0.76–1.05; shank length/SVL 0.08–

0.12; body scales smooth, scales from occiput to above vent 65–76; eyelids movable, with single enlarged medial transparent scale.

Dorsal surfaces brown or brownish tan with tiny blackish marks, sometimes forming indistinct longitudinal rows; a darker lateral stripe from nostril to eye widening behind eye 2–3 scale rows then passing above ear opening to some distance on side, where it becomes diffuse; undersurfaces creamy yellow; sides below the lateral stripe with minute flecks forming 2–3 barely visible lateral darker lines; tail orange-brown in young specimens.

Natural history: E. Greenbaum (field notes) recorded an individual basking in leaf litter on a road adjacent to a coffee plantation at Finca El Milagro, Depto. Santa Ana in July. Mertens (1952d) stated that this lizard is most active during the late afternoon in El Salvador. Rand (1957) noted this species under a brush pile at the bottom of a brush-grown gully in a pasture at San Salvador, Depto. San Salvador in March; other individuals were noted under leaves in a banana plantation.

Specimens examined: Ahuachapán: El Refugio, vicinity of Mariposario of Francisco Serrano, 13°49.46′N, 89°59.98′W, 225 m: SMF 79243. Chalatenango: Hacienda El Morito, road San Salvador–Chalatenango, 2.3 km E after the turnoff to Dulce Nombre de María: SMF 44388; San José del Sacaré, 1097 m: FMNH 10966. Cuscatlán: 0.5 km E Tenancingo: KU 184383. La Libertad: Finca El Paraíso near Nuevo San Salvador [= Santa Tecla]: SMF 42207, 42585–89, 42602, 42675–76, MVZ 40396; Finca Los Cedros, Cumbre, 1000 m: SMF 42895–96. San Miguel: Volcán de San Miguel, 740 m: KU 291286. San Salvador: San Salvador, near Instituto Tropical de Investigaciones Científicas: SMF 44387, UMMZ 117607; San Salvador: SMF 46901, ZMB 35686–87, 35692; same locality at 670 m: FMNH 64989; San Salvador, Ciudad Universitaria: KU 184384; Ciudad de Soyapango: KU 184385. Santa Ana: Finca El Milagro, 13°53.29′N, 89°37.17′W, 1300 m: KU 289795. Sonsonate: Izalco: USNM 192604, 523448; Hacienda Chilata, 610 m: MVZ 40362–86.

Published locality records: Ahuachapán: Parque Nacional El Imposible: YPM 12992 (Leenders 2003, Leenders & Watkins-Colwell 2004). Sonsonate: Município Izalco, Cantón Cruz Grande, Finca Nuevos Horizontes (13.821°N, 89.653°W), 1240 m: YPM 12314, 12439 (Leenders & Watkins-Colwell 2004).

Family Teiidae

This small family includes 18 species (9 genera) of lizards distributed from southern Canada to southern South America. Commonly called macroteiids, these diurnal, alert lizards can move with blinding speed during warm parts of the day. Many species are unisexual (no males; Fitzgerald 2003b). Two genera occur in El Salvador.

Genus *Ameiva*

This genus includes 33 species of lizards that are distributed from Nayarit and Tamaulipas, Mexico, to Ecuador (west of the Andes) and northern Argentina (east of the Andes), and throughout the Antilles and Bahama Islands (Savage 2002). One species occurs in El Salvador.

Ameiva undulata (Wiegmann 1834)
(Lagartija Pintada)
Plate 79, Map 71, Figure 29a–h

1834 *Cn[emidophorus] undulatus* Wiegmann, Herpetol. Mex.: 27; type locality: Mexico.
Ameiva undulata: Bocourt 1874, Günther 1885, K. Schmidt 1928, Ahl 1940, Villa et al. 1988, Köhler 2000, Dueñas et al. 2001, Köhler 2003b, Leenders 2003, Leenders & Watkins-Colwell 2004.
Ameiva undulata parva: Mertens 1952d, Brongersma 1954b, Rand 1957, Peters & Donoso-Barros 1970.
Geographic distribution: From Tamaulipas and Nayarit, Mexico, to Nicaragua (Atlantic versant) and central Costa Rica (Pacific versant; Savage 2002).
Ecological distribution: Dry forest and savanna between sea level and 1530 m. This species is very common around human habitations and clearings.
Description: A large species of the genus (maximum SVL in males 112.4 mm, in females 102.6 mm [Leenders & Watkins-Colwell 2004]); usually 2–5 canthal scales; 3–4 supraocular scales; 6–8 supralabial scales; 5–7 infralabial scales; 5–7 gular scales; 8–17 mesoptychal scales; 206–286 dorsal scales between interparietal plate and level of posterior insertion of hind limbs; 16–23 femoral pores on each side; 23–30 lamellae under fourth toe; 6–8 longitudinal rows and 27–31 transverse rows of ventral plates; 9–16 preanal scales; tail length/SVL 1.88–2.34; HL/SVL 0.23–0.27; HW/SVL 0.13–0.17; shank length/SVL 0.22–0.27.

In preserved specimens, top of head and mid-

Plate 79: *Ameiva undulata* EL SALVADOR: Ahuachapán: El Refugio (225 m). Photo: G. Köhler.

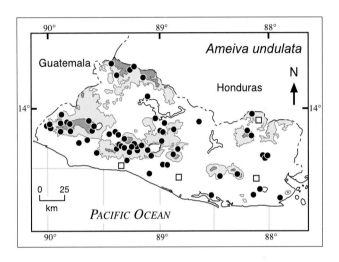

Map 71: Distribution of *Ameiva undulata* in El Salvador.
Closed circles represent examined-specimen locality records; open squares are published locality records. Light shading indicates 600–1200 m elevation; dark shading indicates elevations ≥ 1200 m; large bodies of freshwater are outlined in bold, black lines.

dorsal surface of trunk brown; lateral surfaces dark brown to black above, grading into reddish brown below, and with several vertical pale brown bars which may contact the brown middorsal field but usually separated from it; a dorsolateral cream stripe is more or less evident. In life, adult males of these colorful lizards have middorsal black blotches on an olive brown ground color and orange to orange brown lateral surfaces on head and neck; the lateral body has vertical turquoise bars on a dark brown ground color; a dorsolateral cream stripe is more or less evident; the tail is dark brown with scattered blue scales. Females and juveniles are less colorful and lack the orange

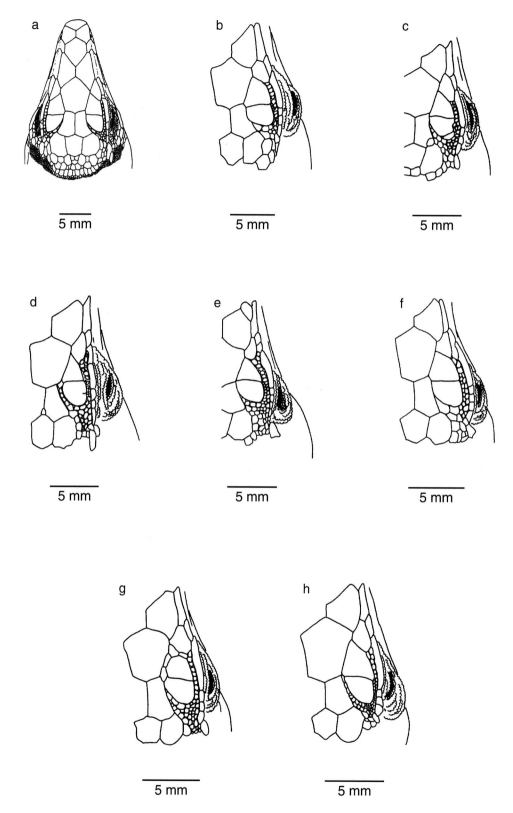

Figure 29: *Ameiva undulata*: Dorsal view of head, variation of superciliar and supraocular scales, a. SMF 42097, b. SMF 52048, c. SMF 42105, d. SMF 52049, e. SMF 52050, f. SMF 42899, g. SMF 42242, h. SMF 42568.

coloration on the head and neck and the turquoise color on the body sides; the dorsolateral cream stripe is usually present.

Natural history: E. Greenbaum (field notes) recorded this species in great abundance around human habitations and roads in numerous lowland habitats throughout El Salvador. Two males were observed head bobbing and circling each other at Parque Nacional El Imposible, Depto. Ahuachapán in July. Mertens (1952d) noted that this lizard is active from the late morning until the late afternoon in El Salvador. Rand (1957) noted this species is common in the lowland brush, forest, and coffee plantations in El Salvador. Campbell (1998a) remarked that this species feeds upon mostly insects; females lay 2–7 eggs from July–September. Leenders (2003) commented that this species is common in open areas during sunny days at Parque Nacional El Imposible, Depto. Ahuachapán. Leenders & Watkins-Colwell (2004) noted gravid females in the dry season with 5–9 oviducal eggs (up to 10 mm × 18 mm) from El Salvador.

Specimens examined: Ahuachapán: Finca Concepción Miramar, 13°48.46′N, 89°48.03′W, 920 m: KU 289929–32, MUHNES C–30–1367–70, C–30–1372–73; El Refugio, vicinity of Mariposario of Francisco Serrano, 13°49.46′N, 89°59.98′W, 225 m: SMF 79330; Parque Nacional El Imposible, La Fincona, 13°50.8′N, 89°58.8′W, 720 m: KU 289743, 289770, MUHNES C–30–1378, SMF 81316–17; Parque Nacional El Imposible, San Benito 780 m: KU 289833–34; El Imposible: MUHNES 1213; Apaneca, 1463 m: MVZ 40328; 3.2 km NW Ahuachapán, 1067 m: MVZ 40329; Finca Las Delicias, 13°52′N, 89°53′W, 1200 m: KU 290069; Finca Santa Leticia, 13°53′N, 89°47′W, 1224 m: MUHNES C–30–1379; Finca La Esperanza, 13°49′N, 89°52′W, 1000 m: KU 290070. Cabañas: Ilobasco: SMF 52048–49; Sensuntepeque, 838 m: MVZ 40330–31; Bosque Cinquera, 13°53.13′N, 88°57.36′W, 400 m: KU 289976, 289998, 290006. Chalatenango: Citalá, 670 m: SMF 52047; San José del Sacaré, 1097 m: FMNH 10963–64; 2.5 km SW Citalá, Cantón San Lorenzo, 1530 m: KU 184155–56; 20 km W Chalatenango: TCWC 23639. Cuscatlán: Cerro de las Pavas, Municipio Cojutepeque: SMF 42101; 0.5 km E Tenancingo: KU 184138–42; Tenancingo: KU 184143; Tenancingo, Río Tizapa: KU 184144; Tenancingo, Río Quezalapa: KU 184145; 2.9 km N Suchitoto: UU 5187. La Libertad: ruinas San Andrés, 13°47.8′N, 89°23.4′W, 450 m: SMF 81314; Los Chorros: LACM 99780;

Finca El Paraíso near Nuevo San Salvador [= Santa Tecla]: SMF 42242–45; Finca Los Cedros, 1050 m: SMF 42897–905, 42921–22; Hacienda Zapotitán, Río Sucio, 457 m: MVZ 40337; Finca La Giralda, 13°39.34′N, 89°22.47′W, 1080 m: KU 289947, 289966, MUHNES C–30–1371; Laguna de Chanmico: UMMZ 117486; Volcán San Salvador, "1917 Lava," 500 m: FMNH 64986; same locality at 750 m: FMNH 64983–84; 2 km SE Colón: KU 62068–70; Hacienda Belmar, ca. La Libertad: LACM 9370; 0.8 km N, 16.1 km W La Libertad: TCWC 17059; Guadalupe, 640 m: MUHNES C–30–1489; Ciudad Merliot, 900 m: YPM 12469. La Paz: Hacienda Miraflores near Zacatecoluca: SMF 42102; 3 km E San Rafael Obrajuela, Río Jalaponga: KU 62065; 7.5 km W San Luis Talpa: KU 184157. La Unión: Bosque del Monte at Maculis, 10 km SE Turnoff Carretera Litoral, 85 km from El Tamarindo: MVZ 143993–96. Morazán: Montecristo Mine, 213 m: MVZ 40304–06; 4.8 km W Montecristo Mine, 198 m: MVZ 40307–08; 1.6 km SE Divisadero, 259 m: MVZ 40309; Divisadero: FMNH 10973–74; E slope Mt. Cacahuatique, 1219 m: MVZ 40313; same locality at 1341 m: MVZ 40316–17; same locality at 1402 m: MVZ 40314–15, 40318–19; same locality at 1433 m: MVZ 40310; N slope Mt. Cacahuatique, 1402 m: MVZ 40311–12; same locality at 1130 m: MUHNES C–30–1487; same locality at 1360 m: KU 291315; Perquín, 13°57.17′N, 88°10.01′W, 1150 m: KU 290016, 290022–25, 291359, MUHNES C–30–1485. San Miguel: Laguna de Olomega, 61 m: MVZ 40320–23; San Pedro: MCZ 57081; Volcán de San Miguel, 700 m: KU 291273, 291275; same locality at 720 m: MUHNES C–30–1486; same locality at 740 m: KU 291274, 291388; same locality at 900 m: MUHNES C–30–1488; same locality at 1140 m: MUHNES C–30–1490. San Salvador: San Salvador, Instituto Tropical de Investigaciones Científicas: SMF 42097–99, 52045, KU 62066–67; 0.4 km NW of Instituto Tropical de Investigaciones Científicas: UMMZ 117487–88; S coast of Lago de Ilopango: SMF 42105–06; Finca Tino Castro near San Salvador: SMF 42232 (*); San Salvador, Barranca on the 65 Avenida Sur: SMF 42381, 42417, 42507–08, 42566–70, 42582–83; San Salvador, 670–700 m: FMNH 64978–79, 64985, 64987, ZMB 35669–73; Colónia Altos del Cerro near slope of San Jacinto Mountain: KU 289969; 1.6 km NW San Salvador: KU 42262; 3 km SE Ilopango, Cantón Asino: KU 184148–51; Cantón El Paraíso: KU 184152; Soyapango, Colónia Amatepec: KU 184153. San Vicente: Finca El Carmen, E part of Volcán San

Vicente, 1319 m: SMF 44368–71, 52050–52; Laguna Apastepeque, 500 m: FMNH 64980–82. Santa Ana: over Hacienda San José, 7 km N of Metapán: SMF 42462–63; W side of Laguna de Coatepeque: SMF 42418; San Juan Mine, 12.1 km SE Metapán, 488 m: MVZ 40324–27; Finca El Milagro, 13°53.29´N, 89°37.17´W, 1300 m: KU 289786, 289796, MUHNES C–30–1377. Sonsonate: Hacienda San Antonio near Sonsonate: SMF 42100, 42103–04, 42485; Atecozol: SMF 52046; Hacienda Chilata, 610 m: MVZ 40332–36, FMNH 10987–90; Bosque Las Lajas, 13°50.04´N, 89°33.56´W, 920 m: MUHNES C–30–1375. Usulután: Espiritu Santo, El Triunfo: SMF 52053; Cerro del Tigre, 13°28.37´N, 88°26.21´W, 1100 m: MUHNES C–30–1366.

Published locality records: Ahuachapán: Município San Pedro Puxtla, Cantón La Concepción, Cooperativa Concepción Miramar (13.810°N, 89.807°W), 950 m: YPM 12293, 12295, 12303–04, 12457, 12460, 12462, 12467 (Leenders & Watkins-Colwell 2004); Parque Nacional El Imposible: YPM 12296, 12298–300, 12454–55, 12459, 12461, 12463 (Leenders & Watkins-Colwell 2004). La Libertad: Município La Libertad, Ciudad Merliot, Colonia Jardines del Volcán, on slope of Volcán El Boquerón (13.76°N, 89.35°W), 900 m: YPM 12469 (Leenders & Watkins-Colwell 2004). La Paz: 6 km N Los Blancos (Rand 1957); Município Zacatecoluca, Finca La Esmeralda, 3 km E Zacatecoluca (13.483°N, 88.850°W), 115 m (Leenders & Watkins-Colwell 2004). San Miguel: Laguna Aramuaca: RMNH 9942 (Brongersma 1954b). Morazán: Município Arambala, Cantón Cumaro, Río Sapo (13.959°N, 88.132°W), 1118 m: YPM 14000–01 (Leenders & Watkins-Colwell 2004). San Vicente: near highway at km 80–81 E: RMNH 9941 (*) (Brongersma 1954b). Sonsonate: Município Izalco, Cantón Las Lajas, Bosque Las Lajas (13.829°N, 89.567°W), 750 m: YPM 12464–66 (Leenders & Watkins-Colwell 2004); Município Izalco, Cantón Cruz Grande, Finca Nuevos Horizontes (13.821°N, 89.653°W), 1200 m: YPM 12294, 12297, 12301–02, 12456, 12458 (Leenders & Watkins-Colwell 2004).

Genus *Aspidoscelis*

Reeder et al. (2002) transferred species of *Cnemidophorus,* exclusive of the *lemniscatus* group, to the genus *Aspidoscelis.* This genus includes over 87 species that are distributed from the United States south to central Costa Rica (Reeder et al.

2002, Savage 2002, Köhler 2003b). Two species occur in El Salvador.

Aspidoscelis deppii (Wiegmann 1834)
(Corredor Rayado)
Plate 80, Map 72, Figure 30a–c

1834 *Cnemidophorus deppii* Wiegmann, Herpetol. Mex.: 28; type locality: Mexico.
Cnemidophorus deppii: Bocourt 1874, Günther 1885, McLain 1899, K. Schmidt 1928, Köhler 2000, Leenders & Watkins-Colwell 2004.
Cnemidophorus deppii deppii: Burt 1931, Ahl 1940, Mertens 1952d, Brongersma 1954b, Rand 1957, Peters & Donoso-Barros 1970.
Cnemidophorus deppei: Villa et al. 1988, Dueñas et al. 2001.
Aspidoscelis deppii: Köhler 2003b.
Geographic distribution: From northern Veracruz and Michoacán, Mexico, to northeastern Nicaragua (exclusive of the Yucatán Peninsula and rainforest regions south of it on the Atlantic versant) and central Costa Rica (Pacific versant; Savage 2002, Köhler 2003b).
Ecological distribution: Dry forest and savanna between sea level and 750 m.
Description: A medium-sized species of the genus (maximum SVL in males 85 mm, in females 68 mm), 3 supraocular scales; 32–39 femoral pores; 27–33 lamellae under fourth toe; 4–6 preanal scales; tail length/SVL 1.47–2.36; HL/SVL 0.20–0.24; HW/SVL 0.12–0.15; snout length/HL 0.44–0.47; shank length/SVL 0.18–0.19.

Dorsal ground color in adults dark grayish brown with nine cream longitudinal stripes, vertebral stripe sometimes darker than the others or even missing, lateral stripes often with spots or fragmented into rows of spots. Limbs dark brown with cream spots, in some specimens forming 3–4 longitudinal rows. Ventral surfaces blue or bluish gray in males, in females undersurfaces creamy white. Juveniles have almost black dorsal ground color, no spots in lateral stripes, no darker coloration on belly, and bluish tail.
Natural history: E. Greenbaum (field notes) encountered great numbers of this species in and around human habitations at Isla San Sebastián, Depto. Usulután in July. Rand (1957) noted this species is common in open grassy areas without shrubs and overgrazed pastures in El Salvador. Savage (2002) noted this species preys upon arthropods. Reproduction takes place in the rainy

Plate 80: *Aspidoscelis deppii* COSTA RICA: Guanacaste: Tamarindo (5 m). Photo: G. Köhler.

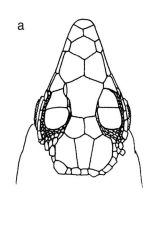

a

1 cm

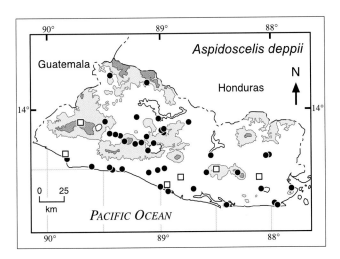

Map 72: Distribution of *Aspidoscelis deppii* in El Salvador.

Closed circles represent examined-specimen locality records; open squares are published locality records. Light shading indicates 600–1200 m elevation; dark shading indicates elevations ≥ 1200 m; large bodies of freshwater are outlined in bold, black lines.

season; 4–6 clutches of 1–4 eggs each are laid by females.

Specimens examined: <u>Cabañas</u>: 8.9 km W Sensuntepeque, 457 m: MVZ 40344–46. <u>Chalatenango</u>: Hacienda El Morito, on the road San Salvador–Chalatenango, 2.3 km E after the turnoff to Dulce Nombre de María: SMF 44382. <u>Cuscatlán</u>: 2 km SE Tenancingo: KU 184289; 3.5 km SE Tenancingo: KU 184278; Tenancingo: KU 184279–80; Tenancingo, El Paso a la Cruz: KU 184281–83; Tenancingo, Río Quezalapa: KU 184284–87; Tenancingo, Copalchan: KU 184288; 2.9 km N Suchitoto: UU 5323. <u>La Libertad</u>: San Andrés near

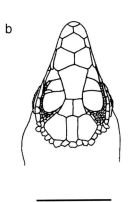

b

1 cm

c

1 cm

Figure 30: *Aspidoscelis deppii:* Variation on dorsal head scalation, a. from series SMF 44372–77, b. SMF 423112, c. from series SMF 44383–84.

Nuevo San Salvador [= Santa Tecla]: SMF 42066;
Laguna de Chanmico, 480 m: SMF 42626; W from
La Liberad: SMF 42311–12; 14 km W La Libertad:
KU 62071–72; La Libertad: UMMZ 117496; Haci-
enda Zapotitán, Río Sucio, 457 m: MVZ 40347–48;
Volcán San Salvador "1917 Lava," 750 m: FMNH
64974; Volcán San Salvador "1917 Lava," 500 m:
FMNH 64975–77; 0.8 km N, 16.1 km W La
Libertad: KU 17092–95. La Paz: El Zapote, Estero
de Jaltepeque: SMF 42064–65; 6 km N Los Blancos:
FMNH 64973; 4 km W El Rosario de La Paz, Río
Jiboa: KU 62073–74; 3 km E San Rafael Obrajuela,
Río Jalponga: KU 62075–78; Hacienda Santa Clara:
KU 184290–313. La Unión: La Unión, near digres-
sion of the road to Conchagua: SMF 44383–84;
M.A.G. Laboratory, 1 km S El Tamarindo: MVZ
143997; 1.5 km S of El Tamarindo: MVZ 143998–99.
Morazán: Montecristo Mine, 213 m: MVZ 40339;
Divisadero, 198 m: MVZ 40340, FMNH 10976,
10978–80; Gigante Mine near Divisadero: FMNH
10983; 1.6 km SE Divisadero, 259 m: MVZ 40349.
San Miguel: Laguna de Olomega, 61 m: MVZ
40341–43; Volcán de San Miguel, 740 m: KU
291276. San Salvador: Apulo near Ilopango, 480 m:
SMF 44378–81; San Salvador: ZMB 35668; San
Diego: ZMB 35658–59; San Salvador, near Airport:
CAS 144029–30; 4 km N Aguilares, 300 m: KU
184316–17; 2.4 km SE Ilopango, Cantón Asino: KU
184324; 3.2 km E Tonacatepeque: LACM 99800.
Santa Ana: Tinteral near Coatepeque: SMF 43109; 6
km S Metapán, Cantón Las Piedras: KU 184314; 6
km S Metapán: KU 184318–23; 5 km S Metapán:
KU 184315. Sonsonate: Acajutla: SMF 42067–70,
44372–77 (coast), CAS-SU 3530, ZMB 26307, 58911–
13. Usulután: San Marcos Lempa, E side of Lempa:
SMF 42071; Río Lempa at Pan American Hwy
Bridge: MVZ 40338; Isla San Sebastián, 13°10.01´N,
88°24.49´W, 20 m: KU 289899–902, 289904–05,
MUHNES C–30–1345–48; Usulután, 12 km S Hwy
El Litoral ca. Río Lempa: LACM 99801–02.

Published locality records: La Paz: near La
Herradura: RMNH 9945 (Brongersma 1954b);
Munícipio Zacatecoluca, Finca La Esmeralda, 3 km
E Zacatecoluca (13.483°N, 88.850°W), 115 m: YPM
12435 (Leenders & Watkins-Colwell 2004). San
Miguel: Laguna Aramuaca: RMNH 9946
(Brongersma 1954b). Santa Ana: NE of Laguna
Verde: RMNH 9943 (Brongersma 1954b). San
Salvador: International Airport (Leenders &
Watkins-Colwell 2004). Sonsonate: Río Zunza
(Zunzal or Zunzita), W of Acajutla: RMNH 9944,
9956 (Brongersma 1954b).

Plate 81: *Aspidoscelis motaguae* (UTA R-39798)
GUATEMALA: Progreso: km 91, Carretera a Cobán
(430 m). Photo: E. N. Smith.

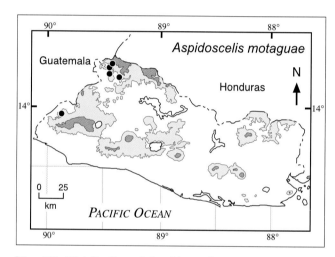

Map 73: Distribution of *Aspidoscelis motaguae* in El
Salvador.
Closed circles represent examined-specimen locality records;
open squares are published locality records. Light shading
indicates 600–1200 m elevation; dark shading indicates elevations ≥ 1200 m; large bodies of freshwater are outlined in bold,
black lines.

Aspidoscelis motaguae (Sackett 1941)

(Corredor Grande)
Plate 81, Map 73, Figure 31

1941 *Cnemidophorus motaguae* Sackett, Notulae
Naturae 77: 1; type locality: Motagua River, Zacapa,
Guatemala.
Cnemidophorus sackii bocourti: Mertens 1952d.
Cnemidophorus motaguae: Peters & Donoso-Barros
1970, Villa et al. 1988, Köhler 2000, Dueñas et al.
2001.
Aspidoscelis motaguae: Köhler 2003b.
Geographic distribution: From Oaxaca, Mexico,

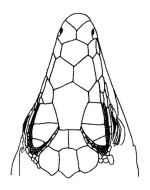

1 cm

Figure 31: *Aspidoscelis motaguae*: Dorsal view of head (from series SMF 44385–86).

to El Salvador and Honduras (Köhler 2003b). Introduced to Florida, USA (Meshaka et al. 2004).
Ecological distribution: Dry forest and savanna between 480 and 1070 m.
Description: A large species of the genus (SVL of largest specimen examined 122 mm), 4 supraocular scales; 44–52 femoral pores; 32–34 lamellae under fourth toe; 6–8 preanal scales; tail length/SVL 1.79–2.34; HL/SVL 0.22–0.23; HW/SVL 0.12–0.14; snout length/HL 0.50–0.53; shank length/SVL 0.20–0.22.

In adults dorsal ground color olive to grayish brown; creamy spots present on back and upper surfaces of hind limbs; gular region and ventral surfaces of limbs and tail cream; belly and anterior part of femoral region black with sky blue spots in males, in females spots cream or pale blue. Juveniles with brown dorsum becoming darker laterally, with six longitudinal white stripes; lateral and dorsolateral stripes broad, paravertebral stripes narrow and indistinct; gular area and ventral surface of tail pale white; belly and limbs yellowish.
Natural history: K. Schmidt & Stuart (1941) noted this species from the "oak-pine zone on the lower mountain slopes and in the dryer parts of the valley among the scrubby vegetation" in Guatemala in July.
Specimens examined: Ahuachapán: 3.2 km NW Ahuachapán, 1067 m: MVZ 40355–56, 40359–60. Santa Ana: Cerro de Cal, Metapán, 860 m: SMF 44385–86; San Juan Mine, 12.1 km SE Metapán, 488 m: MVZ 40350–54, 40357–58; Metapán: KU 184325–29; 5 km S Metapán: KU 184331–42; 6 km S Metapán: KU 184330, 184343–45.

Family Xantusiidae

This family includes 23 species (3 genera) of nocturnal lizards that have a disjunct distribution from the southwestern United States to central Panama, and Cuba. All night lizards lack eyelids, and many species are microhabitat specialists. With the exception of one Cuban species, all night lizards seem to be viviparous (Bezy & Grismer 2003). One genus occurs in El Salvador.

Genus *Lepidophyma*

This genus includes 17 species of lizards that are distributed from Michoacán and Tamaulipas, Mexico, to central Panama (Atlantic versant) and central El Salvador (Pacific versant; Savage 2002, Köhler 2003b). One species occurs in El Salvador.

Lepidophyma smithii Bocourt 1876
(Escorpión Nocturno del Pacífico)
Plate 82, Map 74, Figure 32ab

1876 *Lepidophyma Smithii* Bocourt, Journ. Zool. Paris 5: 402; type locality: Tehuantepec and western Guatemala.
Lepidophyma smithii smithi: Mertens 1952d.
Lepidophyma flavimaculatum smithi: Peters & Donoso-Barros 1970.
Lepidophyma smithii: Bezy 1989, Köhler 2000, Dueñas et al. 2001, Köhler 2003b, Leenders 2003.
Geographic distribution: From Guerrero, Mexico, along the Pacific versant to central El Salvador (Köhler 2003b).
Ecological distribution: Dry forest, premontane evergreen forest, subtropical humid forest, and pine-oak forest between 200 and 1240 m.
Description: An elongated lizard of a moderate size (SVL of largest specimen examined 93.1 mm) with rough, tubercular skin; head covered with large symmetrical plates; body scales small, pointed; enlarged pointed tubercles scattered over the dorsum and sides of body; venter with 10 longitudinal rows of juxtaposed, smooth rectangular plates; tail length/SVL 1.26–1.64; HL/SVL 0.19–0.23; HW/SVL 0.14–0.16; axilla–groin distance/SVL 0.39–0.47; limbs strong, well developed; shank length/SVL 0.11–0.13; lamellae beneath 4th toe 18–24; divided lamellae beneath 4th toe 3–7; number of supralabial scales 8–9, supralabial scales to point below the center of eye 5; number of transverse rows of tubercles in axilla–groin distance 16–21;

Plate 82: *Lepidophyma smithii* EL SALVADOR: Ahuachapán: El Refugio (225 m). Photo: G. Köhler.

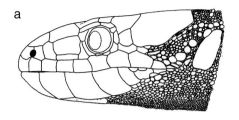

a

5 mm

b

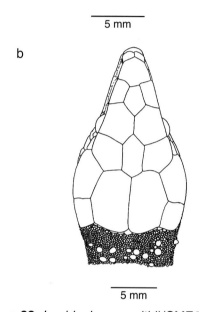

5 mm

Figure 32: *Lepidophyma smithii* (SMF 79339): a. lateral view of head, b. dorsal view of head.

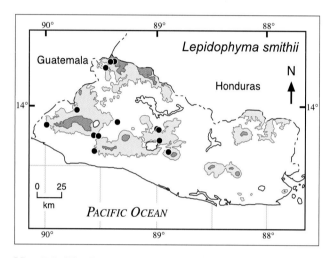

Map 74: Distribution of *Lepidophyma smithii* in El Salvador.
Closed circles represent examined-specimen locality records; open squares are published locality records. Light shading indicates 600–1200 m elevation; dark shading indicates elevations ≥ 1200 m; large bodies of freshwater are outlined in bold, black lines.

total number of femoral pores 15–18; no movable eyelids, eye covered with a transparent spectacle; pupil round.

Dorsal background color brown to grayish brown with distinct yellowish or cream spots; head beige to brown, upper and lower labials boldly marked with dark brown spots or bars against a lighter background; chin cream with darker reticulations; ventral scales creamy yellow.

Natural history: G. Köhler (field notes) collected a specimen on a rotten log at El Refugio, Depto. Ahuachapán. M. Veselý (field notes) observed several specimens at night in holes between stones in a wall (about 3 m high) at Finca El Carmen, Depto. San Vicente in late May; when disturbed,

the lizards quickly retreated into the holes. Mertens (1952d) noted that this lizard was found in rotten wood in El Salvador.

Specimens examined: <u>Ahuachapán</u>: El Refugio, vicinity of Mariposario of Francisco Serrano, 13°49.46´N, 89°59.98´W, 225 m: SMF 79339, 81485. <u>Cuscatlán</u>: Tenancingo, El Sitio de los Sánchez: KU 184272; Cojutepeque: KU 184273–74; Tenancingo, 650 m: KU 184275–77. <u>La Libertad</u>: Hacienda Talqualuya, N of San Juan Opico, 390 m: SMF 51996–98; Cantón San Diego: KU 184271. <u>San Vicente</u>: Finca El Carmen, 13°36.8´N, 88°50.3´W, 1240 m: SMF 81482. <u>Santa Ana</u>: Parque Nacional Montecristo, oficinas de Parques Nacionales, 800 m: SMF 81483–84; Montecristo: MUHNES 1216; Metapán: KU 184270. <u>Sonsonate</u>: km 43 road San Salvador–Sonsonate: SMF 44357; Finca La Joya, km 48 road San Salvador–Sonsonate, 587 m: SMF 44358–60; Hacienda Chilata, 610 m: MVZ 40071–73.

Suborder Serpentes (Snakes)

There are approximately 2750 species (ca. 440 genera; 18 families) of snakes currently known from a wide array of habitats across the globe (excluding the Arctic and Antarctic regions). Snakes, together with lizards and amphisbaenians (worm-like reptiles) form a group called squamates. Snakes can be distinguished from most lizards by the absence of limbs, eyelids, and ear openings, and the presence of forked tongues and fangs (many exceptions are known). Snakes can be fossorial, terrestrial, semi-aquatic, fully aquatic (freshwater or marine environments), or arboreal. Snakes range in size from tiny blindsnakes to large pythons and anacondas (10 m) that have been known to attack humans. Most snakes lay eggs, but viviparity has evolved at least 35 times independently; some species are parthenogenetic (reproduction from virgin females; Zug et al. 2001, Pianka 2003a). There are seven families of snakes in El Salvador.

Key to the Snakes of El Salvador

1 a. Ventrals and dorsals equal in size **2**
   b. Ventral scutes considerably enlarged **3**
2 a. Fourteen scale rows around midbody .... *Leptotyphlops goudotii*
   b. Twenty scale rows around midbody.. *Ramphotyphlops braminus*
3 a. Tail distinctly laterally compressed .... *Pelamis platurus*
   b. Tail cylindrical or subcylindrical in cross section, not distinctly
      laterally compressed **4**
4 a. Large deep pit in loreal region between eye and nostril **5**
   b. Loreal region without deep pit **9**
5 a. A rattle on end of tail .... *Crotalus durissus*
   b. No rattle present **6**
6 a. Top of head covered with nine large plates .... *Agkistrodon bilineatus*
   b. Scales on top of head small and irregular **7**
7 a. Dorsal scale rows at midbody 21 .... *Cerrophidion godmani*
   b. Dorsal scale rows at midbody more than 21 .... **8**
8 a. Ventrals 150 or less; supraocular long and narrow; extremely stout body
      with rugose scales; no whitish vertebral line .... *Atropoides nummifer*
   b. Ventrals 150 or more; supraocular large and broad;
      relatively slender body with keeled scales; usually a whitish
      vertebral line present .... *Porthidium ophryomegas*
9 a. A pair of non-erectile, grooved fangs located in the front of mouth;
      no loreal .... *Micrurus nigrocinctus*
   b. No pair of non-erectile, grooved fangs located in the front of mouth;
      loreal present or absent **10**
10 a. Dorsals in 60 or more scale rows at midbody; frontal and parietal
      areas covered by small irregular scales .... *Boa constrictor*
   b. Dorsals in less than 50 scale rows at midbody; snout, frontal,
      and parietal areas covered by large symmetrical shields **11**
11 a. Internasal fused with anterior portion of nasals .... *Stenorrhina freminvillii*
   b. Internasal not fused with anterior portion of nasals **12**
12 a. Dorsal scales at midbody in an even (14–18) number of rows .... *Spilotes pullatus*
   b. Dorsal scales at midbody in an odd number of rows.. **13**
13 a. Dorsal scales at midbody in 27 or more rows **14**
   b. Dorsal scales at midbody in 25 or less rows **15**
14 a. Ventral scutes do not extend across venter; no loreal, prefrontal
      meets supralabials; scales smooth .... *Loxocemus bicolor*
   b. Ventral scutes extend across entire venter; loreal present, separating prefrontal

       from supralabials; posterior body scales keeled .... **Senticolis triaspis** (part)
15 a. Dorsal scale rows uniform in number throughout the body, no dorsal reductions **16**
    b. Dorsal scale rows one head length anterior to vent at least two less
       than at midbody **37**
16 a. Dorsal scales keeled **17**
    b. Dorsal scales smooth **18**
17 a. Dorsum red in life (pale brown or gray in preservative); head black,
       a yellow nuchal collar present .... ***Ninia sebae***
    b. Dorsum uniform gray; nuchal collar absent .... ***Ninia espinali***
18 a. Anal plate entire, preocular absent **19**
    b. Anal plate divided, preocular present or absent **25**
19 a. Supralabials not conspicuously enlarged, nor in contact with postocular,
       or anterior and posterior temporal **20**
    b. Supralabial below anterior temporal enlarged and in
       contact with postocular, and anterior and posterior temporal;
       much higher than neighboring labials **21**
20 a. Dorsal pattern with yellow blotches (red in life); supraocular present,
       separating frontal from orbit .... ***Geophis fulvoguttatus***
    b. Dorsal pattern without yellow blotches; supraocular absent,
       frontal enters orbit .... ***Geophis rhodogaster***
21 a. Dorsal scale rows 15 or less; vertebral scale row distinctly larger
       than paravertebrals **22**
    b. Dorsals scale rows 17; vertebral and paravertebral rows subequal **24**
22 a. Dorsal scales in 13 rows.. **23**
    b. Dorsal scales in 15 rows.. ***Sibon nebulatus***
23 a. No anterior temporal, 5th supralabial in contact with parietal .... ***Sibon carri***
    b. One anterior temporal, separating parietals from supralabials .... ***Sibon anthracops***
24 a. Dark (black) annuli on body fewer than 20 .... ***Tropidodipsas sartorii***
    b. Dark annuli (brown) on body more than 25 .... ***Tropidodipsas fischeri***
25 a. Head greatly enlarged, neck extremely narrow and elongate;
       eyes very large and bulging out from head .... ***Imantodes gemmistratus***
    b. Head distinct from neck or not, but not greatly enlarged;
       eyes not markedly enlarged nor bulging out from head **26**
26 a. Preocular absent **27**
    b. Preocular present **30**
27 a. Subcaudals 30 or less **28**
    b. Subcaudals 40 or more **29**
28 a. Dark brown vertebral stripe present; ventrals 115–129 .... ***Tantilla vermiformis***
    b. No dark brown vertebral stripe; ventrals 139–160 .... ***Tantilla brevicauda***
29 a. Vertebral stripe pale yellow .... ***Tantilla taeniata***
    b. Vertebral stripe dark brown .... ***Tantilla armillata***
30 a. Pattern with black bands or rings **31**
    b. Pattern without black bands or rings.. **33**
31 a. With middorsal-round orange blotches in life; dorsal scales at midbody
       in 15 rows; ventrals 170 or more; subcaudals 60 or less .... ***Scolecophis atrocinctus***
    b. Without middorsal-round orange blotches in life; dorsal scales at
       midbody in 17 rows; ventrals 160 or less; subcaudals 80 or more **32**
32 a. Pattern with black bands on anterior part of body, not extending onto venter
       (posterior part of body usually without bands); subcaudals 120 or more; usually
       one anterior and two posterior temporals .... ***Scaphiodontophis annulatus***
    b. Pattern with complete black rings; subcaudals 115 or less;
       usually one anterior and one posterior temporal .... ***Pliocercus elapoides***

33 a. Dorsum uniformly pale to dark brown; rostral plate usually
        protruding beyond mouth opening; dorsal scales at midbody in 15–17 rows;
        preocular absent, loreal enters orbit .... ***Enulius flavitorques***
    b. Dorsal pattern of longitudinal stripes; rostral plate not enlarged
        nor protuding beyond mouth opening; dorsal scales at midbody in 17–21 rows;
        preocular present, separating loreal from eye **34**
34 a. Dorsal scales in 17 rows **35**
    b. Dorsal scales in 19 or 21 rows **36**
35 a. White head with brown mottling (black with bright orange pigment in life);
        lateral darker stripes completely absent .... ***Rhadinaea pilonaorum***
    b. Head coloration not as above; at least one obvious dark brown
        line or stripe on side of body .... ***Rhadinaea kinkelini***
36 a. Dorsal scales in 19 rows .... ***Rhadinaea montecristi***
    b. Dorsal scales in 21 rows .... ***Rhadinaea godmani***
37 a. Dorsal scale rows at midbody 27 or more;
        ventrals 240 or more .... ***Senticolis triaspis*** (part)
    b. Dorsal scale rows at midbody 25 or less; ventrals 215 or less **38**
38 a. Dorsal scale rows at midbody 15 .... **39**
    b. Dorsal scale rows at midbody 17 or more **40**
39 a. Dorsum uniform green in life (blue in preservative) .... ***Leptophis modestus***
    b. Dorsum with a broad nut-brown or yellow-brown middorsal
        band and dark brown or black lateral stripes (on rows 2
        through 5 or 6) .... ***Leptophis mexicanus***
40 a. 2–3 loreals .... ***Trimorphodon biscutatus***
    b. One or no loreal **41**
41 a. Loreal absent, prefrontals in contact with supralabials; dorsal scale
        rows at midbody 17; head narrow and pointed **42**
    b. Loreal present, separating prefrontals from supralabials or if loreal is absent,
        dorsal scale rows at midbody 17 or more; head shape normal **43**
42 a. Dorsum green in life (blue in preservative);
        usually 10 supralabials .... ***Oxybelis fulgidus***
    b. Dorsum pale brown to gray (in life and in preservative);
        usually 8 or 9 supralabials .... ***Oxybelis aeneus***
43 a. Anal plate entire **44**
    b. Anal plate divided **47**
44 a. Dorsal scales keeled **45**
    b. Dorsal scales smooth **46**
45 a. Lateral stripe involving 3rd and 4th scale rows; no dark brown
        markings on supralabials; no occipital blotches; ventrals 141–181;
        subcaudals 82–131 .... ***Thamnophis proximus***
    b. Lateral stripe involving only 2nd or 3rd scale row or both, at least anteriorly;
        dark brown markings present on supralabials; occipital blotches present;
        ventrals 132–154; subcaudals 56–80 .... ***Thamnophis fulvus***
46 a. Pattern of black, red, and yellow (or white) rings .... ***Lampropeltis triangulum***
    b. No black, red, and yellow (or white) rings; anterior part of body grayish brown;
        tail and posterior part of body black .... ***Drymarchon corais***
47 a. Some or all of dorsal scales keeled **48**
    b. Dorsal scales smooth **49**
48 a. Dorsum uniform green in life (blue in preservative);
        ventrals 151–171 .... ***Drymobius chloroticus***
    b. Pattern of a green or yellow spot on each scale;
        ventrals 137–158 .... ***Drymobius margaritiferus***

49   a. Dorsal scale rows reduced to 13 at about one head length anterior to vent;
    a small subocular below preocular; a distinct loreal depression,
    canthal ridge markedly pronounced .... ***Masticophis mentovarius***

    b. Dorsal scale rows reduced to not less than 15 at about one head length
    anterior to vent; a small subocular below preocular present or not;
    no distinct loreal depression **50**

50   a. One anterior temporal **51**

    b. Two anterior temporals **55**

51   a. Dorsal pattern of stripes extending the length of the body **52**

    b. Dorsal pattern consisting of blotches or bands **53**

52   a. Dorsal scales at midbody in 23 or 25 rows; ventrals 153–174 .... ***Coniophanes piceivittis***

    b. Dorsal scales at midbody in 21 rows; ventrals 109–146 .... ***Coniophanes fissidens***

53   a. Dorsal color pattern consisting of dark brown bands on a
    light brown or tan ground color forming alternating bands that
    extend completely across the body .... ***Leptodeira nigrofasciata***

    b. Dorsal color pattern consisting of dark brown or blackish spots, blotches,
    or bands on a lighter brown or grayish ground color, or blotches fused to form
    a zig-zag pattern, but no bands extend completely across the body **54**

54   a. Ventrals 200 or more .... ***Leptodeira septentrionalis***

    b. Ventrals 180 or less .... ***Leptodeira annulata***

55   a. Dorsal scales at midbody in 19 rows **56**

    b. Dorsal scales at midbody in 17 rows **57**

56   a. Pale (yellowish) ground color with dark (brown or black)
    longitudinal stripes .... ***Conophis lineatus***

    b. Dark (grayish brown) ground color with pale (dirty white)
    longitudinal stripes .... ***Crisantophis nevermanni***

57   a. Head green in life; dorsal pattern of a pair of creamish paravertebral stripes;
    three postoculars; 195–210 ventrals .... ***Leptodrymus pulcherrimus***

    b. Head grayish brown in life; dorsum unicolor or with a dark brown
    vertebral stripe; two postoculars; 163–195 ventrals **58**

58   a. A dark brown middorsal stripe present .... ***Dryadophis dorsalis***

    b. No dark brown middorsal stripe .... ***Dryadophis melanolomus***

Clave para las Serpientes de El Salvador

1   a. Escamas ventrales y dorsales de igual tamaño **2**

    b. Escamas ventrales considerablemente agrandadas **3**

2   a. Catorce filas de escamas alrededor de la mitad del cuerpo .... ***Leptotyphlops goudotii***

    b. Veinte filas de escamas alrededor de la mitad
    del cuerpo .... ***Ramphotyphlops braminus***

3   a. Cola comprimida lateralmente .... ***Pelamis platurus***

    b. Cola cilíndrica o subcilíndrica en sección transversal, no comprimida lateralmente **4**

4   a. Foseta loreal grande entre el ojo y nostrilo **5**

    b. Foseta loreal ausente **9**

5   a. Cascabel presente al final de la cola .... ***Crotalus durissus***

    b. Sin cascabel al final de la cola **6**

6   a. Dorso de la cabeza cubierto con 9 escamas
    laminares grandes .... ***Agkistrodon bilineatus***

    b. Dorso de la cabeza cubierto con escamas pequeñas e irregulares **7**

7   a. Veintiun filas de escamas dorsales al nivel de la mitad del
    cuerpo .... ***Cerrophidion godmani***

    b. Más de 21 filas de escamas dorsales al nivel de la mitad del cuerpo **8**

8   a. Ventrales 150 o menos; supraocular larga y angosta; cuerpo grueso
        con escamas rugosas; sin línea vertebral clara .... ***Atropoides nummifer***
     b. Ventrales 150 o más; supraocular larga y ancha;
        cuerpo relativamente delgado con escamas quilladas;
        normalmente con línea vertebral clara .... ***Porthidium ophryomegas***
9   a. Boca con par de colmillos no eréctiles, con canales, localizados en la
        parte frontal; escama loreal ausente .... ***Micrurus nigrocinctus***
     b. Boca sin colmillos como los descritos en 9a; escama loreal presente o ausente **10**
10   a. Sesenta o más filas de escamas dorsales al nivel de la
        mitad del cuerpo; áreas parietal y frontal cubiertas por escamas
        pequeñas e irregulares .... ***Boa constrictor***
     b. Cincuenta o menos filas de escamas dorsales al nivel de la mitad
        del cuerpo; hocico y áreas parietal y frontal cubiertos por escamas
        laminares grandes y simétricas **11**
11   a. Internasal fusionada con la porción anterior de
        las nasales .... ***Stenorrhina freminvillii***
     b. Internasal no fusionada con la porción anterior de las nasales **12**
12   a. Número par (14, 16, 18) de filas de escamas dorsales al nivel de la
        mitad del cuerpo .... ***Spilotes pullatus***
     b. Número impar de filas de escamas dorsales al nivel de la mitad del cuerpo **13**
13   a. Número de filas de escamas dorsales al nivel de la mitad del cuerpo ≥ 27 .... **14**
     b. Número de filas de escamas dorsales al nivel de la mitad del cuerpo ≤ 25 .... **15**
14   a. Placas ventrales no se extienden a través del vientre; sin loreal;
        prefrontal en contacto con supralabiales; escamas lisas .... ***Loxocemus bicolor***
     b. Placas ventrales se extienden a través de todo el vientre;
        loreal separa prefrontal de supralabiales; parte posterior del cuerpo
        con escamas quilladas .... ***Senticolis triaspis*** (parte)
15   a. Número de filas de escamas dorsales no varía a lo largo del cuerpo **16**
     b. Número de filas de escamas dorsales a una cabeza de distancia antes de la
        cloaca por lo menos dos menos que en la mitad del cuerpo **37**
16   a. Escamas dorsales quilladas **17**
     b. Escamas dorsales lisas **18**
17   a. En vida, dorso rojo (café claro o gris en preservante); cabeza negra con
        un collar amarillo al nivel de la nuca .... ***Ninia sebae***
     b. Dorso color gris uniforme; collar en la nuca ausente .... ***Ninia espinali***
18   a. Placa anal entera, preocular ausente **19**
     b. Placa anal dividida, preocular presente o ausente **25**
19   a. Supralabiales no conspicuamente agrandadas, separadas de postocular y de
        temporales anterior y posterior **20**
     b. Supralabiales por debajo de temporal anterior agrandadas
        (mucho más altas que labiales adyacentes) y en contacto con postocular y
        temporales anterior y posterior **21**
20   a. Dorso con manchas amarillas (rojas en vida); supraocular separa
        frontal de la órbita .... ***Geophis fulvoguttatus***
     b. Dorso sin manchas amarillas; supraocular ausente,
        escama frontal entra a la órbita .... ***Geophis rhodogaster***
21   a. Número de filas de escamas dorsales ≤ 15; fila de escamas vertebrales
        más grandes que paravertebrales **22**
     b. Número de filas de escamas dorsales 17; escamas vertebrales y
        paravertebrales de tamaño similar **24**
22   a. Escamas dorsales en 13 filas **23**
     b. Escamas dorsales en 15 filas .... ***Sibon nebulatus***

23 a. Temporal anterior ausente, 5ta supralabial en contacto con parietal .... *Sibon carri*

   b. Una escama temporal anterior separa parietales
de supralabiales .... *Sibon anthracops*

24 a. Menos de 20 anillos oscuros (negro) en el cuerpo .... *Tropidodipsas sartorii*

   b. Más de 25 anillos oscuros (café) en el cuerpo .... *Tropidodipsas fischeri*

25 a. Cabeza grande, cuello extremadamente delgado y elongado;
ojos muy grandes que sobrepasan el perfil de la cabeza .... *Imantodes gemmistratus*

   b. Cabeza no agrandada, diferenciable o no diferenciable del cuello;
ojos no evidentemente grandes, no sobrepasan el perfil de la cabeza **26**

26 a. Preocular ausente **27**

   b. Preocular presente **30**

27 a. Subcaudales ≤ 30 .... **28**

   b. Subcaudales ≥ 40 .... **29**

28 a. Línea vertebral oscura (café) presente; entre
115–129 ventrales .... *Tantilla vermiformis*

   b. Sin línea paravertebral oscura (café); entre
139–160 ventrales .... *Tantilla brevicauda*

29 a. Línea vertebral color amarillo claro .... *Tantilla taeniata*

   b. Línea vertebral color café oscuro .... *Tantilla armillata*

30 a. Patrón de coloración con bandas o anillos negros **31**

   b. Patrón de coloración sin bandas ni anillos negros **33**

31 a. En vida, con manchas mediodorsales anaranjadas;
15 filas de escamas al nivel de la mitad del cuerpo;
ventrales ≥ 170; subcaudales ≤ 60 .... *Scolecophis atrocinctus*

   b. En vida, sin manchas mediodorsales anaranjadas;
17 filas de escamas al nivel de la mitad del cuerpo;
ventrales ≤ 160; subcaudales ≥ 80 .... **32**

32 a. Bandas negras en parte anterior del cuerpo; las bandas no son evidentes en
el vientre ni en la parte posterior del cuerpo; subcaudales ≥ 120; normalmente
una temporal anterior y dos temporales posteriores .... *Scaphiodontophis annulatus*

   b. Anillos negros completos (visibles también en el vientre);
subcaudales ≤ 115; normalmente una temporal anterior y una temporal
posterior .... *Pliocercus elapoides*

33 a. Dorso color café claro u oscuro; rostral normalmente proyectada por
delante del nivel de la abertura de la boca; número de filas de escamas
dorsales al nivel de la mitad del cuerpo 15–17; preocular ausente,
loreal entra en la órbita .... *Enulius flavitorques*

   b. Dorso con líneas longitudinales; rostral no agrandada ni proyectada
por delante del nivel de la abertura de la boca; número de filas de escamas dorsales al
nivel de la mitad del cuerpo 17–21; preocular separa loreal del ojo **34**

34 a. Escamas dorsales en 17 filas **35**

   b. Escamas dorsales en 19 ó 21 filas **36**

35 a. Cabeza blanca con pigmentación café (en vida, negra con
pigmentación naranja brillate); líneas oscuras en los flancos del
cuerpo ausentes .... *Rhadinaea pilonaorum*

   b. Coloración de la cabeza differente a la descrita en 35a; al menos una línea
oscura (café) en cada flanco del cuerpo .... *Rhadinaea kinkelini*

36 a. Escamas dorsales en 19 filas .... *Rhadinaea montecristi*

   b. Escamas dorsales en 21 filas .... *Rhadinaea godmani*

37 a. Número de filas de escamas dorsales al nivel de la mitad del cuerpo ≥ 27;
ventrales ≥ 240 .... *Senticolis triaspis* (parte)

   b. Número de filas de escamas dorsales al nivel de la mitad del cuerpo ≤ 25;

ventrales ≤ 215 .... **38**

38 a. Número de filas de escamas dorsales al nivel de la mitad del cuerpo 15 .... **39**

    b. Número de filas de escamas dorsales al nivel de la mitad del cuerpo ≥ 17 .... **40**

39 a. En vida, dorso color verde uniforme (azul en preservante) .... *Leptophis modestus*

    b. Dorso con una línea ancha mediodorsal color café oscuro o café
amarillento y con líneas laterales color café oscuro o negro
(en filas 2 hasta 5 ó 6) .... *Leptophis mexicanus*

40 a. De 2 a 3 loreales .... *Trimorphodon biscutatus*

    b. Una loreal o loreal ausente **41**

41 a. Loreal ausente, prefrontales en contacto con supralabiales;
17 filas de escamas dorsales al nivel de la mitad del cuerpo;
cabeza angosta y punteaguda **42**

    b. Cuando presente, loreal separa prefrontales de supralabiales;
cuando la loreal esta ausente, el número de filas de escamas dorsales al nivel
de la mitad del cuerpo ≥ 17; cabeza con forma normal **43**

42 a. En vida, dorso verde (azul en preservante);
normalmente 10 supralabiales .... *Oxybelis fulgidus*

    b. Color del dorso desde gris hasta café claro (en vida y en preservante);
normalmente 8 ó 9 supralabiales .... *Oxybelis aeneus*

43 a. Anal entera **44**

    b. Anal dividida **47**

44 a. Escamas dorsales quilladas **45**

    b. Escamas dorsales lisas **46**

45 a. Línea lateral sobre la 3ra y 4ta fila de escamas; sin manchas
oscuras en las supralabiales; sin manchas occipitales; ventrales 141–181;
subcaudales 82–131 .... *Thamnophis proximus*

    b. Línea lateral sobre la 2da y/o 3ta fila de escamas; manchas oscuras
(café) en las supralabiales; manchas occipitales presentes; ventrales 132–154;
subcaudales 56–80 .... *Thamnophis fulvus*

46 a. Patrón de coloración con anillos negros, rojos y amarillos
(o blancos) .... *Lampropeltis triangulum*

    b. Sin anillos color negro, rojo o amarillo (o blanco);
parte anterior del cuerpo color café grisáseo, cola y parte posterior
del cuerpo color negro .... *Drymarchon corais*

47 a. Algunas o todas las escamas dorsales quilladas **48**

    b. Escamas dorsales lisas **49**

48 a. En vida, dorso color verde uniforme (azul en preservante);
ventrales 151–171 .... *Drymobius chloroticus*

    b. Cada escama con un punto verde o amarillo;
ventrales 137–158 .... *Drymobius margaritiferus*

49 a. Número de filas de escamas dorsales a una cabeza de distancia antes de
la cloaca reducido a 13; subocular pequeña por debajo de preocular;
depresión loreal evidente, borde cantal pronunciado .... *Masticophis mentovarius*

    b. Número de filas de escamas dorsales a una cabeza de distancia antes
de la cloaca reducido a no menos de 15; subocular pequeña por debajo de
preocular presente o ausente; sin depresión loreal evidente **50**

50 a. Una temporal anterior **51**

    b. Dos temporales anteriores **55**

51 a. Dorso con líneas que se extienden a lo largo del cuerpo **52**

    b. Dorso con patrón de coloración que incluye manchas o bandas **53**

52 a. Escamas dorsales al nivel de la mitad del cuerpo en 23 ó 25 filas;
ventrales 153–174 .... *Coniophanes piceivittis*

   b. Escamas dorsales al nivel de la mitad del cuerpo en 21 filas;
      ventrales 109–146 .... *Coniophanes fissidens*
53 a. Dorso cubierto con un patrón de coloración que consiste en bandas
      gruesas color café oscuro que contrastan con bandas delgadas color café claro;
      las bandas están claramente definidas en el dorso y en los lados
      del cuerpo .... *Leptodeira nigrofasciata*
   b. Dorso con un patrón de coloración que consiste en la presencia
      de puntos, bandas o manchas color café oscuro o negro sobre un fondo café
      claro o grisáceo; también es posible observar machas fusionadas en forma de zig-zag;
      las bandas no están claramente definidas en los lados del cuerpo **54**
54 a. Ventrales ≥ 200 .... *Leptodeira septentrionalis*
   b. Ventrales ≤ 180 .... *Leptodeira annulata*
55 a. Escamas dorsales al nivel de la mitad del cuerpo en 19 filas **56**
   b. Escamas dorsales al nivel de la mitad del cuerpo en 17 filas **57**
56 a. Dorso claro (amarillento) con líneas longitudinales oscuras
      (café o negro) .... *Conophis lineatus*
   b. Dorso oscuro (café grisáceo) con líneas longitudinales claras
      (blanco sucio) .... *Crisantophis nevermanni*
57 a. En vida, cabeza verde; dorso con dos líneas paravertebrales claras;
      tres postoculares; 195–210 ventrales .... *Leptodrymus pulcherrimus*
   b. En vida, cabeza café grisácea; dorso uniforme (con un solo color) o con una
      línea vertebral oscura (café); dos postoculares; 163–195 ventrales **58**
58 a. Línea mediodorsal oscura (café) presente .... *Dryadophis dorsalis*
   b. Línea mediodorsal oscura (café) ausente .... *Dryadophis melanolomus*

Family Boidae

Currently, this family includes 41 species (7 genera) with a wide distribution from western North America to southern South America, the Antilles, West Indies, southeastern Europe and Asia (including Sri Lanka), Africa (including Madagascar and Réunion Island), Moluccas and New Guinea through Melanesia to Somoa (McDiarmid et al. 1999, Barker & Barker 2003). One genus occurs in El Salvador.

Genus *Boa*

The four species of this genus are distributed from northern Mexico to southern South America, Madagascar, and Réunion Island (McDiarmid et al. 1999). One species occurs in El Salvador.

Boa constrictor Linnaeus 1758
(Mazacuata)
Plate 83, Map 75

1758 *Boa constrictor* Linnaeus, Systema Naturae,
ed. 10: 215; type locality: India (in error).
Constrictor constrictor imperator: Ahl 1940;
Mertens 1952d.
Boa constrictor imperator: Peters & Orejas-Miranda 1970.
Boa constrictor: Villa et al. 1988, Köhler 1996, McDiarmid et al. 1999, Dueñas et al. 2001, Köhler 2001a, 2003b, Leenders 2003, Leenders & Watkins-Colwell 2003a, 2004.

Geographic distribution: From Sonora and Tamaulipas, Mexico, through Central America to central Argentina (Atlantic versant) and northwestern Peru (Pacific versant; Savage 2002); also in the Lesser Antilles. Meshaka et al. (2004) noted the presence of this species in Florida, USA, but it is not clear if breeding populations are established.

Ecological distribution: Dry forest, premontane evergreen forest, and subtropical humid forest between sea level and 1200 m.

Description: A very large snake (SVL of largest specimen 2170 mm [Leenders & Watkins-Colwell 2004]); relative tail length 13–16% of SVL in males, 8–9% in females; naris situated between 2 or 3 nasal scales; 17–21 supralabials; 20–23 infralabials;

Plate 83: *Boa constrictor* EL SALVADOR: Ahuachapán: Parque Nacional El Imposible, San Benito (750 m). Photo: T. Leenders.

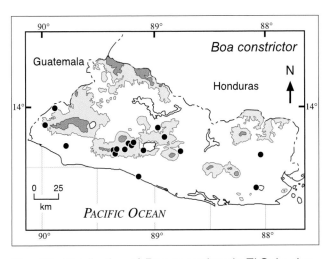

Map 75: Distribution of *Boa constrictor* in El Salvador. Closed circles represent examined-specimen locality records; open squares are published locality records. Light shading indicates 600–1200 m elevation; dark shading indicates elevations ≥ 1200 m; large bodies of freshwater are outlined in bold, black lines.

dorsal scales smooth, without apical pits, in 65–70 rows at midbody, and 35–40 rows one head length anterior to vent; ventrals 237–243 in males, 232–238 in females; subcaudals 55–63 in males, 49–53 in females; anal plate entire.

Dorsal ground color gray, grayish brown, brown, or yellowish brown, with a series of darker saddle-like blotches becoming more reddish brown and contrasting on the tail, where they form dark brown rings alternating with cream rings; another series of smaller creamish centered and rhomboidal blotches laterally; top of head shares dorsal ground color; a narrow dark brown median stripe originating on the snout and extending onto neck, forming a cruciform mark in frontal area in some specimens; a dark brown postocular stripe extending to angle of jaw; ventral surface cream and pinkish to almost salmon with numerous dark brown spots or blotches, especially on lateral portions of ventrals.

Natural history: Campbell (1998a) remarked that this species can be active by day or night. Females give live birth to 12–64 young between May and August. Leenders & Watkins-Colwell (2003a) noted this species eats lizards, birds and mammals. Two snakes from Parque Nacional El Imposible, Depto. Ahuachapán consumed a Big-eared Climbing Rat (*Ototylomys phyllotis*) and a Deppe's Squirrel (*Sciurus deppei);* the snakes were captured in the months of January and February.

Conservation status: CITES: Appendix II.

Specimens examined: Ahuachapán: 12 km NW Ahuachapán, Cantón El Jobo: KU 183855; Parque Nacional El Imposible, San Benito, 750 m: Plate 83. Cuscatlán: Tenancingo, 3 km E Tenancingo, Mazacuayo: KU 183853; 15 km SE Tenancingo, Cantón El Tablón: KU 183856. La Libertad: Finca Los Naranjos, vicinity Nuevo San Salvador [= Santa Tecla], 1200 m: SMF 42449, 42581, 42870, 43061; Finca Rosario, 1060 m: SMF 42584; Finca Astillero, about 1000 m: SMF 42873, 42929–30; Finca Paraíso, Santa Tecla: MVZ 40401. La Paz: 9 km SW San Luis Talpa, El Pimental: KU 183854. Morazán: 3.2 km W Montecristo Mine, 183 m: MVZ 40402; Município Arambala, Cantón Cumaro, Río Sapo (13.959°N, 88.132°W): YPM 13994 (Leenders & Watkins-Colwell 2004). San Miguel: Laguna de Olomega, 61 m: MVZ 40399–400. San Salvador: Instituto Tropical de Investigaciones Científicas, San Salvador, 700 m: SMF 43198 (skull), 77401; San Salvador: ZMB 35706–07; 3 km SE Ilopango, Cantón Asino: KU 183851; San Salvador, Ciudad Universitaria: KU 183857. San Vicente: 2.4 km S, 10.8 km E San Vicente: TCWC 17170. Sonsonate: brook near Santo Domingo de Guzman, 200 m: SMF 43194.

Published locality records: Ahuachapán: Parque Nacional El Imposible, La Fincona, 13°50.8′N, 89°58.8′W, 780 m: YPM 12327 (Leenders & Watkins-Colwell 2003a).

Family Colubridae

This is the largest family of snakes, which includes approximately 1700 species (ca. 300

genera) and accounts for 70% of all snake species. This family is nearly cosmopolitan—it is absent only from Antarctica, central and western Australia, and high latitudes of North America and Eurasia. Generalizations about morphology are difficult because this group encompasses a tremendous diversity of taxa. However, one New World subfamily, Xenodontinae, includes some species that are mildly venomous to humans. Most colubrids lay eggs, but some species give live birth (Savitzky 2003). New species continue to be described from around the world (e.g., Grismer et al. 2003, Nieto-Montes de Oca 2003).

Genus *Coniophanes*

This genus includes 14 species of snakes that are distributed from southern Texas and Sinaloa, Mexico, through Central America to northwestern Peru (Savage 2002). Two species occur in El Salvador.

Coniophanes fissidens (Günther 1858)
(Culebra Vientre-punteado)
Plate 84, Map 76, Figure 33

1858 *Coronella fissidens* Günther, Cat. Snakes Brit. Mus. 1858: 36; type locality: Mexico.
Coniophanes fissidens punctigularis: Mertens 1952d.
Coniophanes fissidens: Peters & Orejas-Miranda 1970, Villa et al. 1988, Dueñas et al. 2001, Köhler 2001a, 2003b, Leenders 2003, Leenders & Watkins-Colwell 2004.
Geographic distribution: From southern Michoacán and southern San Luis Potosí, Mexico, through Central America to central Ecuador, exclusive of southwestern and western Nicaragua (Savage 2002).
Ecological distribution: Dry forest, premontane evergreen forest, subtropical humid forest, and savanna between sea level and 1280 m.
Description: A medium-sized snake (SVL of largest specimen examined 357 mm); relative tail length 50–54% of SVL in males, 40–44% in females; divided nasal; 1 loreal; 1 preocular; 2 postoculars; 1 anterior and 2 posterior temporals; 8 supralabials, with the 4th and 5th entering orbit; dorsal scales smooth, without apical pits, in 21 rows at midbody, and 17 rows one head length anterior to vent; ventrals 121–126 in males, 127–129 in females; subcaudals 79–88 in males, 76–80 in females; anal plate divided.

Head brown, becoming darker laterally, upper

Plate 84: *Coniophanes fissidens* (KU 289798) EL SALVADOR: San Salvador: San Salvador (ca. 670 m). Photo: E. Greenbaum.

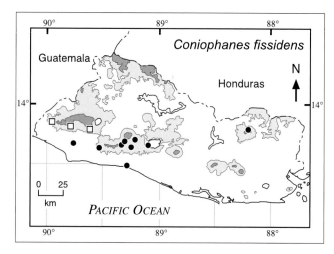

Map 76: Distribution of *Coniophanes fissidens* in El Salvador.
Closed circles represent examined-specimen locality records; open squares are published locality records. Light shading indicates ≥ 600–1200 m elevation; dark shading indicates elevations ≥ 1200 m; large bodies of freshwater are outlined in bold, black lines.

lips creamish white with irregular brown dots and flecks; dorsal and lateral surfaces of body grayish brown with dark brown vertebral stripes (2–3 scale rows wide) extending from snout to the tip of tail; two white spots in nuchal region usually present and followed by two creamish dorsolateral longitudinal stripes, 2–6 scale rows wide, almost white and very narrow anteriorly, becoming slightly broader and grading into pale brown posteriorly; sides of body dark brown; ventral side of head, body, and tail creamish white or yellow, becoming salmon-orange on the edges of the ventrals, with scattered small black spots on chin and throat scales and lateral margins of ventrals and subcaudals.

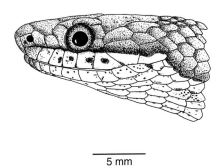

5 mm

Figure 33: *Coniophanes fissidens* (SMF 42814): Lateral view of head.

Plate 85: *Coniophanes piceivittis* (KU 291285) EL SALVADOR: San Miguel: Volcán de San Miguel (740 m). Photo: O. Komar.

Natural history: Mertens (1952d) noted that this snake is crepuscular and nocturnal, and feeds on small frogs in El Salvador. Campbell (1998a) noted this species can be active by day or night, and feeds upon small vertebrates, reptile eggs, earthworms, and lepidopteran larvae. Females lay clutches of 1–5 eggs from March–July. Stafford & Meyer (2000) noted caudal urotomy is common in this species. Savage (2002) noted this species can inflict a painful bite to humans; swelling can last for several days.

Specimens examined: La Libertad: Finca El Paraíso near Nuevo San Salvador [= Santa Tecla]: SMF 42707, 42812–14, 43026; Finca Los Cedros, vicinity Nuevo San Salvador [= Santa Tecla]: SMF 43105; Finca La Peña, near Nuevo San Salvador [= Santa Tecla]: (Live zoo specimen); 6.9 km E La Libertad, 20 m: KU 86173. Morazán: Cerro Cacahuatique, 1030 m: KU 291310. San Salvador: San Salvador: KU 289798, AMNH 67243; 3 km SE Ilopango, Cantón Asino: KU 183858. Sonsonate: Hacienda San Antonio near Sonsonate: SMF 42495; Hacienda Chilata, 610 m: MVZ 40418.

Published locality records: Ahuachapán: Parque Nacional El Imposible: YPM 12366 (Leenders 2003, Leenders & Watkins-Colwell 2004); Município San Pedro Puxtla, Cantón La Concepción, Cooperativa Concepción Miramar (13.810°N, 89.807°W), 950 m: YPM 12365 (Leenders & Watkins-Colwell 2004). Sonsonate: Município Izalco, Cantón Cruz Grande, Finca Nuevos Horizontes (13.821°N, 89.653°W), 1280 m: YPM 12305, 12364 (Leenders & Watkins-Colwell 2004).

***Coniophanes piceivittis* Cope 1870**
(Culebra de Tres Rayas)
Plate 85, Map 77, Figure 34ab

1870 *Coniophanes piceivittis* Cope, Proc. Amer. Phil.

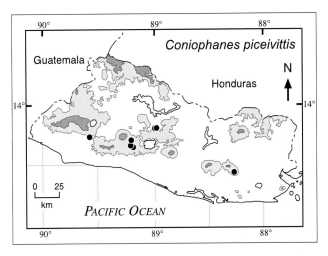

Map 77: Distribution of *Coniophanes piceivittis* in El Salvador.
Closed circles represent examined-specimen locality records; open squares are published locality records. Light shading indicates 600–1200 m elevation; dark shading indicates elevations ≥ 1200 m; large bodies of freshwater are outlined in bold, black lines.

Soc. 11(1869): 149; type locality: Chihuitan, Oaxaca, Mexico.
Coniophanes piceivittis piceivittis: Mertens 1952d.
Coniophanes piceivittis: Peters & Orejas-Miranda 1970, Villa et al. 1988, Dueñas et al. 2001, Köhler 2001a, 2003b, Leenders 2003.
Geographic distribution: From southern Tamaulipas and Guerrero, Mexico, to the Isthmus of Tehuantepec, south and east to northwestern Costa Rica; Atlantic drainage uplands of central Honduras and Nicaragua (Savage 2002).
Ecological distribution: Dry forest between 450 and 740 m.

a

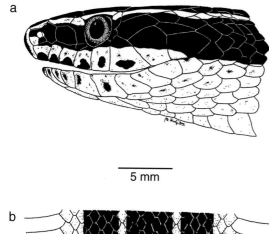

5 mm

b

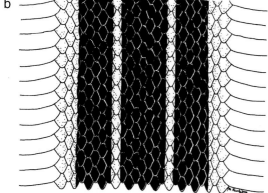

Figure 34: *Coniophanes piceivittis* (SMF 60745): a. lateral view of head, b. dorsal color pattern.

Description: A medium-sized snake (SVL of largest specimen examined 465 mm); relative tail length 37% of SVL in males, 33–55% in females; divided nasal; 1 loreal; 2 preoculars; 2 postoculars; 1 anterior and 2 posterior temporals; 8 supralabials, with the 4th and 5th entering orbit; dorsal scales smooth, without apical pits, in 25 rows at midbody, and 19–21 rows one head length anterior to vent; ventrals 165 in males, 162–170 in females; subcaudals 91 in males, 82–88 in females; anal plate divided.

Head dark brown dorsally and laterally, except lower portions of supralabials; infralabials and chin region are cream with some brown mottling; a narrow yellow stripe extends from rostral along canthus rostralis and above eye to upper temporal region (may be discontinuous); dorsal ground color dark brown with a pair of dorsolateral yellow (cream in preservative) longitudinal stripes (on all of dorsal scale row 9 and 1/2 to 2/3 of adjacent scale rows) beginning 3–4 scales behind parietals; dark brown lateral coloration reaches to 3rd dorsal scale row where it covers about half of the scales; all of scale rows 1 and 2 and adjacent part of the 3rd dorsal scale row yellowish to cream as are the ventrals; venter immaculate or with few scattered brown dots.

Natural history: O. Komar (field notes) collected an adult female with eggs among rubbish at a coffee plantation at Volcán de San Miguel, Depto. San Miguel in May. Mertens (1952d) reported a specimen found under a rock in El Salvador.

Specimens examined: <u>Cuscatlán</u>: Tenancingo, Copalchan, El Sitio de los Sánchez: KU 183859; 2.5 km E Tenancingo, Río Quezalapa, 450 m: KU 183860. <u>San Miguel</u>: Volcán de San Miguel, 740 m: KU 291285. <u>San Salvador</u>: Doble vía near Parque Cuscatlán: SMF 60745; San Salvador, Ciudad Universitaria, 700 m: KU 183861; San Salvador, CAMRS: USNM 167215; Planes de Renderos: UU 5394. <u>Sonsonate</u>: Finca La Joya, 587 m: km 48 road San Salvador–Sonsonate: SMF 43187.

Genus *Conophis*

This genus includes two species of mildly venomous colubrids that are distributed from Veracruz, Mexico, to eastern Honduras and the Yucatán Peninsula on the Atlantic versant, and from Nayarit, Mexico, to Costa Rica on the Pacific versant (Savage 2002, Köhler 2003b).

Conophis lineatus (Duméril, Bibron & Duméril 1854)
(Lagartijera Rayada)
Plate 86, Map 78, Figure 35ab

1854 *Tomodon lineatum* Duméril, Bibron & Duméril, Erp. Gén. 7: 936; type locality: Mexico.
Conophis lineatus: K. Schmidt 1928, Peters & Orejas-Miranda 1970, Villa et al. 1988, Köhler 1996, Dueñas et al. 2001, Köhler 2001a, 2003b, Leenders 2003.
Conophis pulcher plagosus: Mertens 1952d.
Conophis lineatus dunni: Wellman 1963.
Geographic distribution: From Veracruz, Mexico, to eastern Honduras on the Atlantic versant, and from Oaxaca, Mexico, to southwestern Costa Rica (possibly) on the Pacific versant (Savage 2002).
Ecological distribution: Dry forest and savanna between sea level and 1170 m.
Description: A medium-sized snake (SVL of largest specimen examined 818 mm); relative tail

Plate 86: *Conophis lineatus* (KU 289911) EL SALVA-DOR: Usulután: Isla San Sebastián (20 m). Photo: E. Greenbaum.

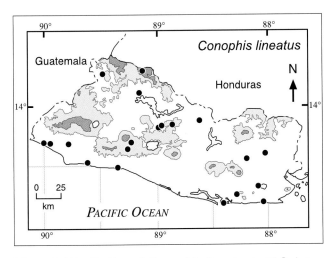

Map 78: Distribution of *Conophis lineatus* in El Salvador.
Closed circles represent examined-specimen locality records; open squares are published locality records. Light shading indicates 600–1200 m elevation; dark shading indicates elevations ≥ 1200 m; large bodies of freshwater are outlined in bold, black lines.

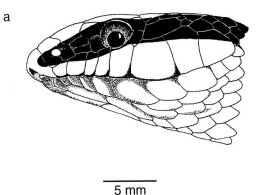

5 mm

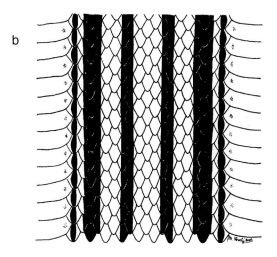

Figure 35: *Conophis lineatus* (SMF 42019): a. lateral view of head, b. dorsal color pattern.

length 26–49% of SVL in males, 21–30% in females; divided nasal; 1 loreal; 1 to 2 preoculars; 2 to 3 postoculars; 1–3 anterior and 2–4 posterior temporals; 8 supralabials, with the 4th and 5th entering orbit; 9–10 infralabials; dorsal scales smooth, without apical pits, in 19 rows at midbody, and 17 rows one head length anterior to vent; ventrals 161–171 in males, 165–178 in females; 58–83 subcaudals in males, 54–74 in females; anal plate divided.

Dorsum pale brown to gray with six dark brown or black longitudinal stripes extending the length of the body and well onto the tail. The first stripe is very narrow and runs through the first dorsal scale row, sometimes it is fragmented. The second stripe involves the 3rd and 4th, or 2nd, 3rd, and 4th dorsal scale rows, and the third (paramedian) stripe involves the 7th and 8th, or 7th, 8th, and 9th dorsal scale rows. The venter is immaculate. Head with a dark brown or black lateral stripe from temporal region to nostril, reaching the edge of the rostral. The paramedian stripes extend across the parietals and along the supraocular-frontal suture to the frontal-prefrontal border.

Natural history: E. Greenbaum (field notes) recorded an adult of this species on a beach near a bird nest at midday at Isla San Sebastián, Depto. Usulután in July. Campbell (1998a) noted this diurnal species eats lizards, small mammals, and bird eggs; females lay 4–6 eggs in June or July. Stafford & Meyer (2000) noted this species has large rear fangs that can produce burning pain, bleeding, and swelling in humans; snakes were noted as potential prey items. Savage (2002) noted the effects of a bite from this species are dangerous and can last up to several days.

Specimens examined: <u>Ahuachapán</u>: Barra de Santiago: KU 183865. <u>Cabañas</u>: Ilobasco: MUHNES 546; Sensuntepeque, Cantón Sapo de Oro: KU 183870. <u>Chalatenango</u>: Los Esesmiles, Cerro El Pital, western slopes near La Palma, 1170 m: SMF 43215; 20 km W Chalatenango: TCWC 23640. <u>Cuscatlán</u>: 2 km SE Tenancingo, Tenancingo: KU 183863; 0.5 km E Tenancingo: KU 183867; 7 km E Tenancingo, Cantón El Tablón: KU 183868. <u>La Libertad</u>: Finca El Paraíso, near Nuevo San Salvador [= Santa Tecla]: SMF 42203; Mizata, km 89 Carretera de la Litoral: KU 183864; Puerto de La Libertad: USNM 192600. <u>La Paz</u>: Hacienda La Providencia: KU 183866 (*). <u>La Unión</u>: Playa El Icacal, 5 m: MUHNES C–30–1350. <u>Morazán</u>: Montecristo Mine, 213 m: MVZ 40436; 4.8 km W Montecristo Mine, 198 m: MVZ 40437; Divisadero: FMNH 10999. <u>San Miguel</u>: Laguna de Olomega, 61 m: MVZ 40438–39. <u>San Miguel</u>: San Antonio: MUHNES 545. <u>San Salvador</u>: Instituto Tropical de Investigaciones Científicas, San Salvador, 770 m: SMF 43147, 77407–08, UU 5245. <u>Santa Ana</u>: SE Metapán, Hacienda San Diego: KU 183869. <u>Sonsonate</u>: El Zope: SMF 81295; ca. 19.3 km WNW Acajutla: MVZ 80002. <u>Usulután</u>: Isla San Sebastián, 13°10.01′N, 88°24.49′W, 20 m: KU 289911.

Genus *Crisantophis*

This monotypic genus is distributed from Guatemala along the Pacific versant to Costa Rica (Savage 2002).

Crisantophis nevermanni (Dunn 1937)
(Lagartijera de Nevermann)
Plate 87, Map 79, Figure 36ab

1937 *Conophis nevermanni* Dunn, Copeia 1937: 214; type locality: Río Poas de Aserri, (= a few kilometers south of San José), Costa Rica.
Crisantophis nevermanni: Hidalgo 1981a, Villa 1988, Dueñas et al. 2001, Köhler 2001a, 2003b.

Plate 87: *Crisantophis nevermanni* COSTA RICA: Guanacaste: Taboga (5 m). Photo: W. Van Devender.

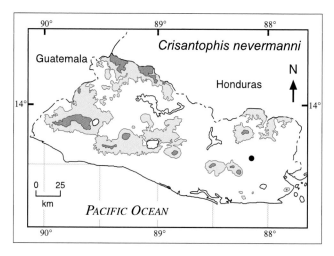

Map 79: Distribution of *Crisantophis nevermanni* in El Salvador.
Closed circles represent examined-specimen locality records; open squares are published locality records. Light shading indicates 600–1200 m elevation; dark shading indicates elevations ≥ 1200 m; large bodies of freshwater are outlined in bold, black lines.

Geographic distribution: Identical to genus.
Ecological distribution: Dry forest and savanna below 300 m.
Description: A medium-sized snake (SVL of single specimen examined 630 mm); relative tail length 28% of SVL; divided nasal; 1 loreal; 2 preoculars; 2 postoculars; 2 anterior and 2–3 posterior temporals; 8 supralabials, with the 4th and 5th entering orbit; 9–10 infralabials; dorsal scales smooth, without apical pits, in 19 rows at midbody, and 17 rows one head length anterior to vent; 166 ventrals, 84 subcaudals; anal plate divided.

Dorsal and lateral surfaces of body dark brown with four narrow, dirty white stripes; lateral stripes

a

5 mm

b

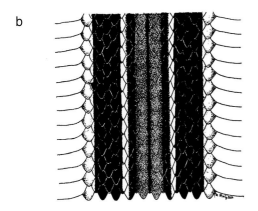

Figure 36: *Crisantophis nevermanni* (SMF 79844): a. lateral view of head, b. dorsal color pattern.

on 1st and 2nd rows, dorsolateral stripes on 6th and 7th rows; supralabials and infralabials dirty white with dark brown sutures; ventral surfaces dirty white with dark brown mottling on lateral margins of ventral scales.

Natural history: The single Salvadoran specimen was collected in "moist forest" in May (Hidalgo 1981a). Savage (2002) noted this is a diurnal and terrestrial species. Prey items include frogs, toads, and other snakes. A captive female laid three eggs in May and contained seven more.

Specimens examined: <u>San Miguel</u>: 10 km N San Miguel, Cantón San Antonio Chávez, 250 m: MUHNES 216.

Genus *Dryadophis*

The taxonomic composition of this genus has been debated for decades. Recent publications that include the three Central American species recognize *Dryadophis* as the valid genus for *D. dorsalis*, *D. melanolomus*, and *D. pleei* (e.g., Dueñas et al.

2001, Köhler 2001a, 2003b, Leenders 2003), which is consistent with a previous systematic evaluation of this group (Smith & Larsen 1974). However, Savage (2002) recognized *Mastigodryas* as the valid genus for these snakes, including the two species that occur in El Salvador, *M. dorsalis* and *M. melanolomus*. As this book went to press, Dixon & Tipton (2004) presented evidence that the nomenclature of Savage (2002) is correct, and with time, this change is likely to receive general acceptance by herpetologists.

Dryadophis dorsalis (Bocourt 1890)
(Lagartijera Lisa de Montaña)
Plate 88, Map 80

1890 *Drymobius (Eudryas) dorsalis* Bocourt, Misc. Sci. Mex., Rept. 1890: 724; type locality: Guatemala.
Eudryas dorsalis: Ahl 1940.
Dryadophis dorsalis: Stuart 1941, Mertens 1952d, Villa et al. 1988, Dueñas et al. 2001, Köhler 2001a, 2003b, Leenders 2003.
Mastigodryas dorsalis: Peters & Orejas-Miranda 1970.

Geographic distribution: From Guatemala to Nicaragua on both versants (Köhler 2003b).
Ecological distribution: Cloud forest and pine-oak forest between 450 and 2200 m.
Description: A medium-sized snake (SVL of largest specimen examined 1180 mm); relative tail length 35–48% of SVL in males, 40–44% in females; divided nasal; 1 loreal; 1 preocular; 2 postoculars; 9–10 supralabials, 4th, 5th and 6th enter orbit; 10–12 infralabials; 2 anterior and 2–3 posterior temporals; dorsal scales smooth, with two apical pits, in 17 rows at midbody, and 15 rows one head

Plate 88: *Dryadophis dorsalis* NICARAGUA: Matagalpa: Selva Negra (1300–1400 m). Photo: G. Köhler.

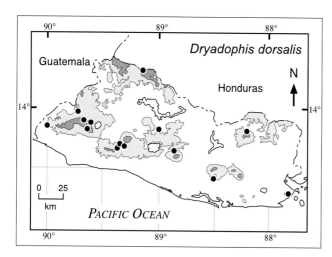

Map 80: Distribution of *Dryadophis dorsalis* in El Salvador.
Closed circles represent examined-specimen locality records; open squares are published locality records. Light shading indicates 600–1200 m elevation; dark shading indicates elevations ≥ 1200 m; large bodies of freshwater are outlined in bold, black lines.

length anterior to vent; ventrals 181–194 in males, 175–195 in females; subcaudals 133–142 in males, 126–134 in females; anal plate divided.

Dorsal color brown or olive-green with a distinct longitudinal dark brown dorsal stripe (on vertebral scale row and upper portions of adjacent scale rows) extending from neck to the tail; dorsal scales on anterior portion of body white edged; supralabials and scales on chin and throat yellow; ventrals yellowish becoming greenish laterally with two indistinct longitudinal whitish lines.

Natural history: E. Greenbaum (field notes) encountered a freshly killed DOR at the Usulután locality during the day in July. M. Veselý (field notes) observed two juveniles basking on plants (ca. 30–50 cm above the ground) on the edge of a footpath at Cerro Verde, Depto. Santa Ana in May.

Specimens examined: Ahuachapán: Parque Nacional El Imposible, La Fincona: MUHNES 1109. Chalatenango: Los Esesmiles, Cerro El Pital, 2225 m: MVZ 40409–10. Cuscatlán: 0.4 km N Tenancingo: KU 183920. La Libertad: Finca Los Cedros, about 1000 m: near Nuevo San Salvador [= Santa Tecla]: SMF 42430, 43199; Finca San José, 1250 m: near Nuevo San Salvador [= Santa Tecla]: SMF 43102; Los Chorros between Nuevo San Salvador [= Santa Tecla] and Colón, 700 m: SMF 43108. La Unión: Volcán Conchagua: KU 183918. Morazán: N slope Mt. Cacahuatique, 1341 m: MVZ

40408. San Vicente: Finca El Carmen, 1319 m: SMF 43200. Santa Ana: Chalchuapa, Laguna Cuscachapa, 13°58.8´N, 89°40.5´W, 690 m: MUHNES 1214; Cerro Verde, 13°49.5´N, 89°37.4´W, 1960 m: SMF 81477; Finca Los Andes, Volcán de Santa Ana: VH 95; Las Cruces coffee plantation, 1372 m: MVZ 40411. Usulután: rd to Santiago de María, 1 km after Desvío a Ozatlán, 13°24´N, 88°30´W, 450 m: KU 289864.

***Dryadophis melanolomus* (Cope 1868)**
(Lagartijera Lisa Olivácea)
Plate 89, Map 81

1868 *Masticophis melanolomus* Cope, Journ. Acad. Nat. Sci. Philadelphia 1868: 134; type locality: Yucatán, Mexico.
Dryadophis melanolomus: Hidalgo 1981b, Villa et al. 1988, Dueñas et al. 2001, Köhler 2001a, 2003b, Leenders 2003.
Geographic distribution: From Tamaulipas, Mexico, to western Panama on the Atlantic versant, and from Nayarit, Mexico, to central Panama on the Pacific versant (Savage 2002).
Ecological distribution: Dry forest and savanna between sea level and 750 m.
Description: A medium-sized snake (SVL of largest specimen examined 980 mm); relative tail length 36–39% of SVL in males, 35–38% in females; divided nasal; 1 loreal; 1 preocular; 2 postoculars; 9 supralabials, 4th, 5th and 6th enter orbit; 8–9 infralabials; 2 anterior and 2 posterior temporals; dorsal scales smooth, with two apical pits, in 17 rows at midbody, and 15 rows one head length anterior to vent; ventrals 186 in a female; subcaudals 132 in a female; anal plate divided. Three specimens of *D. melanolomus* from the Bay Islands (KU collection) and four specimens of *D. melanolomus* from Nicaragua (SMF collection) were included in the study to provide the following data: ventrals 176–182 in males, 183–193 in females; subcaudals 93–107 in males, 96–99 in females.

Adult specimens have uniformly olive-brown or tan dorsal coloration; ventral scales creamy yellow with tan lateral parts; supralabials, infralabials, and scales on chin and throat with brown mottling on posterior margins; contrary to the more or less uniformly colored adults, the juveniles exhibit a banded pattern which is usually more distinct on the anterior third of the body.
Natural history: Mertens (1952d) noted that this snake is easily irritated and tends to bite; when

Plate 89: *Dryadophis melanolomus* NICARAGUA: Rivas: Mobacho (5 m). Photo: G. Köhler.

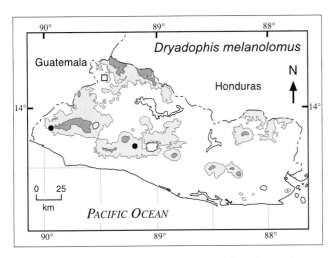

Map 81: Distribution of *Dryadophis melanolomus* in El Salvador.
Closed circles represent examined-specimen locality records; open squares are published locality records. Light shading indicates 600–1200 m elevation; dark shading indicates elevations ≥ 1200 m; large bodies of freshwater are outlined in bold, black lines.

excited it vibrates its tail rapidly. Campbell (1998a) noted this diurnal species feeds on small vertebrates and reptile eggs; females lay 2–5 eggs from August–November. Savage (2002) noted that juveniles might eat insects and clutch size increases with body size in adult females.

Specimens examined: Ahuachapán: Parque Nacional El Imposible: MUHNES 1194. San Salvador: San Salvador: ZMB 35704–05.

Published locality records: Santa Ana: flat fields surrounding Laguna San Diego at Hacienda San Diego, 6 km S Metapán, 470 m (Hidalgo 1981b).

Genus *Drymarchon*

Indigo snakes (genus *Drymarchon*) comprise a widespread group of large colubrid snakes (up to 3 m total length). *Drymarchon* has a disjunct distribution in the southeastern United States, Trinidad and Tobago, and from southern Texas, USA, and southern Sonora, Mexico, to southern Brazil, Paraguay, and northern Argentina on the Atlantic versant, and to northwestern Peru on the Pacific versant (Savage 2002). Throughout most of the 20th century, *Drymarchon* has been considered monotypic (e.g., McCranie 1980). Recently, two former subspecies (*D. couperi* and *D. melanurus*) were raised to the status of full species and a new species, *D. caudomaculatus*, was described from Venezuela (Collins 1991, Wüster et al. 2001). However, because the multivariate study of Wüster et al. (2001) included only eight Central American specimens (none from El Salvador), we prefer to recognize *"melanurus"* as a subspecies of *D. corais* until the systematics of the Indigo snakes is examined with additional specimens or molecular data.

Drymarchon corais (Boie 1827)
(Voladora de Cola Negra)
Plate 90, Map 82

1827 *Coluber corais* Boie, Isis von Oken 1827: 537; type locality: America.
Drymarchon corais melanurus: Ahl 1940.
Drymarchon corais unicolor: Mertens 1952d, Peters & Orejas-Miranda 1970, McCranie 1980.
Drymarchon corais: Villa et al. 1988, Köhler 1996, Dueñas et al. 2001, Köhler 2001a, Köhler 2003b, Leenders 2003.

Geographic distribution: Identical to genus.
Ecological distribution: Dry forest, premontane evergreen forest, subtropical humid forest, pine-oak forest, and cloud forest between 200 and 1200 m.
Description: A very large snake (SVL of largest specimen examined 2030 mm); relative tail length 18–24% of SVL in males, 17–24% in females; single nasal; 1 loreal; 1 preocular; 2 postoculars; 7–9 supralabials, 4th and 5th enter orbit; 8–9 infralabials; 2 anterior and 2 posterior temporals; dorsal scales smooth, with two apical pits, in 17 rows at midbody, and 15 rows one head length anterior to vent; ventrals 174–203 in males, 195–201 in females; subcaudals 65–83 in males, 54–81 in females; anal plate entire.

Dorsal and lateral surfaces of head and body

Plate 90: *Drymarchon corais* (KU 289805) EL SALVA-DOR: Ahuachapán: Finca Concepción Miramar (920 m). Photo: E. Greenbaum.

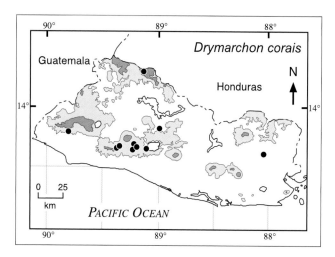

Map 82: Distribution of *Drymarchon corais* in El Salvador.
Closed circles represent examined-specimen locality records; open squares are published locality records. Light shading indicates 600–1200 m elevation; dark shading indicates elevations ≥ 1200 m; large bodies of freshwater are outlined in bold, black lines.

grayish to reddish brown or olive-tan becoming gradually darker posteriorly so that the posterior part of body and tail are uniformly dark grayish brown to black (also on ventral surfaces); dorsum usually with black mottling that may show fusion to black diagonal streaks; lateral head with four black streaks radiating out from below eye on posterior portions of supralabials, usually continuing onto infralabials; a distinct black oblique bar is usually present on the side of the neck; ventrals cream with transverse black streaks extending 1/3 to 1/2 across venter.

Natural history: E. Greenbaum (field notes) recorded an adult from a tree during the day at Finca Concepción Miramar, Depto. Ahuachapán in February. Fitch (1970) noted this species lays 4–11 eggs in subtropical areas. Campbell (1998a) noted that this diurnal species feeds upon most terrestrial vertebrates; females lay eggs from May–July. Stafford & Meyer (2000) noted adult males may engage in ritualized combat. Savage (2002) added that fish and turtles are included in the diet of this species.

Specimens examined: Ahuachapán: Finca Concepción Miramar, 13°48.46´N, 89°48.03´W, 920 m: KU 289805. Chalatenango: Los Esesmiles, Cerro El Pital: MVZ 40421. Cuscatlán: 0.2 km E Tenancingo: KU 183872. La Libertad: Finca Astillero, about 1050 m: near Nuevo San Salvador [= Santa Tecla]: SMF 42872; Finca San José, about 1150 m: near Nuevo San Salvador [= Santa Tecla]: SMF 42877; Finca Sta. Elena near Cuscatlán, 900 m: SMF 43195. Morazán: Divisadero, 198 m: MVZ 40420. San Salvador: Instituto Tropical de Investigaciones Científicas, San Salvador, 700 m: SMF 77409–10, 81486; San Salvador: ZMB 35716–17; 2.3 km SE Ilopango, Cantón Asino: KU 183873; Planes de Renderos: UU 5250.

Genus *Drymobius*

This genus includes four species of snakes that are distributed from southern Texas, USA, and Sonora, Mexico, through Central America to Ecuador, the Guianas, Bolivia, Peru, and Brazil (Savage 2002). Two species occur in El Salvador.

Drymobius chloroticus (Cope 1886)
(Ranera Verdosa Montaña)
Plate 91, Map 83

1886 *Dendrophidium chloroticum* Cope, Proc. Amer. Phil. Soc. 23: 278; type locality: Guatemala. *Drymobius chloroticus*: Uzzell & Starrett 1958, Wilson 1970, 1975, Villa et al. 1988, Dueñas et al. 2001, Köhler 2001a, 2003b.
Geographic distribution: From Oaxaca and southern San Luis Potosí, Mexico, to central Nicaragua (Köhler 2003b).
Ecological distribution: Cloud forest and pine-oak forest between 1800 and 2200 m.
Description: A medium-sized snake (SVL of largest specimen examined 825 mm); relative tail length 45–48% of SVL in males, 46% in single

Plate 91: *Drymobius chloroticus* NICARAGUA: Matagalpa: Selva Negra (1300–1400 m). Photo: G. Köhler.

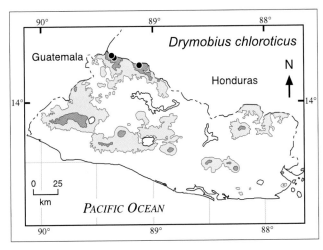

Map 83: Distribution of *Drymobius chloroticus* in El Salvador.
Closed circles represent examined-specimen locality records; open squares are published locality records. Light shading indicates 600–1200 m elevation; dark shading indicates elevations ≥ 1200 m; large bodies of freshwater are outlined in bold, black lines.

female; divided nasal; 1 loreal; 1–2 preoculars; 2–3 postoculars; 2 anterior and 2 posterior temporals; 9 supralabials, 4th, 5th and 6th enter orbit, 9–10 infralabials; dorsal scales keeled (except the first 3 rows), with two apical pits (a single pit on some scales on anterior body), in 15–17 rows at midbody, and 15 rows one head length anterior to vent; ventrals 160–167 in males, 153 to more than 165 (specimen damaged) in females; subcaudals 117–118 in males, data for females not available (incomplete tails); anal plate divided.

Dorsal ground color of head, body, and tail uniform bright green (bluish green in preservative),

dorsal coloration extending onto lateral portions of ventrals and subcaudals; lower margins of supralabials and ventral surfaces of head, body, and tail yellow or cream.

Specimens examined: <u>Chalatenango</u>: Los Esesmiles, Cerro El Pital: MVZ 40427. <u>Santa Ana</u>: Hacienda Montecristo: SMF 81333, 81344; Hacienda Los Planes de Montecristo, Metapán, 1800 m: VH 107; same locality at 2150 m: SMF 81516; same locality at 2200 m: KU 62096.

Drymobius margaritiferus (Schlegel 1837)
(Ranera Salpicada)
Plate 92, Map 84, Figure 37

1837 *Drymobius margaritiferus* Schlegel, Essai Physion. Serpens 2: 184; type locality: New Orleans (in error).
Drymobius margaritiferus occidentalis: Mertens 1952d, Rand 1957, Wilson 1974a.
Drymobius margaritiferus: Wilson & Meyer 1985, Villa et al. 1988, Dueñas et al. 2001, Köhler 2001a, 2003b, Leenders 2003, Leenders & Watkins-Colwell 2004.
Geographic distribution: From southern Texas, USA, to northern Colombia on the Atlantic versant, and from southern Sonora, Mexico, through Central America to Panama (Savage 2002).
Ecological distribution: Dry forest and savanna between sea level and 800 m.
Description: A medium-sized snake (SVL of

Plate 92: *Drymobius margaritiferus* (KU 289908) EL SALVADOR: Usulután: Isla San Sebastian (20 m). Photo: E. Greenbaum.

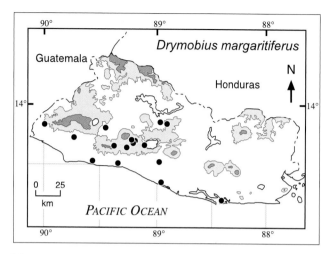

Map 84: Distribution of *Drymobius margaritiferus* in El Salvador.
Closed circles represent examined-specimen locality records; open squares are published locality records. Light shading indicates 600–1200 m elevation; dark shading indicates elevations ≥ 1200 m; large bodies of freshwater are outlined in bold, black lines.

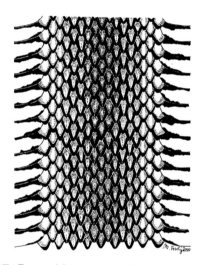

Figure 37. *Drymobius margaritiferus* (SMF 81284): Dorsal color pattern.

largest specimen examined 840 mm); relative tail length 50–65% of SVL in males, 57–61% in females; divided nasal; 1 loreal; 1 preocular; 2 postoculars; 2 anterior and 2 posterior temporals; 9 supralabials, 4th, 5th and 6th enter orbit, 8–11 infralabials; dorsal scales keeled, with two apical pits, in 17 rows at midbody, and 15–16 rows one head length anterior to vent; ventrals 143–158 in males, 143–149 in females; subcaudals 133–138 in males, 127–133 in females; anal plate divided.

Dorsum dark brown with speckled appearance because of yellow, yellowish green, or orange spots on each dorsal scale, scales edged posteriorly with black (more pronounced on dorsal than on lateral surface of body); top of head tan to greenish brown with a dark brown or black inverted V-shaped mark on the nape; infralabials, chin, and throat yellow, venter yellow or cream with black on lateral edges of ventral plates.

Natural history: E. Greenbaum (field notes) recorded an adult near a shallow body of water at midday at Isla San Sebastián, Depto. Usulután in July. An active adult was collected from a shallow pond in a meadow at night at Bosque Cinquera, Depto. Cabañas in August; the pond contained calling *Physalaemus pustulosus* and *Leptodactylus melanonotus*. Rand (1957) collected an adult specimen during the day in tall grass on the brush-grown gully of a pasture at San Salvador, Depto. San Salvador in March. Campbell (1998a) noted this diurnal species eats small vertebrates, reptile eggs, and crickets; females lay 2–7 eggs from April–August. Stafford & Meyer (2000) noted that bites from this species may result in excessive bleeding to humans because of an anticoagulant.

Specimens examined: <u>Ahuachapán</u>: Parque Nacional El Imposible, 13°50.50´N, 89°58.51´W, 720 m: MUHNES C–30–1354. <u>Cabañas</u>: Bosque Cinquera, 13°53.13´N, 88°57.36´W, 400 m: KU 289988; 4 km SW Tejutepeque: KU 183876. <u>La Libertad</u>: Finca El Paraíso, near Nuevo San Salvador [= Santa Tecla]: SMF 42248, MVZ 40434; Finca Los Cedros: SMF 43103; Hacienda Zapotitán, Río Sucio, 457 m: MVZ 40423; Mizata, km 89 Carretera de la Litoral: KU 183875; Puerto de La Libertad: USNM 192599. <u>La Paz</u>: Santiago Nonualco: KU 183877; La Herradura: USNM 167216. <u>San Salvador</u>: Instituto Tropical de Investigaciones Científicas: SMF 81334; San Salvador, Parque Zoológico Nacional, 13°58.8´N, 89°11.9´W, 700 m: SMF 81284; San Salvador, near Parque Saburo-Hirao: MUHNES 31–560; San Salvador: FMNH 64950; San Salvador, Ciudad Universitaria: KU 183878; 2.4 km SE Ilopango, Cantón Asino: KU 183879–90. <u>Sonsonate</u>: Sonsonate: MVZ 78745. <u>Usulután</u>: Isla San Sebastián, 13°10.01´N, 88°24.49´W, 20 m: KU 289908. <u>Depto. unknown</u>: no specific locality: SMF 42817 (*).

Published locality records: <u>Ahuachapán</u>: Parque Nacional El Imposible, 750–780 m: YPM 12429 (Leenders & Watkins-Colwell 2004).

Genus *Enulius*

This genus includes five species of small, slender snakes that are distributed from Sinaloa, Mexico, to Colombia; also in Atlantic slope of Honduras, Nicaragua, Costa Rica, Panama, and Colombia.

Enulius flavitorques (Cope 1869)
(Collareja Común)
Plate 93, Map 85

1869 *Liophis flavitorques* Cope, Proc. Acad. Nat. Sci. Philadelphia 1868: 307; type locality: Río Magdalena, Colombia.
Enulius flavitorques: Mertens 1952d, Villa et al. 1988, Köhler 1996, Dueñas et al. 2001, Köhler 2001a, 2003b.
Geographic distribution: From southern Jalisco, Mexico, through Central America to Colombia on the Pacific versant; also on the Atlantic versant in Honduras, Nicaragua, and Colombia (Savage 2002).
Ecological distribution: Dry forest, premontane evergreen forest, subtropical humid forest, and savanna between sea level and 1100 m.
Description: A small snake (SVL of largest specimen examined 403 mm); relative tail length 34–54% of SVL in males, 38–54% in females; rostral projecting; divided nasal; 1 loreal; no preocular; 2 postoculars; 7 supralabials, 3rd and 4th enter orbit; 7 infralabials; 1 anterior and 2 posterior temporals; dorsal scales smooth, with one apical scale pit, in 17 rows throughout; ventrals 185–206 in males, 189–207 in females; subcaudals 69–107 in males, 89–113 in females; anal plate divided.

Dorsal surface of head dark brown from tip of snout posteriorly to about midlength of parietal scales; creamish nuchal collar present, covering posterior half of parietal scales and temporals, 1–2 dorsal rows, and 2–3 posterior supralabials; dorsal surfaces of body and tail uniformly dark brown, gradually becoming paler brown laterally to upper edge of 1st scale row on each side; ventral surface of head, body, and tail creamish white.
Natural history: O. Komar (field notes) recorded an adult from under a log on the side of a road in a coffee plantation at Volcán de San Miguel, Depto. San Miguel in May. Mertens (1952d) found a specimen in loose ground substrate in El Salvador. Savage (2002) noted this fossorial, diurnal, oviparous species has long fangs to feed upon small snake and lizard eggs.

Plate 93: *Enulius flavitorques* HONDURAS: Francisco Morazán: Santa Lucia. Photo: A. Sosa.

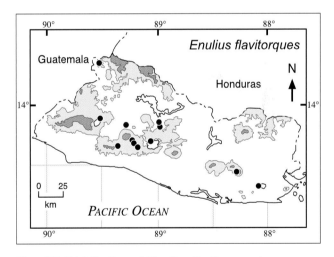

Map 85: Distribution of *Enulius flavitorques* in El Salvador.
Closed circles represent examined-specimen locality records; open squares are published locality records. Light shading indicates 600–1200 m elevation; dark shading indicates elevations ≥ 1200 m; large bodies of freshwater are outlined in bold, black lines.

Specimens examined: <u>Cuscatlán</u>: 0.6 km E Tenancingo: KU 183883; N Tenancingo, Santa Rita: KU 183884; E of Tenancingo: KU 183885–86. <u>La</u>

Libertad: Quetzaltepeque: CAS 94256; Finca Los Naranjos, Cumbre, about 1100 m: SMF 43004. San Miguel: Volcán de San Miguel, 740 m: KU 291282. San Salvador: Apulo, Lago de Ilopango, 460 m: SMF 43214; Instituto Tropical de Investigaciones Científicas, San Salvador, 700 m: SMF 77411–12; San Salvador, Colónia Zacamil: KU 183887; Planes de Renderos: UU 5503. San Miguel: Laguna de Olomega, 61 m: MVZ 40405–07. Santa Ana: Finca Serbia, 13°53´N, 89°31´W, 900 m: KU 289970.

Genus *Geophis*

This genus is composed of 40 species of snakes that are distributed from northern Mexico south and east through Central America to western Colombia (Savage 2002, Nieto-Montes de Oca 2003). Two species occur in the highlands of El Salvador.

Geophis fulvoguttatus Mertens 1952
(Culebrita Manchas Rojitas)
Plate 94, Map 86

1952 *Geophis fulvoguttatus* Mertens, Zool. Anz. 149: 134; type locality: Hacienda Montecristo, 2200 m, Cordillera Metapán, Depto. Santa Ana, El Salvador.
Geophis fulvoguttatus: Mertens 1952d, Downs 1967, Campbell et al. 1983, Villa et al. 1988, Köhler 1996, Dueñas et al. 2001, Köhler 2001, 2003b.
Geographic distribution: Northwestern El Salvador and western Honduras (Köhler 2003b).
Ecological distribution: Cloud forest and pine-oak forest between 1780 and 2200 m.
Description: A small snake (SVL of largest specimen examined 335 mm); relative tail length 13–16% of SVL in males, 20% in a single female;

Plate 94: *Geophis fulvoguttatus* (KU 57996) EL SALVADOR: Santa Ana: Hacienda Montecristo (2200 m). Preserved specimen. Photo: E. Greenbaum.

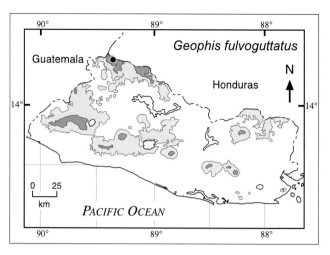

Map 86: Distribution of *Geophis fulvoguttatus* in El Salvador.
Closed circles represent examined-specimen locality records; open squares are published locality records. Light shading indicates 600–1200 m elevation; dark shading indicates elevations ≥ 1200 m; large bodies of freshwater are outlined in bold, black lines.

divided nasal; 1 loreal; no preocular; 1 postocular; 6 supralabials, 3rd and 4th enter orbit; 7 infralabials; no anterior and 1 posterior temporal; dorsal scales smooth, without apical pits, in 17 rows throughout; ventrals 135–157; subcaudals 24–36; anal plate entire.

Dorsal and lateral surfaces dark grayish brown with 18–22 yellow to red (pale brown in preservative) blotches on posterior part of body; ventral surfaces of head and body yellowish white, lateral edges of ventral scales mottled with dark brown; ventral surfaces of tail grayish brown.
Specimens examined: Santa Ana: Hacienda Montecristo, Cordillera de Metapán, 2200 m: SMF 43248, MUHNES 489, KU 57996, 183881.

Geophis rhodogaster (Cope 1868)
(Culebrita Gris)
Plate 95, Map 87

1868 *Colophrys rhodogaster* Cope; Proc. Acad. Nat. Sci. Philadelphia 1868: 130; type locality: "the elevated country in the neighborhood of the city of Guatemala."
Geophis rhodogaster: Downs 1967, Villa et al. 1988, Dueñas et al. 2001, Köhler 2001a, 2003b.
Geophis fulvoguttatus: Köhler 1996.
Geographic distribution: From eastern Chiapas, Mexico, to northwestern El Salvador (Köhler 2003b).

Plate 95: *Geophis rhodogaster* EL SALVADOR: Chalatenango: Cerro El Pital (2100 m). Photo: O. Komar.

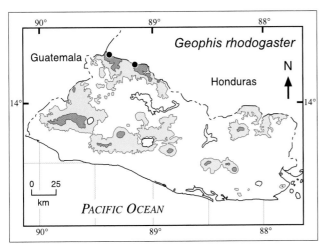

Map 87: Distribution of *Geophis rhodogaster* in El Salvador.
Closed circles represent examined-specimen locality records; open squares are published locality records. Light shading indicates 600–1200 m elevation; dark shading indicates elevations ≥ 1200 m; large bodies of freshwater are outlined in bold, black lines.

Ecological distribution: Cloud forest and pine-oak forest between 1780 and 2200 m.

Description: A small snake (SVL of largest specimen examined 312 mm); relative tail length 18–27% of SVL in males, 18–26% in females; rostral projecting; divided nasal; 1 loreal, no preocular, 1 postocular, 6 supralabials, 3rd and 4th enter orbit, 6–7 infralabials, no anterior and 2 posterior temporals, dorsal scales smooth, without apical pits, in 17 rows throughout; ventrals 129–137 in males, 140–144 in females; subcaudals 39–42 in males, 31–34 in females; anal plate entire.

Dorsal and lateral surfaces of body and tail dark grayish to reddish brown with a row of yellow spots on 2nd dorsal row; head dark brown with yellow flecks and mottling on rostral, nasals, loreal, and labials (the latter almost immaculate yellow); ventral surfaces of head, body, and tail yellowish white.

Natural history: O. Komar (field notes) received an individual from a worker tending to a shrubby fenceline in an agricultural field during the day at Cerro El Pital, Depto. Chalatenango in June.

Specimens examined: <u>Chalatenango</u>: Cerro El Pital, 2100 m: KU 291579. <u>Santa Ana</u>: Hacienda Montecristo, Cordillera de Metapán, 14°25´N, 89°22´W, 1780–1800 m: SMF 77413, VH 106; same locality at 2200 m: KU 57997–58000; Montecristo: MUHNES 490, 1141.

Genus *Imantodes*

This genus includes six species of elongate snakes that are distributed from Sonora and southern Tamaulipas, Mexico, south along both slopes to northwestern Ecuador and northeastern Argentina (Savage 2002). One species occurs in El Salvador.

Imantodes gemmistratus (Cope 1861)
(Cordelilla Manchada)
Plate 96, Map 88

1861 *Himantodes gemmistratus* Cope, Proc. Acad. Nat. Sci. Philadelphia 1861: 296; type locality: Near Izalco, San Salvador, El Salvador.
Himantodes cenchoa: Cope 1860.
Imantodes gemmistratus: K. Schmidt 1928, Mertens 1952d, Villa et al. 1988, Dueñas et al. 2001, Köhler 2001a, 2003b, Leenders 2003.

Geographic distribution: From southern Sonora and northern Veracruz, Mexico, to the Yucatán Peninsula (Atlantic versant) and eastern Panama (Pacific versant); sporadic records on the Atlantic versant in Honduras, Costa Rica, Panama, and Colombia (Savage 2002).

Ecological distribution: Dry forest between sea level and 750 m.

Description: A medium-sized snake (SVL of largest specimen examined 630 mm); relative tail length 37–44% of SVL in males, 38–45% in females; divided nasal; 1 loreal; 1 preocular; 2–3 postoculars; 8 supralabials, 4th and 5th, or 3rd, 4th and 5th enter orbit, 10–11 infralabials; 1–2 anterior and 1–3

Plate 96: *Imantodes gemmistratus* (KU 190964) GUATEMALA: Baja Verapaz: 3.5 km E La Unión Barrios, Río Sananjá (1646 m). Photo: J. A. Campbell (KU CT 7071).

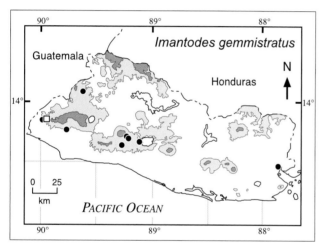

Map 88: Distribution of *Imantodes gemmistratus* in El Salvador.
Closed circles represent examined-specimen locality records; open squares are published locality records. Light shading indicates 600–1200 m elevation; dark shading indicates elevations ≥ 1200 m; large bodies of freshwater are outlined in bold, black lines.

posterior temporals; dorsal scales smooth, without apical pits, in 17 rows throughout; ventrals 219–229 in males, 213–244 in females; subcaudals 123–125 in males, 112–136 in females; anal plate divided.

Dorsal ground color of head and body pale brown to orange-tan with saddle-like, irregularly shaped orangish brown blotches with black edges; saddles on anterior body tend to fuse with smaller lateral blotches, forming irregular crossbars; on posterior body lateral blotches become smaller and

separated from dorsal saddles; top of head with several dark brown flecks (mostly on frontal and parietal plates); ventral surfaces cream or white with numerous irregular black spots.

Natural history: Campbell (1998a) noted that this mostly nocturnal species feeds upon lizards in the genus *Norops;* females lay 2–3 eggs during the rainy season. Savage (2002) noted this species is primarily arboreal and is often found just 1 m above the ground as it travels through low trees and shrubs.

Specimens examined: <u>Ahuachapán</u>: Finca San Benito: MUHNES 1149. <u>La Libertad</u>: Finca El Paraíso, Nuevo San Salvador [= Santa Tecla]: SMF 42249. <u>La Unión</u>: 19 km SW of El Salvador-Nicaragua [sic] border on Pan American Hwy: USNM 226390. <u>San Salvador</u>: San Salvador: ZMB 35700–701; San Salvador, Instituto Tropical de Investigaciones Científicas: KU 62099–100, SMF 81340; 3 km SE Ilopango, Cantón Asino: KU 183889–90. <u>Santa Ana</u>: Río Guajoyo near Cantón Paraíso de Culebras, 630 m: 43213. <u>Sonsonate</u>: Hacienda San Antonio, near Sonsonate: SMF 42219.

Published locality records: <u>Ahuachapán</u>: Parque Nacional El Imposible (Leenders 2003).

Genus *Lampropeltis*

This genus includes eight species of constricting snakes that are distributed from southeastern Canada and the northern United States to Ecuador and northern Venezuela (Savage 2002). One species occurs in El Salvador.

Lampropeltis triangulum (Lacepède 1789)
(Falsa Coral Roja)
Plate 97, Map 89, Figure 38

1789 *Coluber Triangulum* Lacepède, Hist. Nat. Quadr. Ovip. Serp. 2: 86; type locality: America.
Lampropeltis doliata polyzona: Mertens 1952d.
Lampropeltis triangulum oligozona: Peters & Orejas-Miranda 1970.
Lampropeltis triangulum stuarti: K. Williams 1978, 1994.
Lampropeltis triangulum: Villa et al. 1988, Dueñas et al. 2001, Köhler 2001a, 2003b, Leenders 2003.
Geographic distribution: From southeastern Canada and most of the continental United States, Mexico, and Central America to Ecuador and northern Venezuela (Savage 2002).
Ecological distribution: Dry forest, premontane

5 mm

Figure 38: *Lampropeltis triangulum* (SMF 75879): Lateral view of head.

Plate 97: *Lampropeltis triangulum* EL SALVADOR: no specific locality. Photo: T. Leenders.

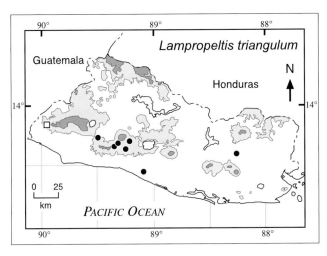

Map 89: Distribution of *Lampropeltis triangulum* in El Salvador.
Closed circles represent examined-specimen locality records; open squares are published locality records. Light shading indicates 600–1200 m elevation; dark shading indicates elevations ≥ 1200 m; large bodies of freshwater are outlined in bold, black lines.

evergreen forest, and subtropical humid forest between 400 and 1000 m.

Description: A medium-sized snake (SVL of largest specimen examined 1270 mm); relative tail length 16–19% of SVL in males, 16–17% in females; divided nasal; 1 loreal; 1 preocular; 2–3 postoculars; 7–8 supralabials, 3rd and 4th enter orbit; 1–2 anterior and 2–3 posterior temporals; dorsal scales smooth, without apical pits, in 21–23 rows at midbody, and 17–19 rows one head length anterior to vent; ventrals 221–231 in males, 234–244 in females; subcaudals 52–55 in males, 51–54 in females; anal plate entire.

A snake with a pattern similar to coral snakes

through head, body, and tail; the sequence of bands is red-black-yellow (white in preservative)-black-red; red scales without black pigment or only slightly black tipped, whereas the yellow (white in preservative) scales are moderately black tipped; most of the head is black with a V-shaped yellow mark across the snout; a yellow collar separates black head cap from first black ring that usually begins at the posterior edges of the parietals or slightly posterior to these.

Natural history: Campbell (1998a) noted that this species is mostly nocturnal and feeds upon lizards, snakes, mammals, and reptile eggs; females lay 5–12 eggs that hatch from July–August after 35–50 days of incubation. Savage (2002) added that this species preys on birds and their eggs.

Specimens examined: <u>La Libertad</u>: Finca El Paraíso near Nuevo San Salvador [= Santa Tecla]: SMF 42251–52, 42845; Finca Los Cedros, about 1000 m: Cumbre near Nuevo San Salvador [= Santa Tecla]: SMF 43166; 6.8 km W Ateos: LACM 38194. <u>La Paz</u>: Municipio de San Luis La Harradura, ca. Comalapa airport, 400 m: KU CT 11895. <u>San Miguel</u>: Municipio de Chapeltique: MUHNES C–30–1532. <u>San Salvador</u>: San Salvador: SMF 75878–79.
Published locality records: <u>Ahuachapán</u>: Parque Nacional El Imposible (Leenders 2003).

Genus *Leptodeira*

The nine species of this genus are distributed from southern Texas, United States, and Sonora, Mexico, to southeastern Brazil on the Atlantic versant and northern Chile on the Pacific versant (Savage 2002). Three species occur in El Salvador.

Leptodeira annulata (Linneaus 1758)
(Escombrera Común)
Plate 98, Map 90

Plate 98: *Leptodeira annulata* (MUHNES C-30-1351)
EL SALVADOR: San Salvador: Colónia Costa Rica
(670 m). Photo: E. Greenbaum.

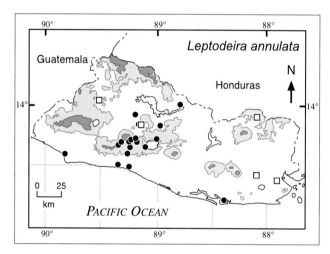

Map 90: Distribution of *Leptodeira annulata* in El
Salvador.
Closed circles represent examined-specimen locality records;
open squares are published locality records. Light shading
indicates 600–1200 m elevation; dark shading indicates elevations ≥ 1200 m; large bodies of freshwater are outlined in bold,
black lines.

1758 *Coluber annulatus* Linnaeus, Systema
Naturae, ed. 10: 215; type locality: Amazon Basin;
restricted by Duellman (1958) to lower Río Amazon,
Pará, Brazil.
Leptodeira rhombifera: Mertens 1952d, Brongersma
1954a, Rand 1957.
Leptodeira annulata annulata: Ahl 1940.
Leptodeira rhombifer: Rand 1957.
Leptodeira annulata rhombifera: Duellman 1958,
Uzzell & Starrett 1958, Peters & Orejas-Miranda
1970.

Leptodeira annulata: Villa et al. 1988, Köhler 1996,
Dueñas et al. 2001, Köhler 2001a, 2003b, Leenders
2003, Leenders & Watkins-Colwell 2004.
Geographic distribution: From southern
Tamaulipas and Guerrero, Mexico, through Central
America to southeastern Brazil and northern
Argentina on the Atlantic versant (including
Margarita, Trinidad, and Tobago), and to Ecuador
on the Pacific versant. Sporadic records from the
Atlanic drainage of Honduras, Nicaragua, Costa
Rica, and Panama (Savage 2002).
Ecological distribution: Dry forest, premontane
evergreen forest, subtropical humid forest, and
savanna between sea level and 1200 m.
Description: A medium-sized snake (SVL of
largest specimen examined 640 mm); relative tail
length 25–37% of SVL in males, 24–35% in females;
divided nasal; 1 loreal; 2–3 preoculars; 2 (rarely 3)
postoculars; 8 supralabials, 4th and 5th enter orbit;
9–11 infralabials; 1 anterior and 2 (rarely 1) posterior temporals; dorsal scales smooth, with two
apical pits, in 21–23 rows at midbody, and 17 (rarely
19) rows one head length anterior to vent; ventrals
160–175 in males, 161–175 in females; subcaudals
62–85 in males, 65–84 in females; anal plate divided.

Dorsal ground color tan, gray, olive-brown, or
pale brown with large brown blotches edged in dark
brown or black that are usually wider dorsally;
dorsal blotches can be fused or separated by 1–3
scales in the vertebral scale row; dark brown
lateral spots alternating with dorsal blotches are
present on the body and tail; head scales usually
darker in the center; dark brown postocular stripe
extends to posterior supralabial scale; supralabials
and anterior infralabials dark brown posteriorly;
ventral surface pale yellow or cream.
Natural history: E. Greenbaum (field notes)
collected an adult specimen as it crawled through a
village at night at Isla San Sebastián, Usulután in
July. O. Komar (field notes) collected several adults
during the day under leaf litter next to a river at
Guadalupe, Depto. La Libertad in April. Mertens
(1952d) noted that this snake is nocturnal and feeds
mostly on frogs in El Salvador. Brongersma (1954a)
noted a *Physalaemus pustulosus* in the stomach of
a male collected near a highway west of La Unión,
km 180–181 E, Depto. La Unión. Rand (1957) noted
this species feeds upon *Physalaemus pustulosus*
and *Smilisca baudinii* around shallow bodies of
water in pastures in San Salvador, Depto. San
Salvador. Uzzell & Starrett (1958) collected a male

at night from low bushes over a stream in "pastureland" 22.1 km N San Salvador, Depto. San Salvador. Savage (2002) noted this nocturnal species feeds upon frogs and toads. Bites can cause "a severe reaction" in humans. Leenders & Watkins-Colwell (2004) collected an adult female under a log at the edge of a small puddle in a drying bed of Río Sapo (Depto. Morazán) where metamorphs and tadpoles of *Scinax staufferi* and *Rana maculata* were present.

Specimens examined: Ahuachapán: Valle Doña María: SMF 77418 (*). Cuscatlán: 25.8 km E San Salvador: KU 41544; Tenancingo, Copalchan: KU 183894–95. La Libertad: Finca El Paraíso, Nuevo San Salvador [= Santa Tecla]: SMF 42250, 42260; Finca San José, about 1200 m: near Nuevo San Salvador [= Santa Tecla]: SMF 42865; Los Chorros among Nuevo San Salvador [= Santa Tecla] and Colón: SMF 43053; La Libertad: KU 183893; 10 km E La Libertad: KU 183903; Puerto de La Libertad: USNM 192601; Guadalupe: KU 291290–92, MUHNES C–30–1533–34. San Salvador: Instituto Tropical de Investigaciones Científicas, San Salvador, 700 m: SMF 43219–26, 77414–17, KU 62101–05, 63828; San Antonio Abad, San Salvador: SMF 43227; same locality at 670 m: MVZ 40446; Colónia Luz, west of San Salvador: SMF 43228; San Salvador: ZMB 35698; San Salvador, 670 m: FMNH 64957, 64961–63; Colonia Costa Rica: MUHNES C–30–1351; 22.1 km N San Salvador on rd to Citalá: UMMZ 117283; no specific locality: FMNH 64958–60 (*); 29 km N San Salvador: KU 140070; 3 km SE Ilopango, Cantón Asino: KU 183892, 183896–902, 183908; San Salvador, Ciudad Universitaria, 700 m: KU 183904, 183906–07. Sonsonate: 20 km WSW Acajutla, 20 m: KU 103204. Usulután: Isla San Sebastián, 13°10.01′N, 88°24.49′W, 20 m: KU 289913.

Published locality records: La Unión: near highway, W of La Unión, km 180–181 E: RMNH 9952 (Brongersma 1954a). Morazán: Município Arambala, Cantón Cumaro, Río Sapo (13.959°N, 88.132°W), 674 m: YPM 14003 (Leenders & Watkins-Colwell 2004). San Miguel: Laguna Aramuaca: RMNH 9951 (Brongersma 1954a). San Salvador: 22.1 km N San Salvador (Uzzell & Starrett 1958). Santa Ana: near Río Amayo, about 3 km E of the Agua Caliente railroad crossing: RMNH 9949 (Brongersma 1954a).

Leptodeira nigrofasciata Günther 1868
(Escombrera Falsa Coral Negra)
Plate 99, Map 91

Plate 99: *Leptodeira nigrofasciata* (KU 291293) EL SALVADOR: La Libertad: 2 km S Zaragoza (640 m). Photo: O. Komar.

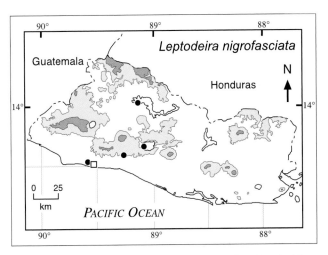

Map 91: Distribution of *Leptodeira nigrofasciata* in El Salvador.
Closed circles represent examined-specimen locality records; open squares are published locality records. Light shading indicates 600–1200 m elevation; dark shading indicates elevations ≥ 1200 m; large bodies of freshwater are outlined in bold, black lines.

1868 *Leptodeira nigrofasciata* Günther, Ann. Mag. Nat. Hist. 1(4): 425; type locality: Nicaragua.
Leptodeira nigrofasciata: Hidalgo 1980a, Dueñas et al. 2001, Köhler 2001a, 2003b, Leenders 2003.
Geographic distribution: From Guerrero, Mexico, along the Pacific versant to Costa Rica; also on the Caribbean versant of northwestern Honduras (Savage 2002).
Ecological distribution: Dry forest and savanna between sea level and 420 m.
Description: A medium-sized snake (SVL of largest specimen examined 325 mm); relative tail length 31–32% of SVL in males (no Salvadoran females available); divided nasal; 1 loreal; 1

preocular; 2 postoculars; 8 supralabials, 3rd, 4th, and 5th enter orbit; 10 infralabials; 1 anterior and 2 posterior temporals; dorsal scales smooth, with two apical pits, in 19 rows at midbody, and 17 rows one head length anterior to vent; ventrals 170–184 in males; subcaudals 65–78 in males, no data available for Salvadoran females; anal plate divided.

Dorsal ground color cream to pale gray with large, dark brown transverse blotches, extending onto lateral portions of ventrals; dorsal blotches usually separated from each other by 1–2 scales; middorsally top of head dark brown, upper and lower labials with dark brown spots; chin spotted with dark brown medially; tail with transverse dark brown bands; ventral surface dirty white.

Natural history: O. Komar (field notes) collected an adult under leaf litter near a river during the day at Guadalupe, Depto. La Libertad in April. Duellman (1958) noted a *Gymnophthalmus speciosus* as a prey item of this species. Savage (2002) noted this species is nocturnal and terrestrial.

Specimens examined: Cuscatlán: Colima Dry Forest, 14°03´N, 89°08´W, 244–420 m: uncollected specimen, ID confirmed by E. Greenbaum & O. Komar. La Libertad: Playa El Balsamar, approx. 30 km W La Libertad, 10 m: VH 72; Guadalupe: KU 291293. San Salvador: 3 km SE Ilopango, Cantón Asino: KU 183909. Depto. unknown: no specific locality: MUHNES 738 (*).

Published locality records: La Libertad: km 56 on the road from San Salvador–La Libertad, between Mizata and Bocana La Perla, 10 m (Hidalgo 1980a).

Leptodeira septentrionalis (Kennicott 1859)
(Escombrera de Manchitas)
Plate 100, Map 92

1859 *Dipsas septentrionalis* Kennicott, in Baird: Reptiles of the Boundary 2: 16; type locality: Matamores, Tamaulipas, Mexico.
Leptodeira annulata polysticta: Mertens 1952d.
Leptodeira septentrionalis polysticta: Duellman 1958, Uzzell & Starrett 1958, Peters & Orejas-Miranda 1970.
Leptodeira septentrionalis: Villa et al. 1988, Dueñas et al. 2001, Köhler 2001a, 2003b, Leenders 2003, Leenders & Watkins-Colwell 2004.

Geographic distribution: From southern Texas, USA, to northern Colombia on the Atlantic versant, and discontinuously from Sinaloa, Mexico, to north-

Plate 100: *Leptodeira septentrionalis* (MUHNES C-30-1352) EL SALVADOR: Ahuachapán: Finca Concepción Miramar (920 m). Photo: E. Greenbaum.

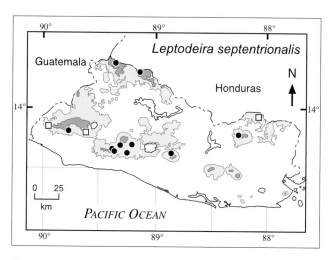

Map 92: Distribution of *Leptodeira septentrionalis* in El Salvador.
Closed circles represent examined-specimen locality records; open squares are published locality records. Light shading indicates 600–1200 m elevation; dark shading indicates elevations ≥ 1200 m; large bodies of freshwater are outlined in bold, black lines.

western Peru on the Pacific versant (Savage 2002).
Ecological distribution: Premontane evergreen forest, subtropical humid forest, and pine-oak forest between 700 and 2050 m.
Description: A medium-sized snake (SVL of largest specimen examined 645 mm); relative tail length 29–33% of SVL in males with complete tails, 15–30% in females with complete tails; divided nasal; 1 loreal; 3 preoculars; 2 postoculars; 8 supralabials, 4th and 5th enter orbit; 8–10 infralabials; 1 anterior and 2 posterior temporals;

dorsal scales smooth, with two apical pits, in 21–25 rows at midbody, and 15–17 rows one head length anterior to vent; ventrals 205–208 in males, 202–205 in females; subcaudals 84–97 in males with complete tails, 80–92 in females with complete tails; anal plate divided. Leenders & Watkins-Colwell (2004) listed 196–205 ventrals and 79–100 subcaudals for Salvadoran specimens of both genders.

Dorsal ground color tan or pale brown with dark brown transverse blotches, which can be broken and offset to vertebral line; smaller dark brown lateral spots alternating with dorsal blotches are present on sides of body and tail; top of head with scattered dark brown blotches; dark brown postocular stripe extends to posterior supralabial scale; infralabials, chin, and throat cream color; venter tan or pale brown.

Natural history: E. Greenbaum (field notes) encountered this species at night near shallow pools with calling *Physalaemus pustulosus* at Finca Concepción Miramar, Depto. Ahuachapán in August. Another individual was encountered as it crawled through vegetation at night above a stream with calling *Ptychohyla salvadorensis* at Finca La Giralda, Depto. La Libertad in August. W. E. Duellman (field notes) collected a specimen from a relatively dry log in cloud forest at Cerro Montecristo, Depto. Santa Ana in February. Duellman (1958) noted this species eats frogs, toads, anuran eggs, and lizards. Females produce clutches of 4–13 eggs, and long-term storage of sperm is possible (Haines 1940). Stafford & Meyer (2000) noted this species will feed upon eggs masses of leaf-breeding frogs (e.g., *Agalychnis*). Savage (2002) noted this nocturnal and semiarboreal species can inflict a painful bite to humans. Leenders & Watkins-Colwell (2004) reported an individual captured from the branches of a tree overhanging a cascading mountain stream (ca. 2 m above the water) at Nahuaterique (Depto. Morazán); upon capture the snake regurgitated a recently consumed adult *Rana maculata*.

Specimens examined: Ahuachapán: Finca Concepción Miramar, 13°48.46´N, 89°48.03´W, 920 m: MUHNES C–30–1352. Chalatenango: Cerro El Pital, Municipio de Las Pilas, 2000 m: VH 60. La Libertad: Finca El Paraíso, Nuevo San Salvador [= Santa Tecla]: SMF 42210, 43025; Hacienda San José: SMF 56100; Finca La Giralda, 13°39.34´N, 89°22.47´W, 1080 m: KU 289953; 2.3 km E Colón Los Chorros: UMMZ 117282. Morazán: Cerro

Cacahuatique, 985 m: KU 291316; same locality at 1035 m: MUHNES C–30–1535; same locality at 1090 m: KU 291311. San Salvador: San Salvador: ZMB 35699. Santa Ana: Hacienda Montecristo, 1800 m: UMMZ 117281; S slope Cerro Montecristo, 2050 m: KU 63837. San Vicente: Finca El Carmen, Volcán de San Vicente: SMF 77419 (erroneously identified as *L. annulata* in Köhler 1996).

Published locality records: Ahuachapán: Parque Nacional El Imposible: YPM 12430, 14058 (Leenders 2003, Leenders & Watkins-Colwell 2004). Morazán: Município Arambala, Cantón Cumaro, Nahuaterique, near border crossing with Honduras (13.995°N, 88.093°W), 1389 m: YPM 14060 (Leenders & Watkins-Colwell 2004). Santa Ana: Município Santa Ana, Cantón Los Flores, Parque Nacional Los Andes and Volcán Santa Ana (13.869°N, 89.620°W): YPM 14061 (Leenders & Watkins-Colwell 2004); Município Metapán, Cantón Metapán, Parque Nacional Montecristo (14.401°N, 89.362°W): YPM 14059 (Leenders & Watkins-Colwell 2004).

Genus *Leptodrymus*

This monotypic genus is distributed in Guatemala and Honduras on the Atlantic versant and from Guatemala to central Costa Rica on the Pacific slope (Savage 2002).

Leptodrymus pulcherrimus (Cope 1874)
(Bejuquilla Rayada)
Plate 101, Map 93

1874 *Masticophis pulcherrimus* Cope, Proc. Acad. Nat. Sci. Philadelphia 1874: 65; type locality: Western side of Central America.
Leptodrymus pulcherrimus: Mertens 1952d, Peters & Orejas-Miranda 1970, Villa et al. 1988, Dueñas et al. 2001, Köhler 2001a, 2003b, Leenders 2003.
Geographic distribution: Identical to genus.
Ecological distribution: Dry forest and savanna between sea level and 300 m.
Description: A medium-sized snake (SVL of only specimen 760 mm); relative tail length 55% of SVL in single male; divided nasal; 1 loreal; 1 preocular; 3 postoculars; 2 anterior and 2 posterior temporals; dorsal scales smooth, with two apical pits, in 17 rows at midbody, and 15 rows one head length anterior to vent; ventrals 208 in single male; subcaudals 152 in single male; anal plate divided.

Top of head and upper lateral side of head

Plate 101: *Leptodrymus pulcherrimus* HONDURAS: Atlántida: La Ceiba. Photo: J. Ferrari.

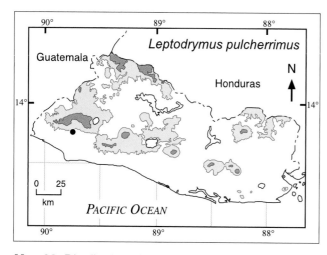

Map 93: Distribution of *Leptodrymus pulcherrimus* in El Salvador.
Closed circles represent examined-specimen locality records; open squares are published locality records. Light shading indicates 600–1200 m elevation; dark shading indicates elevations ≥ 1200 m; large bodies of freshwater are outlined in bold, black lines.

bright green (pale brown in preservative); supralabials, infralabials, chin, and throat cream or white; dorsum tan to pale brown with two distinctive longitudinal dark brown bands running from nostril through the eye, throughout dorsum onto tail; these stripes cover the lower halves of scales in 2nd dorsal row, all of 3rd row and almost all of 4th row; venter cream or dirty white.
Natural history: Mertens (1952d) reported a specimen from under a log in El Salvador; the animal moved too quickly to be captured. Savage (2002) commented that this species is common in Costa Rica, and forages in bushes and small trees.
Specimens examined: <u>Sonsonate</u>: road Sonsonate–Nahuizalco, 300 m: SMF 43192.

Genus *Leptophis*

The nine species of this genus are distributed from Sonora and Tamaulipas, Mexico, to Bolivia and Argentina (Atlantic versant) and Ecuador (Pacific versant); also on the islands of Trinidad and Tobago (Savage 2002). Two species occur in El Salvador.

Leptophis mexicanus Duméril, Bibron & Duméril 1854
(Chocoya Dorso-bronceada)
Plate 102, Map 94

1854 *Leptophis mexicanus* Duméril, Bibron & Duméril, Erp. Gén., 7: 536; type locality: Mexico.
Thalerophis mexicanus mexicanus: Brongersma 1954a.
Leptophis mexicanus mexicanus: Uzzell & Starrett 1958.
Leptophis mexicanus: Peters & Orejas-Miranda 1970, Villa et al. 1988, Dueñas et al. 2001, Köhler 2001a, 2003b.
Geographic distribution: From Tamaulipas, Mexico, along the Atlantic versant to northeastern Costa Rica with disjunct populations on the Pacific versant from Oaxaca and Chiapas, Mexico, to central El Salvador and northwestern Costa Rica (Savage 2002).
Ecological distribution: Dry forest and savanna between sea level and 740 m.
Description: A medium-sized snake (SVL of largest specimen examined 600 mm); relative tail length 47–66% of SVL in males, 65–72% in females; divided nasal; 1 loreal; 1 preocular; 2 postoculars; 8 supralabials, 4th and 5th enter orbit; 9–10 infralabials; 0–2 anterior and 0–2 posterior temporals; dorsal scales keeled (except first row), with single apical pits, in 15 rows at midbody, and 11 rows one head length anterior to vent; ventrals 154–165 in males, 161–163 in females; subcaudals 95–151 in males, 134–161 in females; anal plate divided.

Dorsal coloration of body tan or grayish brown with a golden-brown middorsal area that widens posteriorly; the scales on the sides are more heavily powdered with blackish dots than those of the vertebral region; the adjacent borders of scale rows 2 and 3 may be marked by blackish rims, but these do not form a distinct black line; the skin between the dorsal scales is black; dorsal surfaces of head and neck metallic bluish green or bronzish green; a distinct black stripe extends from nostril

Plate 102: *Leptophis mexicanus* BELIZE: Stann Creek: Dangriga. Photo: W. Van Devender.

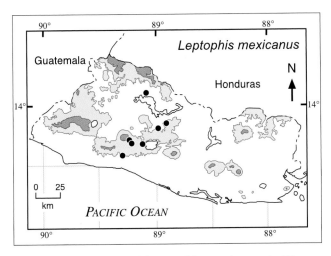

Map 94: Distribution of *Leptophis mexicanus* in El Salvador.
Closed circles represent examined-specimen locality records; open squares are published locality records. Light shading indicates 600–1200 m elevation; dark shading indicates elevations ≥ 1200 m; large bodies of freshwater are outlined in bold, black lines.

through eye to neck, and continues vaguely in a form of black posterior edges of bluish green lateral scales; ventral surfaces including upper and lower labials and two lowermost dorsal scale rows cream or pale gray.

Natural history: Campbell (1998a) noted this diurnal and arboreal species feeds upon amphibians and lizards; females lay 2–11 eggs from March–October. Stafford & Meyer (2000) noted bites from this species may result in localized pain to humans. Savage (2002) added this species may eat snakes, bird eggs, and tadpoles.

Specimens examined: <u>Cabañas</u>: 3.5 km W Tejutepeque: KU 183911. <u>Chalatenango</u>: 20 km W Chalatenango: TCWC 23646. <u>Cuscatlán</u>: Cuscatlán: MUHNES 769; 1 km E Tenancingo, Cantón El Llano, 600 m: KU 183914. <u>La Libertad</u>: 44 km (by rd.) W La Libertad: AMNH 115666; 2 km S Zaragoza, Cantón Guadalupe, 13°33.1'N, 89°17.3'W, 740 m: KU 291580. <u>San Salvador</u>: San Salvador: SMF 53134; 0.4 km NW of Instituto Tropical de Investigaciones Científicas: UMMZ 117287; 2.4 km SE Ilopango, Cantón Asino: KU 183912–13.

***Leptophis modestus* (Günther 1872)**
(Chocoya de Montaña)
Plate 103, Map 95

1872 *Ahaetulla modesta* Günther, Ann. Mag. Nat. Hist. 9(4): 26; type locality: Río Chisoy [= Chixoy = Negro] below the town of Cubulco [Baja Verapaz], Guatemala [in error according to McCranie & Wilson 1993b].
Leptophis modestus: Hoyt 1964, Mertens 1973, Wilson & Meyer 1985, Villa et al. 1988, McCranie & Wilson 1993b, Dueñas et al. 2001, Köhler 2001a, 2003b.

Geographic distribution: From northeastern Chiapas, Mexico, and central Guatemala to northwestern El Salvador and southwestern Honduras (Köhler 2003b).

Ecological distribution: Cloud forest between 2150 and 2200 m.

Description: A medium-sized snake (SVL of largest specimen examined 1020 mm); relative tail length 65% of SVL in single male with complete tail, 52–71% in females; divided nasal; 1–2 loreals (Holm [1995] reported a Honduran specimen that

Plate 103: *Leptophis modestus* (KU 187328) GUATE-MALA: Baja Verapaz: Unión Barrios (1615 m). Photo: J. A. Campbell (KU CT 6810).

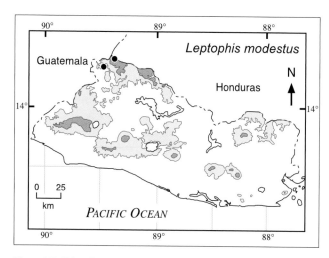

Map 95: Distribution of *Leptophis modestus* in
El Salvador.
Closed circles represent examined-specimen locality records;
open squares are published locality records. Light shading
indicates 600–1200 m elevation; dark shading indicates elevations ≥ 1200 m; large bodies of freshwater are outlined in bold,
black lines.

lacks a loreal); 1–2 preoculars; 2–3 postoculars; 8–9
supralabials, 4th and 5th enter orbit; 9–11
infralabials; usually 1 anterior and 2 posterior
temporals; dorsal scales keeled (except first row),
with single apical pits, in 15 rows at midbody, and
11 rows one head length anterior to vent; ventrals
167–176 in males, 170–180 in females; subcaudals
179 in single male with complete tail, 155–179 in
females; anal plate divided.

Dorsal color greenish olive; ventral surface pale
yellow anteriorly, darkening to pale bluish green
posteriorly; edges of ventrals with a fine, dark blue
line; lower labials and throat immaculate pale
yellow; pale green of head suffuses onto
supralabials that have pale yellow edges; black
postocular bar extends from edge of eye along
supralabial-temporal suture to ultimate labial; ventral surface of tail pale bluish green to pale blue.
Specimens examined: Santa Ana: Hacienda
Montecristo, Cordillera de Metapán, 2150–2200 m:
SMF 67353–55, KU 62106–69, 80722, 81370, 81372,
81517; Metapán: KU 183915.

Genus *Masticophis*

This genus includes eight species of snakes that
are distributed from the southern United States to
Colombia and Venezuela (Köhler 2003b). One
species occurs in El Salvador.

Masticophis mentovarius (Duméril, Bibron & Duméril 1854)
(Zumbadora)
Plate 104, Map 96, Figure 39

1854 *C[oryphodon] Mento-varius* Duméril, Bibron &
Duméril, Erp. Gén. 7: 187; type locality: Mexico.
Coluber mentovarius: Ahl 1940.
Coluber mentovarius mentovarius: Mertens 1952d.
Masticophis mentovarius mentovarius: Peters &
Orejas-Miranda 1970, Johnson 1977, 1982.
Masticophis mentovarius: Villa et al. 1988, Dueñas
et al. 2001, Köhler 2001a, 2003b, Leenders 2003.
Geographic distribution: From southern San
Luis Potosí, southern Sonora, and northern
Veracruz, Mexico, to northwestern Costa Rica on
the Pacific versant; disjunct populations in the
Yucatán Peninsula, Guatemala, Belize, Honduras,
northeastern Nicaragua, western Panama, Colombia, and Venezuela (Savage 2002).
Ecological distribution: Dry forest and savanna
between sea level and 1200 m.
Description: A very large snake (SVL of largest
specimen examined 1580 mm); relative tail length
34–40% of SVL in males, 33–37% in females;
divided nasal; 1 loreal; 1 large preocular and a
small subpreocular; 2–3 postoculars; 2 anterior and
2–3 posterior temporals; 7 (rarely 6 or 8)
supralabials, with the 4th (rarely the 3rd or the 5th)
entering orbit; 7–10 infralabials; dorsal scales
smooth, with two apical pits, in 17 rows at midbody,
and 13 rows one head length anterior to vent;
ventrals 188–205 in males, 197–204 in females;
subcaudals 111–123 in males, 110–124 in females;
anal plate divided. A distinct loreal depression is
present.

Dorsal surfaces of body and tail uniformly
brown or olive-brown, often with minute apical
black spots on body scales; head mostly brown,
anterior portions of temporals and postoculars with
lighter margins, preocular scale with elongate
vertical cream spot; supralabials cream on lower
portions, infralabials and ventrolateral scales on
throat irregularly marked with dark brown pigment; ventral surface cream.
Natural history: Campbell (1998a) noted this
diurnal species feeds upon lizards, birds, and
rodents; females lay 7–30 eggs from March–April.
Stafford & Meyer (2000) noted this species will eat
other snakes. Savage (2002) noted this species
probably feeds upon bird eggs; juveniles feed upon
arthropods. This species is capable of

Plate 104: *Masticophis mentovarius* HONDURAS: Francisco Morazán: Tegucigalpa (930 m). Photo: J. Ferrari.

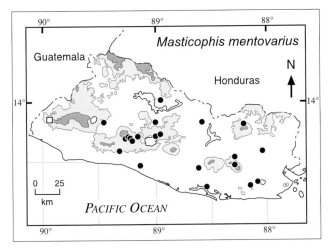

Map 96: Distribution of *Masticophis mentovarius* in El Salvador.
Closed circles represent examined-specimen locality records; open squares are published locality records. Light shading indicates 600–1200 m elevation; dark shading indicates elevations ≥ 1200 m; large bodies of freshwater are outlined in bold, black lines.

pseudautotomy (non-spontaneous, intervertebral breakage of a tail that does not usually result in regeneration).
Specimens examined: <u>Cabañas</u>: 2 km N Villa Dolore, 200 m: SMF 51948. <u>Chalatenango</u>: Municipio La Laguna, on rd 1 km S of town: MUHNES C–30–1537. <u>Cuscatlán</u>: Cojutepeque: SMF 51947; 6 km WSW Cojutepeque at Lago de Ilopango, 550 m: KU 183923; Copalchan, Tenancingo: KU 206430. <u>La Libertad</u>: Ciudad Arce: SMF 42029, Zaragoza: SMF 42061. <u>La Paz</u>: 23 km E La Libertad, 30 m: KU 116970. <u>Morazán</u>: N slope

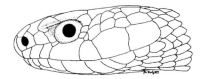

5 mm

Figure 39: *Masticophis mentovarius* (SMF 78866): Lateral view of head.

Mt. Cacahuatique, 1219 m: MVZ 40412; Montecristo Mine, 213 m: MVZ 40415. <u>San Miguel</u>: km 110 on the road from San Salvador–San Miguel: SMF 42030; Laguna de Olomega, 61 m: MVZ 40413; Volcán de San Miguel, 400 m: KU 291259. <u>San Salvador</u>: Planes de Renderos near San Salvador, 750 m: SMF 42565; Instituto Tropical de Investigaciones Científicas, 700 m: KU 62110, SMF 42031–32, 42062, 81335, 81338, 81371, UU 5375; San Salvador: SMF 42059–60, 51946, 81332, ZMB 35712–15; road to Sta. Tecla in San Salvador, 960 m: SMF 42888; 1 km E Soyapango near San Salvador: SMF 43196. <u>Usulután</u>: Puerto El Triunfo: SMF 45406; San Pedro: MCZ 57098; 2 km SE San Marcos Lempa, 20 m: KU 116969.
Published locality records: <u>Ahuachapán</u>: Parque Nacional El Imposible (Leenders 2003).

Genus *Ninia*

This genus includes eight semifossorial species of snakes that are distributed from San Luis Potosí (Atlantic slope) and Oaxaca (Pacific slope), Mexico, south through Central America to Ecuador, Guyana, and the upper Amazon basin (Savage 2002). Two species occur in El Salvador.

Ninia espinali McCranie & Wilson 1995
(Gargantilla de Espinal)
Plate 105, Map 97

1995 *Ninia espinali* McCranie & Wilson, J. Herpetol. 29(2): 228; type locality: El Portillo de Ocotepeque (14°28′N, 89°04′W), 1910 m, Depto. Ocotepeque, Honduras.
Ninia espinali: Greenbaum et al. 2002b, Köhler 2003b.
Geographic distribution: Southwestern Honduras and extreme northern El Salvador (Köhler 2003b).

Plate 105: *Ninia espinali* (MUHNES C-30-1538) EL SALVADOR: Chalatenango: Cerro El Pital (2270 m). Photo: O. Komar.

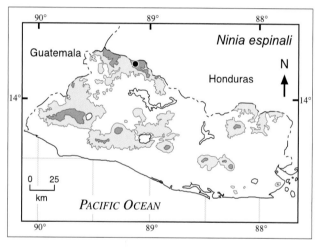

Map 97: Distribution of *Ninia espinali* in El Salvador. Closed circles represent examined-specimen locality records; open squares are published locality records. Light shading indicates 600–1200 m elevation; dark shading indicates elevations ≥ 1200 m; large bodies of freshwater are outlined in bold, black lines.

Ecological distribution: Cloud forest around 2270 m.
Description: A small snake (SVL of largest specimen examined 332 mm); the only El Salvador specimens (1 male, 1 female) show the following characters: relative tail length 27% of SVL in male, 23% in female; divided nasal; 1 loreal; no preoculars; usually 1 postocular (2 postoculars on one side in the female); 1 anterior and 2 posterior temporals; 6–7 supralabials, with the 3rd, 4th, and 5th entering orbit; 7–8 infralabials; dorsal scales

strongly keeled, without apical pits, in 19 rows throughout; ventrals 152 in male, 150 in female; subcaudals 66 in male, 50 in female; anal plate entire.

Dorsal color uniformly gray to grayish brown, reaching onto lateral edges of ventrals; supralabials and ventral surfaces of head and body pale cream, immaculate, or with dark gray fleckings; anal plate and subcaudals with irregular dark brown spots or blotches.
Natural history: O. Komar (field notes) and Greenbaum et al. (2002b) recorded these snakes from under logs near cloud forest during the day at Cerro El Pital, Depto. Chalatenango in May.
Specimens examined: <u>Chalatenango</u>: Cerro El Pital, 2270 m: KU 291246, MUHNES C–30–1538.

Ninia sebae **(Duméril, Bibron & Duméril 1854)**
(Gargantilla de Cafetal)
Plate 106, Map 98, Figure 40

1854 *Streptophorus sebae* Duméril, Bibron & Duméril, Erp. Gén., 7: 515; type locality: Mexico.
Ninia sebae sebae: Mertens 1952d, Rand 1957, K. Schmidt & Rand 1957, Uzzell & Starrett 1958, Peters & Orejas-Miranda 1970.
Ninia sebae: Wilson & Meyer 1985, Villa et al. 1988, Köhler 1996, Dueñas et al. 2001, Köhler 2001a, Savage 2002, Köhler 2003b, Leenders 2003, Leenders & Watkins-Colwell 2004.
Geographic distribution: From Veracruz (Atlantic versant) and Oaxaca, Mexico, (Pacific versant) to southern Costa Rica (Savage 2002).
Ecological distribution: Dry forest, premontane evergreen forest, subtropical humid forest, and pine-oak forest between sea level and 1700 m, exceptionally to 2400 m. K. Schmidt & Rand (1957) noted that this snake is very common in coffee plantations.
Description: A small snake (SVL of largest specimen examined 320 mm); relative tail length 31–37% of SVL in males, 23–33% in females; divided nasal; 1 loreal; no (rarely 1) preoculars; 2 postoculars; 1 anterior and 2 posterior temporals; 6–7 supralabials, with the 3rd and 4th entering orbit; 5–7 infralabials; dorsal scales keeled, without apical pits, in 19 rows throughout; ventrals 136–143 in males, 137–150 in females; subcaudals 60–64 in males, 50–63 in females; anal plate entire.

Dorsal color uniform red to reddish brown or with dark brown alternating bars that are usually restricted to the anterior half of body; venter

Plate 106: *Ninia sebae* (SMF 81476) EL SALVADOR: Ahuachapán: Parque Nacional El Imposible, La Fincona (720 m). Photo: G. Köhler.

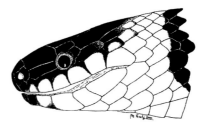

5 mm

Figure 40: *Ninia sebae* (SMF 43230): Lateral view of head.

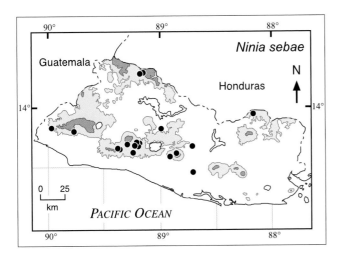

Map 98: Distribution of *Ninia sebae* in El Salvador. Closed circles represent examined-specimen locality records; open squares are published locality records. Light shading indicates 600–1200 m elevation; dark shading indicates elevations ≥ 1200 m; large bodies of freshwater are outlined in bold, black lines.

immaculate; dorsum and lateral sides of head black except for supralabials; venter cream to yellow; a pale white or yellow occipital collar is anterior to a broad, black nuchal blotch.

Natural history: E. Greenbaum (field notes) encountered a gravid female during the day in a rotten log among coffee plants at Finca Concepción Miramar, Depto. Ahuachapán in August; an adult male was collected at night in this same locality as it crawled across a road through the finca. O. Komar (field notes) collected an adult male underneath a rotting wooden plank during the day in pine-oak forest at Perquín, Depto. Morazán in

June. All specimens that Mertens (1952d) collected were found in Salvadoran coffee plantations. Rand (1957) collected an individual under a rock at the bottom of a brush-grown gully in pasture at San Salvador, Depto. San Salvador in March. Landy et al. (1966) reported a caecilian in the stomach of a snake from Mexico. Campbell (1998a) noted this mostly nocturnal species feeds upon earthworms, slugs, and land snails; females lay 1–4 eggs from March–September. Leenders & Watkins-Colwell (2004) noted two females collected from under logs in coffee plantations from Cooperativa Concepción Miramar (Depto. Ahuachapán) contained 2 and 4 oviducal eggs (20–25 mm length, 6–7 mm diameter).

Specimens examined: Ahuachapán: Finca Concepción Miramar, 13°48.46′N, 89°48.03′W, 920 m: KU 289918, 289942; Parque Nacional El Imposible, La Fincona, 13°50.8′N, 89°58.8′W, 720 m: SMF 81476. Chalatenango: La Palma: MUHNES 1199; near La Palma, 14°17.1′N, 89°08.5′W, 2400 m: MUHNES C–30–1199. Cuscatlán: 0.5 km E Tenancingo: KU 183931. La Libertad: Sta. Tecla, Finca El Paraíso: SMF 42208–09, 42214, 42246, 42439, 42706, 42810–11, 42864, 43106–07, 43229–30; Cumbre, Hacienda San José, 1200 m: SMF 42501; Nuevo San Salvador [= Santa Tecla]: KU 183929. Morazán: Perquín: KU 291347. San Salvador: Instituto Tropical de Investigaciones Científicas, 700 m: SMF 77421, KU 62111; San Salvador: ZMB 35693–94, MVZ 40430, FMNH 64949, UMMZ 117293; Colegio Bautista: KU 289803; San Salvador, Parque Zoológico Nacional: MUHNES C–30–1355; San Salvador, Ciudad Universitaria: KU 183930. San Vicente: foothills of Volcánsito (west of Volcán San Vicente), Finca San Jacinto, 840 m: SMF 43231; eastern peak of Volcán San Vicente, Finca El

Carmen, 1319 m: SMF 43232–36, 77420. Usulután:
12 km S hwy El Litoral ca. Río Lempa: LACM
103630.
Published locality records: Ahuachapán:
Município San Pedro Puxtla, Cantón La
Concepción, Cooperativa Concepción Miramar
(13.810°N, 89.807°W), 950–1100 m: YPM 12312,
12362–63 (Leenders & Watkins-Colwell 2004).

Genus *Oxybelis*

These extremely thin and elongate arboreal
snakes (four species) are distributed from southern
Arizona, USA, and Coahuila, Mexico, to Bolivia,
northern Argentina, and southern Brazil on the
Atlantic versant (including Trinidad and Tobago),
and to northern Peru on the Pacific versant (Savage 2002). Two species occur in El Salvador.

Oxybelis aeneus (Wagler 1824)
(Bejuquilla Café)
Plate 107, Map 99

1824 *Dryinus aeneus* Wagler, in Spix: Sp. Nov. Serp.
Bras.: 12; type locality: forest adjacent to the
Solimoens River, near Ega [Tefé], Brazil.
Dryiophis acuminata: Günther 1895.
Oxybelis acuminatus: K. Schmidt 1928, Rand 1957.
Oxybelis aeneus aeneus: Mertens 1952d, Rand 1957.
Oxybelis aeneus: Peters & Orejas-Miranda 1970,
Keiser 1982, Villa et al. 1988, Dueñas et al. 2001,
Köhler 2001a, 2003b, Leenders 2003, Leenders &
Watkins-Colwell 2004.
Geographic distribution: From southern Arizona, USA, and Coahuila, Mexico, to Bolivia on the
Atlantic versant, and Peru on the Pacific versant;
also on Trinidad and Tobago (Savage 2002).
Ecological distribution: Dry forest and savanna
between sea level and 1100 m.
Description: A medium-sized snake (SVL of
largest specimen examined 818 mm); relative tail
length 50–68% of SVL in males, 57–70% in females;
single nasal; no loreal; 1 preocular; 2 postoculars; 1
anterior and 2 posterior temporals; 8–10
supralabials, with the 4th and 5th, or the 4th, 5th,
and 6th entering orbit; 9–11 infralabials; dorsal
scales smooth or weakly keeled, anterior portion of
body with single apical pits (posterior body without
apical pits), in 17 rows at midbody, and 13 rows one
head length anterior to vent; ventrals 176–187 in
males, 179–187 in females; subcaudals 143–170 in
males, 143–170 in females; anal plate divided.

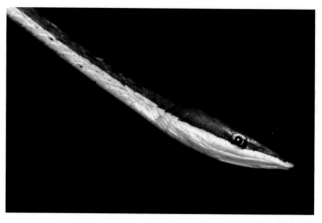

Plate 107: *Oxybelis aeneus* (YPM 12426) EL SALVADOR: Ahuachapán: Parque Nacional El Imposible,
Finca San Benito (760 m). Photo: T. Leenders.

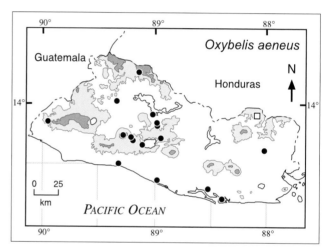

Map 99: Distribution of *Oxybelis aeneus* in El Salvador.
Closed circles represent examined-specimen locality records;
open squares are published locality records. Light shading
indicates 600–1200 m elevation; dark shading indicates elevations ≥ 1200 m; large bodies of freshwater are outlined in bold,
black lines.

Leenders & Watkins-Colwell (2004) list 187–188
ventrals and 168–174 subcaudals for Salvadoran
specimens of both genders.
Dorsal coloration tan or grayish brown; some
dorsal scales with small dark brown spots, more
frequently on proximal part of body; 2–4 indistinct
darker lateral stripes on sides of posterior half of
body; top of head tan with a dark brown line
extending from nostril through eye to neck;
supralabials, infralabials, chin, throat, and anterior
ventrals cream or light yellow (may be dirty white

in preservative); venter grading into tan posteriorly, with two indistinct dark brown lines in lighter anterior portion, and creamish ventromedial line in darker posterior portion.

Natural history: E. Greenbaum (field notes) recorded several individuals from the ground or bushes near the ground at the periphery of a village at midday at Isla San Sebastián, Depto. Usulután in July. Another individual was seen crawling through a tree (3–4 m above ground) during the day at Bosque Cinquera, Depto. Cabañas in August. K. Schmidt (1928) reported the remains of a *Gymnophthalmus speciosus* in the stomach of an *Oxybelis aeneus* from San José del Sacaré (1097 m), Depto. Chalatenango in March. An adult male from Divisadero, Depto. Morazán had a *Sceloporus* in its stomach in December. Mertens (1952d) collected an adult female on *Sclerocarpus* flowers growing on a *Lantana* bush in El Salvador; when caught, the snake opened its mouth but did not attempt to bite. Rand (1957) noted a gravid female (5 eggs) collected from "a bush near the sea" at Los Blancos, Depto. La Paz in May. Campbell (1998a) noted this arboreal, diurnal species feeds upon small vertebrates and insects; females lay 3–5 eggs from March to August. This species is mildly venomous—bites to humans have resulted in itching, swelling, and blistering. Savage (2002) noted that clutch size increases with body size.

Specimens examined: Ahuachapán: Parque Nacional El Imposible, Finca San Benito, 760 m: Plate 107. Chalatenango: San José del Sacaré, 1097 m: FMNH 10997. Cuscatlán: Tenancingo: MUHNES 924; 3 km NE Suchitoto, Orillas de Lago Suchitlán: KU 183932; Cojutepeque: KU 183933; Tenancingo, Cantón El Tablón: KU 183934; 1 km E Tenancingo: KU 183935. La Libertad: Río Lempa, about 8 km from Tacachico: SMF 51943; Las Flores, near La Libertad: SMF 45405; Volcán San Salvador "1917 Lava": FMNH 64955. La Paz: Los Blancos: FMNH 64956. Morazán: Divisadero: FMNH 10998. San Salvador: San Salvador: SMF 42498; San Salvador, Instituto Tropical de Investigaciones Científicas: KU 62112; 3 km SE Ilopango, Cantón Asino: KU 183936–40. Usulután: Puerto El Triunfo: SMF 42034; Isla San Sebastián, 13°10.01´N, 88°24.49´W, 20 m: KU 289907, 289909–10, MUHNES C–30–1356.

Published locality records: Ahuachapán: Parque Nacional El Imposible: YPM 12426 (Leenders & Watkins-Colwell 2004). Morazán: Município Arambala, Cantón Cumaro, Río Sapo (13.959°N,

88.132°W): YPM 13999 (Leenders & Watkins-Colwell 2004).

Oxybelis fulgidus (Daudin 1803)
(Bejuquilla Verde)
Plate 108, Map 100

1803 *Coluber fulgidus* Daudin, Hist. Nat. Rept. 6: 352; type locality: in neighborhood of Port-au-Prince, Santo Domingo (in error).
Dryiophis fulgida: Günther 1895.
Dryophis fulgidus: Cope 1860, 1887.
Oxybelis fulgidus: K. Schmidt 1928, Mertens 1952d, Peters & Orejas-Miranda 1970, Villa et al. 1988, Dueñas et al. 2001, Köhler 2001a, 2003b, Leenders 2003, Leenders & Watkins-Colwell 2003b, 2004.

Geographic distribution: In southern Veracruz, Mexico, and south from the Yucatán Peninsula through Central America to northern Bolivia and northeastern Argentina on the Pacific versant; from the Isthmus of Tehuantepec to eastern Panama on the Atlantic versant (Savage 2002).

Ecological distribution: Dry forest and savanna between sea level and 1320 m.

Description: A large snake (SVL of largest specimen examined 1700 mm); relative tail length 37–50% of SVL in males, 42–44% in females; single nasal; no loreal; 1 preocular; 2 (rarely 1) postoculars; 1 anterior and 2 posterior temporals; 10–11 supralabials, with the 5th, 6th, and 7th entering orbit; 9–10 infralabials; dorsal scales smooth or weakly keeled, on anterior portion of body with single apical pits (posterior body without apical pits), in 17 rows at midbody, and 13 rows one head length anterior to vent; ventrals 201–220 in males, 213 in females; subcaudals 143–181 in

Plate 108: *Oxybelis fulgidus* EL SALVADOR: Ahuachapán: Parque Nacional El Imposible, La Fincona (720 m). Photo: T. Leenders.

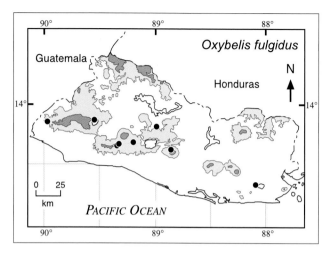

Map 100: Distribution of *Oxybelis fulgidus* in El Salvador.
Closed circles represent examined-specimen locality records; open squares are published locality records. Light shading indicates 600–1200 m elevation; dark shading indicates elevations ≥ 1200 m; large bodies of freshwater are outlined in bold, black lines.

males, 147–161 in females; anal plate divided.

Dorsal coloration uniformly bright green; a dark brown line extends from nasal opening through eye to lower temporal region; supralabials, infralabials, chin, and throat yellowish green; a distinctive white, cream, or yellow longitudinal stripe running on lateral portions of ventral plates throughout body and tail; venter between these stripes pale green.

Natural history: Campbell (1998a) noted this arboreal, diurnal species feeds upon vertebrates; females lay about 10 eggs from April–June. Stafford & Meyer (2000) noted bites from this species may result in localized pain in humans. Leenders & Watkins-Colwell (2003b) observed this species attempting to consume a Ruddy Woodcreeper (*Dendrocincla homochroa)* from a mist net during the day at Parque Nacional El Imposible, Depto. Ahuachapán in February. Leenders & Watkins-Colwell (2004) noted Salvadoran specimens were taken from shrubs and a small tree at heights up to 2.5 m.

Specimens examined: Ahuachapán: Parque Nacional El Imposible, La Fincona, 13°50.8′N, 89°58.8′W, 720 m: Plate 108. Cuscatlán: 0.5 km E Tenancingo: KU 183941. La Libertad: Finca Los Cedros, La Cumbre near Nuevo San Salvador [= Santa Tecla], about 1000 m: SMF 42564; Finca Astillero, La Cumbre near Nuevo San Salvador [=

Santa Tecla], 1050 m: SMF 43152. San Miguel: Laguna de Olomega, 61 m: MVZ 40443. San Salvador: San Salvador, Parque Saburo-Hirao: MUHNES 678. Santa Ana: Lago Coatepeque: VH 47. San Vicente: Finca El Carmen: SMF 81331, 81339.
Published locality records: Ahuachapán: Parque Nacional El Imposible, 750–800 m: YPM 12348, 12427, 12431 (Leenders & Watkins-Colwell 2004).

Genus *Pliocercus*

The genus *Pliocercus* is distributed from Oaxaca and central Veracruz, Mexico, through most of Central America to Colombia and Ecuador. This genus consists of two species, one of which occurs in El Salvador (see dicussion in Köhler 2003b).

Pliocercus elapoides Cope 1860
(Coralillo Cola Larga)
Plate 109, Map 101, Figure 41

1860 *Pliocercus elapoides* Cope, Proc. Acad. Nat. Sci. Philadelphia 1860: 253; type locality: Near Jalapa, Veracruz, Mexico.
Urotheca elapoides: Ahl 1940.
Pliocercus elapoides salvadorensis: Mertens 1952a, d, Peters & Orejas-Miranda 1970.
Pliocercus elapoides: Wilson & Meyer 1985, Villa et al. 1988, Dueñas et al. 2001, Köhler 2001a, 2003b, Leenders 2003.
Pliocercus elapoides diastema: Smith & Chiszar 1996, 2001.
Geographic distribution: From Oaxaca and central Veracruz, Mexico, to eastern El Salvador and central Honduras (Köhler 2003b).
Ecological distribution: Dry forest, premontane evergreen forest, subtropical humid forest, and pine-oak forest between 600 and 1400 m.
Description: A medium-sized snake (SVL of largest specimen examined 300 mm); relative tail length 52–76% of SVL in males, 64–74% in females; divided nasal; 1 loreal; 1–3 preoculars; 2 postoculars; 1 anterior and 1–3 posterior temporals; 7–9 supralabials, with the 4th and 5th, the 4th, 5th, and 6th, or the 5th and 6th entering orbit; 8–10 infralabials; dorsal scales smooth, without apical pits, in 17 rows throughout (rarely 18 rows at midbody and/or one head length anterior to vent); ventrals 121–132 in males, 122–130 in females; subcaudals 75–103 in males, 99–108 in females; anal plate divided.

Dorsal ground color bright red with black rings,

Plate 109: *Pliocercus elapoides* (KU 187344) GUATE-MALA: Baja Verapaz: San José. Photo: J. A. Campbell (KU CT 6829).

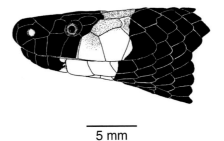

5 mm

Figure 41: *Pliocercus elapoides:* Lateral view of head.

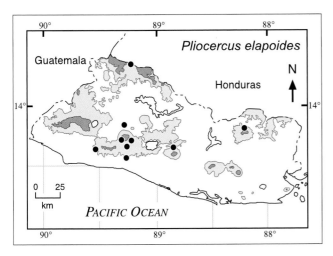

Map 101: Distribution of *Pliocercus elapoides* in El Salvador.
Closed circles represent examined-specimen locality records; open squares are published locality records. Light shading indicates 600–1200 m elevation; dark shading indicates elevations ≥ 1200 m; large bodies of freshwater are outlined in bold, black lines.

which are narrowly bordered anteriorly and posteriorly by yellow or cream-colored rings; red interspaces usually much wider than the black rings; body scales in red and cream areas tipped by black; anterior top of the head black, followed by yellow or cream collar involving posterior tip of rostral, about two thirds of parietals, temporals, and posterior supralabials; anterior supralabials yellow or cream on lower margin; neck collar yellow or cream.
Natural history: Mertens (1952d) found an *Eleutherodactylus rhodopis* in the stomach of a

Pliocercus elapoides in El Salvador. Campbell (1998a) noted this species can be active by day or night, and feeds upon amphibians and their eggs. Females lay 4–8 eggs during the rainy season. This species is mildly venomous and can cause pain and swelling to humans.
Specimens examined: <u>Chalatenango</u>: El Poy: KU 183942. <u>La Libertad</u>: Quezaltepeque: CAS 102964; Finca San José, above Nuevo San Salvador [= Santa Tecla], 1150 m: SMF 42301; Finca El Paraíso, near Nuevo San Salvador [= Santa Tecla]: MVZ 40452, SMF 42211, 42998, 42815. <u>Morazán</u>: N slope Mt. Cacahuatique, 1402 m: MVZ 40447–48. <u>San Salvador</u>: San Salvador: SMF 75766–68. <u>San Vicente</u>: Finca El Carmen: SMF 75724. <u>Sonsonate</u>: Hacienda Chilata, 610 m: MVZ 40449.

Genus *Rhadinaea*

This genus includes 34 species of terrestrial snakes that are distributed from Nuevo León and Sinaloa, Mexico, to southwestern Ecuador; one species occurs in the southeastern United States (Savage 2002). Four species occur in El Salvador—none are common.

Rhadinaea godmani (Günther 1865)
(Hojarasquera de Godman)
Plate 110, Map 102

1865 *Dromicus godmani* Günther, Ann. Mag. Nat. Hist. 3(15): 94; type locality: Duenas, Guatemala.
Rhadinaea zilchi: Mertens 1952b.
Rhadinaea godmani zilchi: Mertens 1952d, Peters & Orejas-Miranda 1970.
Rhadinaea godmani: Uzzell & Starrett 1958, Myers 1974, Wilson & Meyer 1985, Villa et al. 1988, McCranie & Wilson 1992, Dueñas et al. 2001, Köhler 2001a, 2003b, Leenders & Watkins-Colwell 2004.

Plate 110: *Rhadinaea godmani* (YPM 13000) EL SALVADOR: Santa Ana: Volcán de Santa Ana (1717 m). Photo: T. Leenders.

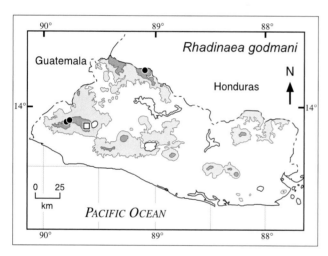

Map 102: Distribution of *Rhadinaea godmani* in El Salvador.
Closed circles represent examined-specimen locality records; open squares are published locality records. Light shading indicates 600–1200 m elevation; dark shading indicates elevations ≥ 1200 m; large bodies of freshwater are outlined in bold, black lines.

Rhadinaea godmani godmani: Peters & Orejas-Miranda 1970.
Geographic distribution: From southern Oaxaca and Chiapas, Mexico, to western Panama (Savage 2002).
Ecological distribution: Cloud forest and pine-oak forest between 1630 and 2225 m.
Description: A medium-sized snake (SVL of largest specimen examined 385 mm); relative tail length 37–40% of SVL in males, 35–37% in females; divided nasal; 1 loreal; 1–2 preoculars; 2

postoculars; 1 anterior and 2 posterior temporals; 8 supralabials, with the 4th and 5th entering orbit; 9 infralabials; dorsal scales smooth, without apical pits, in 21 rows throughout; ventrals 166–174 in males, 175 in a single female; subcaudals 71–94 in males, 80 in the female; anal plate divided.

Dorsal surface of body (median 7 dorsal scale rows) and tail brown with dark brown longitudinal stripes; there are three conspicious, relatively broad dark brown longitudinal stripes, one on the vertebral scale row and adjacent halves of paravertebral rows, the lateral stripes on scale row 5 and adjacent halves of scale rows 4 and 6; other narrower and less distinct lines above and/or below the latter stripes can be present in some specimens; ventral surface of head, body, and tail cream; dorsal surface of head brown; anterior supralabials with cream markings; an oblique cream postocular bar extending across supralabials 6 and 7 (or only on 6th supralabial in some specimens) from lower edge of eye to mouth.
Natural history: Mertens (1952d) reported a specimen found under a log close to a crater lake in El Salvador. Myers (1974) noted most specimens of this species have been collected under logs and boards. Savage (2002) noted that a female from Costa Rica laid five eggs. Leenders & Watkins-Colwell (2004) noted an adult female collected under a log during the day at Parque Nacional Los Andes (Depto. Santa Ana).
Specimens examined: Ahuachapán: Laguna de Las Ranas, 1720 m: SMF 43190; Laguna de Las Ninfas (=Laguna de Apaneca), 1630 m: SMF 43175 (locality erroneously given as Depto. Sonsonate in Mertens 1952b, d, McCranie & Wilson 1992, Leenders & Watkins-Colwell 2004). Chalatenango: Los Esesmiles, Cerro El Pital, 2225 m: MVZ 40416–17.
Published locality records: Santa Ana: Município Santa Ana, Cantón Los Flores, Parque Nacional Los Andes and Volcán Santa Ana (13.869°N, 89.620°W), 1717 m: YPM 13000 (Leenders & Watkins-Colwell 2004).

***Rhadinaea kinkelini* Boettger 1898**
(Hojarasquera de Kinkelin)
Plate 111, Map 103

1898 *Rhadinaea kinkelini* Boettger, Kat. Reptilien-Sammlung Mus. Senckenb. Naturforsch. Ges. 2: 68; type locality: Matagalpa, Nicaragua.
Rhadinaea pinicola: Mertens 1952b, d, Myers 1974,

Plate 111: *Rhadinaea kinkelini* (KU 217398) HONDU-RAS: La Paz: 13.7 km NW Marcala (1530 m). Photo: J. R. McCranie.

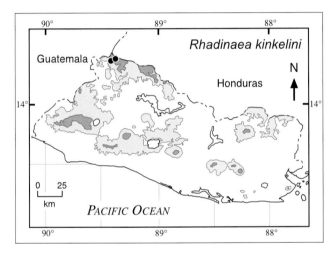

Map 103: Distribution of *Rhadinaea kinkelini* in El Salvador.
Closed circles represent examined-specimen locality records; open squares are published locality records. Light shading indicates 600–1200 m elevation; dark shading indicates elevations ≥ 1200 m; large bodies of freshwater are outlined in bold, black lines.

Villa et al. 1988, Dueñas et al. 2001.
Rhadinaea kinkelini: Myers 1974, Wilson & Meyer 1985, McCranie & Wilson 1991a, Köhler & McCranie 1999, Dueñas et al. 2001, Köhler 2001a, 2003b.
Geographic distribution: From central Guatemala to central Nicaragua (Köhler 2003b).
Ecological distribution: Cloud forest and pine-oak forest between 1500 and 2200 m.
Description: A small snake (SVL of largest specimen examined 225 mm); relative tail length 44% of SVL in single male with complete tail, 34% in single female with complete tail; divided nasal; 1

loreal; 1 preocular; 2 postoculars; 1 anterior and 1–2 posterior temporals; 8 supralabials, with 4th and 5th entering orbit; 6–8 infralabials; dorsal scales smooth, without apical pits, in 17 rows throughout; ventrals 147–162 in males, 159 in single female; subcaudals 76 in single male with complete tail, 73 in single female with complete tail; anal plate divided.

The frontal plate is dark brown with paired, slightly paler blotches medially separated by a slightly darker longitudinal stripe. The body pattern consists of a dark brown vertebral stripe that also involves the adjacent edges of the paravertebral rows, a dark brown dorsolateral stripe (adjacent edges of scale rows 6 and 7), a lateral dark brown stripe (scale row 4 and adjacent edges of scale rows 3 and 5), and three dark brown ventrolateral stripes (one on adjacent edges of scale rows 2 and 3, one on adjacent edges of scale rows 1 and 2, and one along the upper edges of the ventrals and adjacent edges of scale row 1). The center of the lateral dark brown stripe is distinctly paler along the middle portion of the fourth scale row. Iris dark brown.

Taxonomic comments: Because examination of the holotype of *Rhadinaea pinicola* Mertens revealed no coloration or scutellation characters that would distinguish it from *R. kinkelini*, Köhler & McCranie (1999) concluded that the nominal taxon *Rhadinaea pinicola* Mertens is a junior synonym of *R. kinkelini* Boettger.

Natural history: W. E. Duellman (field notes) encountered two adults in damp logs in cloud forest at Cerro Montecristo, Depto. Santa Ana in February. Uzzell & Starrett (1958) collected two males under logs along a road through cloud forest near Hacienda Montecristo, Depto. Santa Ana; these snakes were found "in association" with specimens of *R. montecristi* and *T. fischeri*. Myers (1974) mentioned a specimen ensnared in a spider web from Guatemala.

Specimens examined: <u>Santa Ana</u>: Hacienda San José, 1500 m elevation, Cordillera de Metapán: SMF 43191; Hacienda Montecristo, 2200 m: UMMZ 117290–91, KU 63886–87.

Rhadinaea montecristi Mertens 1952
(Hojarasquera de Montecristo)
Plate 112, Map 104, Figure 42

1952 *Rhadinaea montecristi* Mertens, Zool. Anz. 149: 136; type locality: Hacienda Montecristo, 2200

Plate 112: *Rhadinaea montecristi* (KU 291245) EL SALVADOR: Chalatenango: Cerro El Pital (2390 m). Photo: O. Komar.

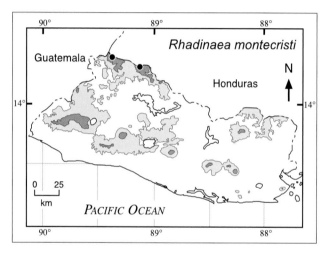

Map 104: Distribution of *Rhadinaea montecristi* in El Salvador.
Closed circles represent examined-specimen locality records; open squares are published locality records. Light shading indicates ≥ 600–1200 m elevation; dark shading indicates elevations ≥ 1200 m; large bodies of freshwater are outlined in bold, black lines.

m, mountains of Metapán, Depto. Santa Ana, El Salvador.
Rhadinaea montecristi: Mertens 1952b, d, Uzzell & Starrett 1958, Myers 1974, Wilson & Meyer 1985, Villa et al. 1988, McCranie & Wilson 1991b, Köhler 1996, Dueñas et al. 2001, Köhler 2001a, 2003b.
Geographic distribution: Northwestern El Salvador, southeastern Guatemala, and southwestern Honduras (Köhler 2003b).
Ecological distribution: Cloud forest between 2150 and 2390 m.
Description: A small snake (SVL of largest speci-

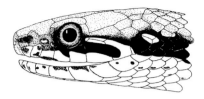

5 mm

Figure 42. *Rhadinaea montecristi* (SMF 79362): Lateral view of head.

men examined 370 mm); relative tail length 34–49% of SVL in males, 31–37% in females; divided nasal; 1 loreal; 1–2 preoculars; 1–2 postoculars; 1 anterior and 2 posterior temporals; 8 supralabials, with the 4th and 5th entering orbit; 8 (rarely 9 or 10) infralabials; dorsal scales smooth, without apical pits, in 19 rows throughout; ventrals 158–167 in males, 164–174 in females; subcaudals 71–90 in males, 62–79 in females; anal plate divided.

Dorsal surfaces of head, body, and tail brown with a more or less distinct dark brown vertebral stripe; two prominent blackish longitudinal stripes on sides of body, the upper one is broader (on scale row 3 and adjacent halves of scale rows 2 and 4) than the lower (includes lower part of scale row 1 and ventral tips); the upper stripe continues to tip of tail while the ventrolateral stripe terminates at vent; lateral surfaces of body between these stripes pale brown; the anterior supralabials are mostly dirty white, except for the lower portions of the anterior ones that are dark brown; an oblique dark brown stripe runs from the posteroventral corner of the eye to the corner of the mouth; above this dark brown stripe a white postocular stripe runs to the side of the neck and is bordered superiorly by dark brown; there is no creamish collar or nape spots; venter immaculate white or with few scattered black dots that tend to concentrate to form a median line on some parts of body and tail. Iris reddish-tan.
Natural history: O. Komar (field notes) recorded two adults from under logs near cloud forest at Cerro El Pital, Depto. Chalatenango in May. W. E. Duellman (field notes) recorded several adults from the inside of damp logs in cloud forest at Cerro Montecristo, Depto. Santa Ana in February; one stump contained nine individuals. Data for a UMMZ specimen indicated it had preyed upon a *Bolitoglossa heiroreias*. Mertens (1952d) reported a

specimen found under leaf litter in El Salvador.
Specimens examined: <u>Chalatenango</u>: Cerro El
Pital, 2390 m: KU 291245, MUHNES C–30–1540.
<u>Santa Ana</u>: Hacienda Montecristo, Cordillera de
Metapán, 2150–2200 m: SMF 43188–89, 77422–26,
two SMF without numbers, UMMZ 117292, KU
62113–16, 63118–20, 63869–85; same locality at 2300
m: KU 183943–44.

Rhadinaea pilonaorum (Stuart 1954)
(Hojarasquera del Pacífico)
Plate 113, Map 105

1954 *Trimetopon pilonaorum* Stuart, Proc. Biol.
Soc. Washington 67: 176; type locality: Finca La
Gloria, about 12 km northeast of Chiquimulilla, 950
m, Depto. Santa Rosa, Guatemala.
Trimetopon posadasi: Mertens 1952d, Rand 1957.
Rhadinaea pilonaorum: Myers 1974, Dueñas et al.
2001, Köhler 2001a, 2003b.
Geographic distribution: Southeastern Guatemala and western El Salvador (Köhler 2003b).
Ecological distribution: Dry forest and pine-oak
forest between 670 and 1080 m.
Description: (including data from Rand 1957): A
small snake (SVL of largest Salvadoran specimen
212 mm); tail incomplete in all specimens; divided
nasal; 1 loreal; 1 preocular; 1 postocular; 1 anterior
and 1–2 posterior temporals; 7 supralabials, 3rd and
4th enter orbit; 8 infralabials; dorsal scales smooth,
without apical pits, in 17 rows throughout; ventrals
151–153; anal plate divided. Subcaudal counts not
available because tails are incomplete in all examined specimens.

　Head white with brown mottling; dorsal surfaces of body and tail uniform black. In life, dorsum
uniform black; the 1st to 2nd scale rows have pale
blue blotches in the center of each black scale; the
head is black with irregular dark orange blotches;
bright orange coloration is concentrated in sutures
between the head plates; there is a fluorescent
orange ring around the neck starting at the posterior end of the parietals and continuing posteriorly
three scale rows, becoming brighter orange posteriorly; the supralabials and venter are pale blue to
gray with some small blotches of brown; the eye is
red; the venter is almost transparent under the
head; remainder of venter pale blue.
Natural history: E. Greenbaum (field notes) was
given a snake collected under a rotting log next to a
house in a coffee plantation during the day at Finca
La Giralda, Depto. La Libertad in August. Rand

Plate 113: *Rhadinaea pilonaorum* (KU 289967) EL
SALVADOR: La Libertad: Finca La Giralda (1080 m).
Photo: E. Greenbaum.

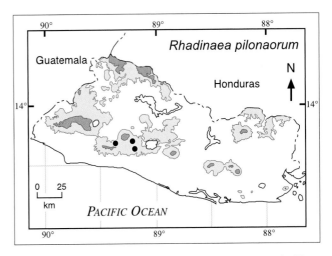

Map 105: Distribution of *Rhadinaea pilonaorum* in El
Salvador.
Closed circles represent examined-specimen locality records;
open squares are published locality records. Light shading
indicates 600–1200 m elevation; dark shading indicates elevations ≥ 1200 m; large bodies of freshwater are outlined in bold,
black lines.

(1957) reported a specimen collected at night at the
bottom of a brush-grown gully in pasture at San
Salvador, Depto. San Salvador in May.
Specimens examined: <u>La Libertad</u>: Finca La
Giralda, 13°39.34′N, 89°22.47′W, 1080 m: KU
289967. <u>San Salvador</u>: San Salvador, 670 m: FMNH
64951; Planes de Renderos: UU 5549.

Genus *Scaphiodontophis*

　This monotypic genus is noted for its
pseudautotomy (intervertebral tail breakage) to

escape predators. The genus is distributed from Tamaulipas, Mexico, to northern and central Colombia on the Atlantic versant, and along the Pacific versant from Oaxaca, Mexico, to Honduras, and from southwestern Costa Rica to eastern Panama (Savage 2002).

Scaphiodontophis annulatus (Duméril, Bibron & Duméril 1854)
(Media Coralilla)
Plate 114, Map 106

1854 *Enicognathus annulatus* Duméril, Bibron & Duméril, Erp. Gén. 7: 335; type locality: Cobán, Alta Verapaz, Guatemala.
Scaphiodontophis albonuchalis: Taylor & Smith 1943.
Sibynophis albonuchalis: Mertens 1952d.
Scaphiodontophis annulatus: Villa et al. 1988, Savage & Slowinski 1996, Dueñas et al. 2001, Köhler 2001a, 2003b, Leenders 2003.
Geographic distribution: Identical to genus.
Ecological distribution: Dry forest, premontane evergreen forest, subtropical humid forest, and pine-oak forest between 600 and 1080 m.
Description: A medium-sized snake (SVL of largest specimen examined 417 mm); relative tail length 76% of SVL in the only specimen (female) with complete tail; 1 loreal; 1 preocular; 2 postoculars; 1 anterior and 2 posterior temporals; 9 supralabials; 9–10 infralabials; dorsal scales smooth, without apical pits; in 17 rows throughout; ventrals 152 in single male, 145–146 in females; subcaudals 117 in the only female with complete tail (no male with complete tail available to us); anal plate divided.

The few specimens of this species we have seen from El Salvador have a pattern similar to coral snakes (yellow bands bordered by black bands and separated by wider red interspaces) in the anterior part of the body, whereas the posterior part of the body and all of the tail is brown with three longitudinal lines of dark brown dots (on the vertebral and the 5th dorsal scale rows); other specimens of this species are known to have a banded pattern throughout the body and tail (Savage & Slowinski 1996); head dark brown or black with a yellowish band across the top of head between eyes and another one on tip of snout; nuchal band some shade of red; ventral surface cream or dirty white, dark brown spots on lateral margins of ventrals and subcaudals can form two additional ventrolateral

Plate 114: *Scaphiodontophis annulatus* EL SALVADOR: La Libertad: Finca La Giralda (1080 m). Photo: E. Greenbaum.

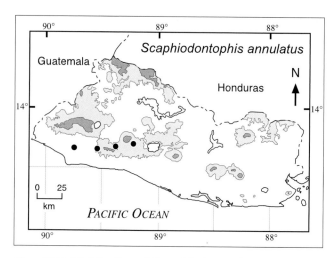

Map 106: Distribution of *Scaphiodontophis annulatus* in El Salvador.
Closed circles represent examined-specimen locality records; open squares are published locality records. Light shading indicates 600–1200 m elevation; dark shading indicates elevations ≥ 1200 m; large bodies of freshwater are outlined in bold, black lines.

longitudinal lines (usually more distinct posteriorly).
Natural history: E. Greenbaum (field notes) was given an adult found under some rubbish in a coffee plantation at Finca La Giralda, Depto. La Libertad in August. Campbell (1998a) noted this diurnal species has a tail that can be easily broken when molested; this species feeds upon lizards and lays 1–10 eggs. Savage (2002) added this species may prey upon frogs; the upper limit for clutch size was reported to be 12.
Specimens examined: <u>La Libertad</u>: Finca La

Giralda, 13°39.34´N, 89°22.47´W, 1080 m: KU 289943. San Salvador: San Salvador, Instituto Tropical de Investigaciones Científicas: KU 62125. Sonsonate: Hacienda San Antonio, near Sonsonate: SMF 42220; Hacienda Chilata, 610 m: MVZ 40429.

Genus *Scolecophis*

This monotypic genus of semifossorial snakes is distributed from Guatemala to central Costa Rica on the Pacific versant; one record from the Atlantic versant of Honduras (Savage 2002).

Scolecophis atrocinctus (Schlegel 1837)
(Falso Coralito de Manchas Anaranjadas)
Plate 115, Map 107, Figure 43

1837 *Calamaria atrocincta* Schlegel, Essai physion. Serpens 2: 48; type locality: Chile (in error). *Scolecophis atrocinctus*: Mertens 1952d, Villa et al. 1988, Köhler 1996, Dueñas et al. 2001, Köhler 2001a, 2003b, Leenders 2003.
Geographic distribution: Identical to genus.
Ecological distribution: Dry forest between sea level and 920 m.
Description: A small snake (SVL of largest specimen examined 380 mm); relative tail length 18–31% of SVL in males, 17–18% in females; divided nasal; 1 loreal; 1 preocular; 2 postoculars; 1 anterior and 1 posterior temporal; 7 supralabials, 3rd and 4th enter orbit; 6–7 infralabials; dorsal scales smooth, with single apical pits, in 13–16 rows at midbody, and 13–15 rows one head length anterior to vent; ventrals 168–193 in males, 194–196 in females; subcaudals 50–52 in males, 45–51 in females; anal plate divided.
    Color pattern of body and tail consists of black rings (3–5 scales at vertebral line), separated by equal or narrower rings (2–4 scales at vertebral row), white laterally but with a distinctive orange-red to fluorescent pink middorsal blotch between each black ring (which disappears in preserved specimens); snout black, followed by white belt including prefrontals, adjacent scales (postnasals, loreals, and anteriormost supralabials, or at least their portions); a black band covering top of head and extending through eyes and supralabials to anterior infralabials; another white blotch extends from chin to postoculars and anterior temporals and is followed by a black ring that fuses dorsally with the anterior black band.
Natural history: One adult, gravid female was

Plate 115: *Scolecophis atrocinctus* (KU 289804) EL SALVADOR: Ahuachapán: Parque Nacional El Imposible, La Fincona (720 m). Photo: E. Greenbaum.

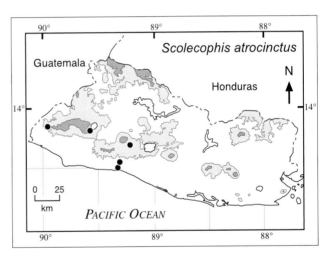

Map 107: Distribution of *Scolecophis atrocinctus* in El Salvador.
Closed circles represent examined-specimen locality records; open squares are published locality records. Light shading indicates 600–1200 m elevation; dark shading indicates elevations ≥ 1200 m; large bodies of freshwater are outlined in bold, black lines.

collected under a rotten log during the day in dry forest at Bosque Las Lajas, Depto. Sonsonate in July and given to E. Greenbaum (field notes). Savage (2002) noted this species preys exclusively on centipedes. One individual was observed climbing a tree.
Specimens examined: Ahuachapán: Parque Nacional El Imposible, 13°50.50´N, 89°58.51´W, 820 m: KU 289804, MUHNES C–30–1358. La Libertad:

2 mm

Figure 43. *Scolecophis atrocinctus* (SMF 75740): Lateral view of head.

road Nuevo San Salvador [= Santa Tecla]–La Libertad, near Hacienda El Triunfo, about 300 m: SMF 43171; Hacienda San Diego near La Libertad, 50 m: SMF 48082. San Salvador: San Salvador: SMF 75740. Sonsonate: Bosque Las Lajas, 13°50.04´N, 89°33.56´W, 920 m: KU 289866.

Genus *Senticolis*

This monotypic genus is distributed from Tamaulipas, Mexico, and Arizona, USA, to central Costa Rica (Savage 2002, Köhler 2003b).

Senticolis triaspis (Cope 1866)
(Ratonera Tropical Común)
Plate 116, Map 108

1866 *Coluber triaspis* Cope, Proc. Acad. Nat. Sci. Philadelphia 1866: 128; type locality: Belize; restricted to the vicinity of the town of Belize, Belize, by Smith & Taylor (1950).
Elaphe triaspis mutabilis: Mertens 1952d, Brongersma 1954a, Peters & Orejas-Miranda 1970.
Senticolis triaspis: Villa et al. 1988, Dueñas et al. 2001, Köhler 2001a, 2003b, Leenders 2003, Leenders & Watkins-Colwell 2004.
Senticolis triaspis mutabilis: Price 1991.
Geographic distribution: Identical to genus.
Ecological distribution: Dry forest, premontane evergreen forest, subtropical humid forest, and pine-oak forest between 200 and 1870 m.
Description (data also from Brongersma 1954a): A medium-sized snake (SVL of largest specimen 1003 mm); relative tail length 23–29% of SVL in males, 23–32% in females; divided nasal; 1 (rarely 0) loreal; 1 preocular; 2 postoculars; 2–3 anterior and 3–4 posterior temporals; 8–9 supralabials, 4th and 5th enter orbit; 10–11 infralabials; dorsal scales smooth (except rows 3–7 that are weakly keeled), with two apical pits, in 29–33 rows at midbody, and 19–23

Plate 116: *Senticolis triaspis* (SMF 81282) EL SALVA-DOR: Ahuachapán: El Refugio (225 m). Photo: G. Köhler.

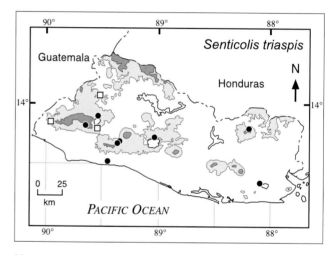

Map 108: Distribution of *Senticolis triaspis* in El Salvador.
Closed circles represent examined-specimen locality records; open squares are published locality records. Light shading indicates 600–1200 m elevation; dark shading indicates elevations ≥ 1200 m; large bodies of freshwater are outlined in bold, black lines.

rows one head length anterior to vent; ventrals 252–260 in males, 255–272 in females; subcaudals 112–113 in males, 95–111 in females; anal plate divided.

Dorsal color of head, body, and tail mostly uniform olive-brown, becoming more yellowish or orange on snout and lateral side of head; a broad dark brown transverse bar across head usually present; ventral surface cream or dirty white; in juveniles dorsal ground color pale brown or grayish brown with a series of irregular, reddish brown and darkly edged blotches distributed from the head to the tip of tail; another series of smaller, similarly colored blotches alternating with the dorsal ones present on lateral sides of body. Some adults retain the juvenile color pattern, although it is less contrasting.

Natural history: Campbell (1998a) noted this species can be active by day or night. This species feeds upon mammals, birds, and lizards; females lay 3–7 eggs throughout the year. Stafford & Meyer (2000) noted this species is mainly terrestrial but is capable of climbing; some individuals have been found feeding on bats in caves. Leenders & Watkins-Colwell (2004) captured a juvenile at the base of a small rock at 1140 h, and a subadult female 1.2 m above ground in a tree (1350 h) at Bosque Las Lajas (Depto. Sonsonate).

Specimens examined: Ahuachapán: El Refugio, vicinity of Mariposario of Francisco Serrano, 13°49.46´N, 89°59.98´W, 225 m: SMF 81282. La Libertad: Finca Astillero La Cumbre, about 1050 m: SMF 43104; Finca Los Cedros, La Cumbre, about 1000 m: SMF 43193; 9.7 km W La Libertad: LACM 51794. Morazán: Cerro Cacahuatique, 1310 m: KU 261392. San Miguel: Laguna de Olomega, 61 m: MVZ 40414. San Salvador: Lago de Ilopango area, 7.4 km ENE Ilopango: KU 183882. Santa Ana: Hacienda Los Planes de Montecristo, Metapán, 1800 m: VH 103; Lago Coatepeque, 13°54´N, 89°33´W: KU 289840. Sonsonate: the top of Volcán de Izalco, 1870 m: VH 70.

Published locality records: Ahuachapán: Parque Nacional El Imposible (Leenders 2003). Santa Ana: road from Santa Ana to Metapán, about 12 km N of Santa Ana: RMNH 9954 (Brongersma 1954a). Sonsonate: Município Izalco, Cantón Las Lajas, Bosque Las Lajas (13.829°N, 89.567°W), 800–970 m: YPM 12428 (Leenders & Watkins-Colwell 2004).

Genus *Sibon*

This genus includes 10 species of snail- and slug-eating snakes that are distributed from Veracruz and Oaxaca, Mexico, along the Atlantic versant to Colombia, Venezuela, Ecuador, the Guianas, and Brazil, and from Nayarit, Mexico, along the Pacific versant to Colombia and Ecuador (Savage 2002). Three species occur in El Salvador.

Sibon anthracops (Cope 1868)
(Tragababosa Falsa Coral)
Plate 117, Map 109

1868 *Leptognathus anthracops* Cope, Proc. Acad.

Plate 117: *Sibon anthracops* (UTA R-39185) GUATEMALA: Progreso: km 67 carretera Sanarate–Jalapa (875 m). Photo: E. N. Smith.

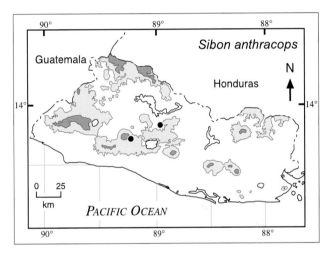

Map 109: Distribution of *Sibon anthracops* in El Salvador.
Closed circles represent examined-specimen locality records; open squares are published locality records. Light shading indicates 600–1200 m elevation; dark shading indicates elevations ≥ 1200 m; large bodies of freshwater are outlined in bold, black lines.

Nat. Sci. Philadelphia 1868: 136; type locality: Central America.
Sibon anthracops: Hidalgo 1979, Kofron 1987, Dueñas et al. 2001, Köhler 2001a, Savage 2002, Köhler 2003b.

Geographic distribution: From the Pacific versant of central El Salvador to Costa Rica; also on the Atlantic versant in Guatemala and Honduras (Köhler 2003b).

Ecological distribution: Dry forest and savanna between 500 and 750 m.

Description: A small snake (SVL of largest

specimen examined 357 mm); relative tail length 35–39% of SVL in males, 35–39% in females; divided nasal; 1 loreal that enters orbit; no preoculars; 2 postoculars; 1 anterior and 2 posterior temporals; 6–7 supralabials, with 3rd and 4th entering orbit; 6–9 infralabials; dorsal scales smooth, without apical pits, in 13 rows throughout; ventrals 170–183 in males, 170–182 in females; 72–89 subcaudals in males, 74–88 in females; anal plate entire.

Dorsal, lateral, and ventral ground color white with 17–18 black bands on body, most of them meeting dorsally and ventrally, some of them alternating; 8–11 black rings on tail; areas between black bands on scale rows 2–7 orange; head black, covering lateral 3/4 of parietals, first supralabial, upper half of those supralabials entering orbit, postoculars, and anterior half of first temporal; first white interspace includes posterior edges of parietals, temporal region, and posterior supralabials, also extending onto second or third scale posterior to parietals; mental, first three infralabials, and anterior half of first pair of chin shields black, rest of chin white.

Natural history: Hidalgo (1979) collected an adult female at night in a tree (*Randia* sp.) 2.6 m above the ground at a locality 3 km E Tenancingo, Depto. Cuscatlán in July. Kofron (1987) noted three adult females had three enlarged, yolked follicles each; a female from El Salvador had follicles ranging in size from 17.9–19.8 mm in July. Savage (2002) noted this nocturnal species can be arboreal or terrestrial.

Specimens examined: Cuscatlán: 3 km E Tenancingo: KU 183946. San Salvador: San Salvador: SMF 73239. Depto. unknown: no specific locality: SMF 68197, KU 183945 (*).

Sibon carri (Shreve 1951)
(Tragababosa de Carr)
Plate 118, Map 110, Figure 44a

1951 *Tropidodipsas carri* Shreve, Copeia 1951: 52; type locality: Escuela Agrícola Panamericana, near Tegucigalpa, Honduras.
Tropidodipsas carri: Mertens 1952d.
Sibon carri: Peters 1960, Peters & Orejas-Miranda 1970, Kofron 1985, Wilson & Meyer 1985, Villa et al. 1988, Köhler 1996, Dueñas et al. 2001, Köhler 2001a, 2003b.

Geographic distribution: Central and eastern Guatemala, and Pacific versant in Honduras and El

Plate 118: *Sibon carri* (UTA R-45493) GUATEMALA: Zacapa: Gualán, carretera al Atlántico, Aldea Juan de Paz. Photo: E. N. Smith.

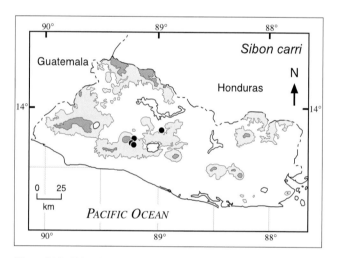

Map 110: Distribution of *Sibon carri* in El Salvador. Closed circles represent examined-specimen locality records; open squares are published locality records. Light shading indicates 600–1200 m elevation; dark shading indicates elevations ≥ 1200 m; large bodies of freshwater are outlined in bold, black lines.

Salvador (Köhler 2003b).

Ecological distribution: Dry forest and savanna between 500 and 750 m.

Description: A small snake (SVL of largest specimen examined 334 mm); relative tail length 18–23% of SVL in males, 20–21% in females; divided nasal; 1 loreal; no preoculars; 1 postocular; 0–1 anterior and 1–2 posterior temporals; 5–6 supralabials, with 3rd and 4th entering orbit; 6–7 infralabials; dorsal scales smooth, without apical pits, in 13 rows throughout; ventrals 155–168 in males, 159–170 in females; subcaudals 40–48 in

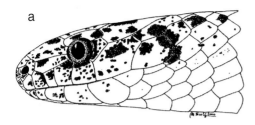

2 mm

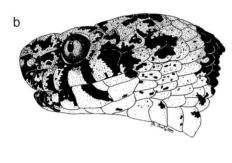

3 mm

Figure 44: a. *Sibon carri* (SMF 58433): Lateral view of head; b. *Sibon nebulatus* (SMF 81283): Lateral view of head.

males, 42–46 in females; anal plate entire.

Dorsal ground color pale brown to dark orange-red with many irregular transverse blotches becoming narrower laterally, often broken and offset to vertebral line and forming a zigzag pattern; interspaces heavily mottled with dark brown and with 1–2 central dark brown spots on the ventrolateral scales; top and sides of the head irregularly mottled with dark brown; ventral surface including infralabials cream or pale white with irregular dark brown spots and streaks.

Natural history: Mertens (1952d) collected a specimen on a trail in the late evening in El Salvador.

Specimens examined: <u>Cuscatlán</u>: 2.4 km SE Tenancingo: KU 183951; 0.3 km E Tenancingo: KU 183952. <u>San Salvador</u>: between Instituto Tropical de Investigaciones Científicas and San Carlos: SMF 43047; Instituto Tropical de Investigaciones Científicas, San Salvador, 700 m: SMF 77427–32, KU 62121–24, UU 5388–91; Ayutuxtepeque: KU 183950.

***Sibon nebulatus* (Linnaeus 1758)**
(Tragababosa Jaspeada)
Plate 119, Map 111, Figure 44b

1758 *Coluber nebulatus* Linnaeus, Systema Naturae, ed. 10: 222; type locality: America.
Sibon nebulata: Hidalgo 1981a, Villa et al. 1988, Kofron 1990, Dueñas et al. 2001.
Sibon nebulatus: Köhler 2001a, 2003b, Leenders 2003.

Geographic distribution: From central Veracruz, Mexico, to Ecuador, the Guianas, and northern Brazil on the Atlantic versant, and from Nayarit, Mexico, to El Salvador on the Pacific versant; also in southwestern Costa Rica and adjacent Panama, Colombia, and Ecuador in the Pacific drainage (Savage 2002).

Ecological distribution: Dry forest, premontane evergreen forest, and subtropical humid forest between 470 and 720 m.

Description (data includes Hidalgo 1981a): A small snake (SVL of largest specimen from El Salvador 707 mm); relative tail length 38% of SVL in single male, 26% in single female; divided nasal; 1 loreal; no preoculars; 2 postoculars; 1 anterior and 2 posterior temporals; 5–6 supralabials, with 3rd and 4th, or 4th and 5th entering orbit; 7–8 infralabials; dorsal scales smooth, without apical pits, in 15 rows throughout; ventrals 178 in single male, 185 in single female; subcaudals 91 in single male, 90 in single female; anal plate entire.

Ground color of head, body, and tail gray or

Plate 119: *Sibon nebulatus* EL SALVADOR: Ahuachapán: Parque Nacional El Imposible, La Fincona (720 m). Photo: G. Köhler.

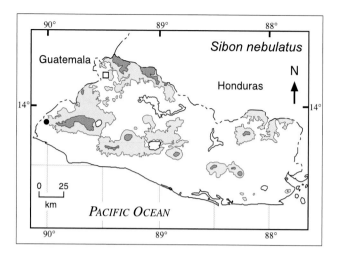

Map 111: Distribution of *Sibon nebulatus* in El Salvador.
Closed circles represent examined-specimen locality records; open squares are published locality records. Light shading indicates 600–1200 m elevation; dark shading indicates elevations ≥ 1200 m; large bodies of freshwater are outlined in bold, black lines.

grayish brown with irregular transverse dark brown or black blotches and bands, reaching at least to lateral edges of ventral plates; some of these bands can fuse to form complete rings; numerous dark brown spots and streaks present on interspaces; ventral surface cream, except for invading dorsal black blotches that are with or without numerous black spots.

Natural history: Hidalgo (1981a) reported an adult female collected at night from a tangle of vines in dry forest (volcanic lava) at Hacienda San Diego, Depto. Santa Ana in November. Campbell (1998a) noted this species is nocturnal and arboreal, feeds upon slugs and shelled snails, and females lay 3–9 eggs from May–August.

Specimens examined: Ahuachapán: Parque Nacional El Imposible, La Fincona, 13°50.8′N, 89°58.8′W, 720 m: SMF 81283.

Published locality records: Santa Ana: 6 km S Metapán, Hacienda San Diego, 470 m (Hidalgo 1981a).

Genus *Spilotes*

This monotypic genus of large snakes is distributed from Tamaulipas, Mexico, to Bolivia, Paraguay, and northeastern Argentina on the Atlantic versant, and from the Isthmus of Tehuantepec along the Pacific versant to western Ecuador (Savage 2002).

***Spilotes pullatus* (Linnaeus 1758)**
(Culebra Mica)
Plate 120, Map 112

1758 *Coluber pullatus* Linnaeus, Systema Naturae, ed. 10: 225; type locality: "Asia" (in error).
Spilotes pullatus mexicanus: K. Schmidt 1928.
Spilotes pullatus: Villa et al. 1988, Dueñas et al. 2001, Köhler 2001a, 2003b, Leenders 2003, Leenders & Watkins-Colwell 2004.

Geographic distribution: Identical to genus.

Ecological distribution: Dry forest, premontane evergreen forest, and subtropical humid forest between sea level and 1000 m.

Description: A large snake (SVL of largest specimen 1874 mm [Leenders & Watkins-Colwell 2004]); relative tail length 34–42% of SVL in males, 36–39% in females; single nasal; 1 loreal; 1 preocular; 2 postoculars; 1–2 anterior and 1–2 posterior temporals; 8–9 supralabials, with the 4th and 5th entering orbit; 8–10 infralabials; dorsal scales keeled, with two apical pits, in 14–18 rows at midbody, and 10–14 rows one head length anterior to vent; ventrals 213–215 in males, 212–218 in females; subcaudals 135–139 in males, 128–139 in females; anal plate single. Leenders & Watkins-Colwell (2004) noted 222 ventrals in a male (YPM 12453) from Parque Nacional El Imposible (Depto. Ahuachapán).

Dorsal color mostly black with irregular, diagonally oriented yellow crossbars; scales in black areas can bear small yellow spots or mottling, and those on yellow crossbars are often tipped or marginated with black; head and ventral coloration resembles that of body; top of head mostly black; however the rostral is usually yellow, and some yellow mottling can be present on other head scales, whereas the supralabials tend to be almost completely yellow; venter predominantly yellow.

Natural history: Campbell (1998a) noted this diurnal, mostly arboreal species feeds upon rodents, birds, and bird eggs; females lay 7–10 eggs from April–July. Stafford & Meyer (2000) noted this species is common around human habitations where it preys upon vermin and domestic foul and their eggs; also noted from ant nests. Leenders & Watkins-Colwell (2004) noted an adult male in a bush ca. 2 m above the ground at Parque Nacional El Imposible (Depto. Ahuachapán); the snake fled into "tree tops" when it was discovered.

Specimens examined: Ahuachapán: Parque Nacional El Imposible, San Benito, 600–750 m:

Plate 120: *Spilotes pullatus* (YPM 12453) EL SALVA-DOR: Ahuachapán: Parque Nacional El Imposible, San Benito, Río Ixcanal (600 m). Photo: T. Leenders.

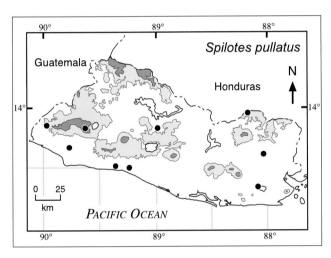

Map 112: Distribution of *Spilotes pullatus* in El Salvador.

Closed circles represent examined-specimen locality records; open squares are published locality records. Light shading indicates 600–1200 m elevation; dark shading indicates elevations ≥ 1200 m; large bodies of freshwater are outlined in bold, black lines.

Plate 120 (YPM 12453). Cuscatlán: Tenancingo, La Laguneta at El Puente: KU 183953. La Libertad: La Libertad: SMF 68174; 10 km E La Libertad: KU 183954. Morazán: Divisadero: FMNH 10996; Finca SW of Perquín, 13°56'N, 88°09'W, 800 m: KU CT 11863. San Miguel: Laguna de Olomega, 61 m: MVZ 40424. Santa Ana: Cerro Verde: MUHNES 753. Sonsonate: Hacienda San Antonio near Sonsonate: SMF 51952.

Genus *Stenorrhina*

The two species of this genus are specialized predators on large arthropods. The genus is distrib-uted from Guerrero and southern Veracruz, Mexico, to north-central Venezuela and western Ecuador (Savage 2002). One species occurs in El Salvador.

Stenorrhina freminvillii Duméril, Bibron & Duméril 1854
(Gargantilla Rayada)
Plate 121, Map 113

1854 *Stenorhina Freminvillii* Duméril, Bibron & Duméril, Erp. Gén. 7: 868; type locality: Mexico.
Stenorhina degenhardtii: K. Schmidt 1928.
Stenorrhina freminvillii lactea: Smith & Taylor 1950, Dunn & Stuart 1951.
Stenorhina freminvillii freminvilli: Brongersma 1954a.
Stenorrhina freminvillii freminvillii: Rand 1957.
Stenorrhina freminvillii: Peters & Orejas-Miranda 1970, Dueñas et al. 2001.
Stenorrhina freminvillei: Villa et al. 1988, Köhler 1996, 2001a, 2003b, Leenders 2003, Leenders & Watkins-Colwell 2004.

Geographic distribution: From the Isthmus of Tehuantepec to central Honduras on the Atlantic versant, and from Guerrero, Mexico, to central Costa Rica on the Pacific versant (Savage 2002).
Ecological distribution: Dry forest, premontane evergreen forest, subtropical humid forest, and pine-oak forest between sea level and 1700 m.
Description: A small snake (SVL of largest specimen examined 410 mm); relative tail length 17–20% of SVL in males, 10–26% in females; divided nasal, anterior section fused with internasal; 0–1 loreal; 1 preocular; 1–2 (rarely 3) postoculars; 1 anterior and 2 posterior temporals; 7 (rarely 8) supralabials, 3rd and 4th enter orbit; 7 (rarely 6 or 8) infralabials; dorsal scales smooth, without apical pits, in 17 rows throughout; ventrals 158–169 in males, 154–176 in females; subcaudals 35–47 in males, 24–40 in females; anal plate divided. Leenders & Watkins-Colwell (2004) noted 16 scale rows one head-length anterior to vent in a male (YPM 12476); a female (YPM 12999) has 197 ventrals and 15 scale rows one head-length anterior to the vent.

Dorsal ground color grayish brown, yellowish brown, or brown, usually with five (one vertebral, two dorsolateral, two lateral) longitudinal black stripes extending the length of the body; vertebral stripe begins at posterior edge of temporals and continues to tip of tail; dorsolateral stripes begin

Plate 121: *Stenorrhina freminvillii* HONDURAS: no specific locality. Photo: G. Köhler.

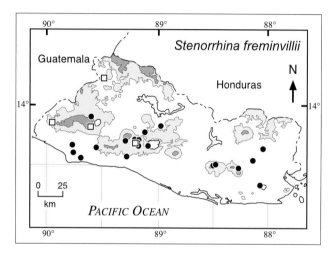

Map 113: Distribution of *Stenorrhina freminvillii* in El Salvador.
Closed circles represent examined-specimen locality records; open squares are published locality records. Light shading indicates 600–1200 m elevation; dark shading indicates elevations ≥ 1200 m; large bodies of freshwater are outlined in bold, black lines.

in nuchal region and extend to about anterior half of tail; lateral stripes originate as a continuous dark brown postocular stripe and reach posterior end of body; in some specimens (especially in darker ones) the stripes are indistinct or absent; posterior margins of dorsal and lateral body scales narrowly edged with black; top of head same as body coloration; supralabials, infralabials, and ventral surface yellow; ventral plates dark brown laterally; a narrow midventral dark brown line on tail. Rand (1957) noted a juvenile with red coloration in San Salvador, Depto. San Salvador.

Natural history: E. Greenbaum (field notes) recorded an invididual from the ground of a coffee plantation during the day at Finca El Milagro, Depto. Santa Ana in July. M. Veselý (field notes) observed a Salvadoran specimen consume a large lycosid spider during the day on a dirt road in May. Mertens (1952d) reported a Salvadoran specimen collected from under a rock. Campbell (1998a) noted this terrestrial species can be active by day or night, and feeds upon insects, spiders and scorpions; females lay 1–2 clutches (5–19 eggs per clutch) per year during the dry or wet season. Savage (2002) noted clutch size increases with body size.

Specimens examined: Cuscatlán: 0.5 km E Tenancingo: KU 183960; Tenancingo: KU 183961. La Libertad: Finca La Peña Cumbre of Santa Tecla, ca. 1000 m: SMF 42887, 43101; Guadalalupe, 640 m: YPM 12476. Morazán: 4.0 km NW Montecristo Mine, 198 m: MVZ 40442. San Miguel: Laguna de Olomega, 61 m: MVZ 40440; 10 km NNE San Miguel, Cantón San Antonio Chávez: KU 183962; Volcán de San Miguel, 740 m: KU 291385. San Salvador: San Marcos, San Salvador: SMF 43153; Instituto Tropical de Investigaciones Científicas, San Salvador, 700 m: KU 62126, SMF 43237, 77435–39, 81369; Colónia Luz, San Salvador: SMF 43238; San Salvador: ZMB 35695–97, FMNH 64952–54; 3.2 km E Tonacatepeque: LACM 103491; San Salvador, Ciudad Universitaria: KU 183957, 183959; 3 km SE Ilopango, Cantón Asino: KU 183958. Santa Ana: Finca El Milagro, 13°53.29´N, 89°37.17´W, 1300 m: KU 289794. Sonsonate: Hacienda San Antonio near Sonsonate: SMF 42222; Hacienda Chilata, 610 m: MVZ 40441; 2.4 km SW CA Hwy 12 (Acajutla-Sonsonate Jct) on Hwy CA 2: LACM 114110; 16.4 km SE Jct Hwys 12/2: TCWC 55531. Usulután: La Poza, 6 km W Usulután: SMF 81368; on the road between Alegría and Berlín: SMF 43239; Laguna de Alegría, 1300 m: SMF 43240.

Published locality records: Ahuachapán: Parque Nacional El Imposible (Leenders 2003). San Salvador: in barranco between the Instituto Tropical de Investigaciones Científicas and Volcán de San Salvador: RMNH 9953 (Brongersma 1954a). Santa Ana: Município Metapán, Cantón Tecomapa, N side of Lago de Güija (14.30°N, 89.50°W), 445 m: YPM 12476 (Leenders & Watkins-Colwell 2004); Município Santa Ana, Cantón Los Flores, Parque Nacional Los Andes and Volcán Santa Ana (13.869°N, 89.620°W), 1700 m: YPM 12999 (Leenders & Watkins-Colwell 2004).

Genus *Tantilla*

As currently understood, the colubrid genus *Tantilla* contains 58 species of snakes in the New World from warm, temperate areas of the United States to east-central Argentina (including Trinidad and Tobago) on the Atlantic versant, and to central Peru on the Pacific versant (Wilson 1999, Wilson & Campbell 2001, Cánseco-Márquez et al. 2002, Savage 2002, Sawaya & Sazima 2003, Stafford 2004, Greenbaum et al. 2004). Four species occur in El Salvador.

Tantilla armillata Cope 1876
(Traga-Cienpiés de Cabeza Negra)
Plate 122, Map 114

1876 *Tantilla armillata* Cope, J. Acad. Nat. Sci. Phila. ser. 2, 8: 587; type locality: Middle Costa Rica.
Tantilla armillata: Mertens 1952d, Rand 1957, Köhler 2003b.
Tantilla melanocephala: Wilson & Mena 1980, Wilson 1982, Villa et al. 1988, Wilson 1992, Dueñas et al. 2001, Köhler 2001a.
Geographic distribution: From Guatemala to central Costa Rica along the Pacific versant; Atlantic drainage of Honduras; upland Nicaragua (Savage 2002).
Ecological distribution: Dry forest between 640 and 750 m.
Description: A very small snake (SVL of largest specimen examined 195 mm); relative tail length 23–27% of SVL in males, 22–26% in females; divided nasal; no loreal; 1 preocular; 2 (rarely 1) postoculars; 1 anterior and 1 posterior temporal; 7 supralabials, 3rd and 4th enter orbit; 6 infralabials; dorsal scales smooth, without apical pits, in 15 rows throughout; ventrals 166–173 in males, 166–172 in females; subcaudals 46–53 in males, 45–53 in females; anal plate divided.

Dorsal ground color brown with a narrow black vertebral line running from about 5th dorsal scale row behind head to the tail; indistinct pale brown longitudinal line on sides of body (covering adjacent halves of 5th and 6th scale rows); about 5–6 black transverse rows of scales on neck and top of head; two yellow spots on posterior portions of parietals (sometimes two more on anterior portions); narrow (1 scale row), yellow nuchal collar present, complete or incomplete; supralabials and anterior infralabials mostly dark brown above, otherwise

Plate 122: *Tantilla armillata* (UTA R-42392) GUATE-MALA: Jutiapa: Aldea El Barreal. Photo: E. N. Smith.

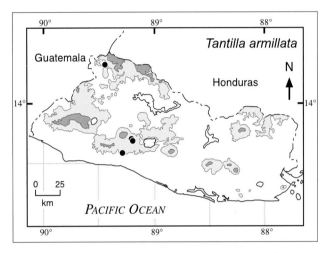

Map 114: Distribution of *Tantilla armillata* in El Salvador.
Closed circles represent examined-specimen locality records; open squares are published locality records. Light shading indicates 600–1200 m elevation; dark shading indicates elevations ≥ 1200 m; large bodies of freshwater are outlined in bold, black lines.

yellow; ventral surface dirty white.
Taxonomic comments: Until recently, *Tantilla armillata* and *T. ruficeps* were considered to be synonyms of the highly variable and geographically widespread species *T. melanocephala* (Wilson & Mena 1980, Wilson 1992). Savage (2002) argued that *T. armillata* is a valid taxon based on its mostly allopatric distribution (in relation to *T. ruficeps*), scutellation, and color pattern.
Natural history: O. Komar (field notes) collected an adult female with a recently laid egg under leaf litter adjacent to a river during the day at Guadalupe, Depto. La Libertad in April. Mertens (1952d) reported a specimen collected at night on a steep trail; a second specimen was found buried 25 cm in the ground in El Salvador. Rand (1957)

collected an adult male at night on a path through pasture at San Salvador, Depto. San Salvador in May.
Specimens examined: <u>La Libertad</u>: Guadalupe: KU 291289. <u>San Salvador</u>: Instituto Tropical de Investigaciones Científicas: SMF 43002, 43241–42; San Salvador, 670 m: FMNH 64964. <u>Santa Ana</u>: Metapán: KU 183963.

Tantilla brevicauda Mertens 1952
(Traga-Cienpiés de Cola Corta)
Plate 123, Map 115

1952 *Tantilla brevicauda* Mertens, Zool. Anz. 149: 137; type locality: El Grito, Los Angeles, 1510 m, Depto. La Libertad, El Salvador.
Tantilla brevicauda: Mertens 1952b, d, Wilson 1982, 1988, Villa et al. 1988, Dueñas et al. 2001, Köhler 2001a, 2003b, Leenders 2003, Leenders & Watkins-Colwell 2004.
Geographic distribution: From south-central Guatemala along the Pacific versant to eastern El Salvador (Köhler 2003b).
Ecological distribution: Dry forest, premontane evergreen forest, subtropical humid forest, and pine-oak forest between 750 and 1510 m.
Description: A very small snake (SVL of largest specimen examined 164 mm); relative tail length 12–13% of SVL in males, 10–11% in females; divided nasal; 0–1 loreal; 1 preocular; 2 (rarely 1) postoculars; 1 anterior and 1 posterior temporal; 7 supralabials, 3rd and 4th enter orbit; 6 infralabials; dorsal scales smooth, without apical pits, in 15 rows throughout; ventrals 142–162 in males, 142–164 in females; subcaudals 21–25 in males, 18–23 in females; anal plate divided.

   Dorsal ground color brown with several narrow dark and pale brown longitudinal stripes, the most distinct dark brown stripe on scale row 3, a faint brownish stripe on scale row 5, and a creamish stripe on the vertebral row; dorsal color reaches onto lateral edges of ventrals, but sharply separated from cream color of ventral surface; head dark brown; white or yellow nuchal collar covers posterior end of parietals, secondary temporals, and one row of nuchal scales; ventral surfaces of tail orange-red in life (Mertens 1952b). Leenders & Watkins-Colwell (2004) noted their adult male specimen (YPM 12367) differs from the color description of Mertens (1952b) by lacking the light vertebral stripe noted in the holotype and paratype, and lack of the bright red underside of the tail.
Natural history: Mertens (1952d) reported a

Plate 123: *Tantilla brevicauda* (YPM 12367) EL SALVADOR: Ahuachapán: Parque Nacional El Imposible, ca. La Fincona (800 m). Photo: T. Leenders.

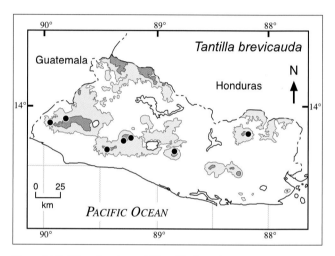

Map 115: Distribution of *Tantilla brevicauda* in El Salvador.
Closed circles represent examined-specimen locality records; open squares are published locality records. Light shading indicates ≥ 600–1200 m elevation; dark shading indicates elevations ≥ 1200 m; large bodies of freshwater are outlined in bold, black lines.

specimen found under a log; a second specimen was buried in loose dirt in El Salvador. Uzzell & Starrett (1958) collected a juvenile under a banana stalk on the ground near Instituto Tropical, San Salvador, Depto. San Salvador. Leenders & Watkins-Colwell (2004) collected an adult male at night as it crossed a trail through secondary vegetation at Parque Nacional El Imposible, Depto. Ahuachapán.
Specimens examined: <u>Ahuachapán</u>: El Imposible: MUHNES 1055; Finca Santa Leticia, 13°53´N, 89°47´W, 1224 m: KU 290044; Parque Nacional El Imposible, La Fincona, 13°50.8´N, 89°58.8´W, 750

m: Plate 123 (YPM 12367). <u>La Libertad</u>: El Grito, Finca Los Angeles, 1510 m, Cumbre de Jayaque: SMF 43243–44; Finca San José, Cumbre de Santa Tecla, 1200 m: SMF 43245. <u>Morazán</u>: E slope Mt. Cacahuatique, 1280 m: MVZ 40403. <u>San Salvador</u>: 0.8 km NW of Instituto Tropical de Investigaciones Científicas: UMMZ 117289. <u>San Vicente</u>: Finca El Carmen, Volcán San Vicente, 1319 m: SMF 43246–47.
Published locality records: <u>Morazán</u>: N slope Mt. Cacahuatique, 1463 m: MVZ 40404 (Wilson 1982).

Tantilla taeniata (Bocourt 1883)
(Traga-Cienpiés Rayada)
Plate 124, Map 116

1883 *Homalocranium taeniatum* Bocourt, Miss. Sci. Mex., Rept.: 587; type locality: Guatemala.
Tantilla taeniata: Wilson 1974b, 1982, 1983, Villa et al. 1988, Campbell 1998b, Wilson & McCranie 1999, Dueñas et al. 2001, Köhler 2001a, 2003b, Stafford 2004.
Geographic distribution: From the Antigua Basin and southeastern Guatemala to northern Nicaragua (Köhler 2003b).
Ecological distribution: Premontane evergreen forest, subtropical humid forest, and pine-oak forest between 1000 and 1100 m.
Description: A very small snake (SVL of largest specimen examined 229 mm); relative tail length 39% in one male and 22% in one female; divided nasal; no loreal; 1 preocular; 2 postoculars; 1 anterior and 1 posterior temporal; 7 supralabials, 3rd and 4th enter orbit; 6 infralabials; dorsal scales smooth, without apical pits, in 15 rows throughout; ventrals 139 in single male, 141 in female; subcaudals 66 in single male, 45 in female; anal plate divided.

Dorsal surfaces of body and tail brown with several pale brown or tan stripes that are edged with dark brown; a vertebral stripe on middorsal scale row and adjacent halves of paravertebral rows, and a lateral stripe on adjacent halves of scale rows 3 and 4; a complete pale brown nape band and pre- and postocular creamish blotches present.
Natural history: The Cerro del Tigre specimen was discovered inside a rotting log in some grass next to a road in July (E. Greenbaum, field notes).
Specimens examined: <u>La Unión</u>: 4 km S La Unión, 1000 m on Volcán de Conchagua: UU 4716. <u>Usulután</u>: Cerro del Tigre, 13°28.37´N, 88°26.21´W, 1100 m: KU 289863.

Plate 124: *Tantilla taeniata* (KU 289863) EL SALVA-DOR: Usulután: Cerro del Tigre (1100 m). Photo: E. Greenbaum.

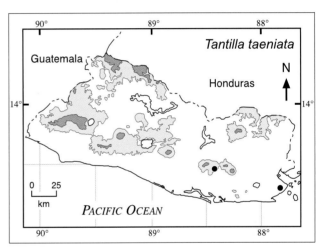

Map 116: Distribution of *Tantilla taeniata* in El Salvador.
Closed circles represent examined-specimen locality records; open squares are published locality records. Light shading indicates 600–1200 m elevation; dark shading indicates elevations ≥ 1200 m; large bodies of freshwater are outlined in bold, black lines.

Tantilla vermiformis (Hallowell 1860)
(Traga-Cienpiés Lombríz)
Plate 125, Map 117

1860 *Lioninia vermiformis* Hallowell, Proc. Acad. Nat. Sci. Philadelphia 1860: 484; type locality: Nicaragua.
Tantilla vermiformis: Wilson 1987, Dueñas et al. 2001, Köhler 2001a, 2003b.
Geographic distribution: From central El Salvador to northwestern Costa Rica (Savage 2002).

Plate 125: *Tantilla vermiformis* COSTA RICA: Guanacaste: 1 km E Los Angeles. Photo: W. Van Devender.

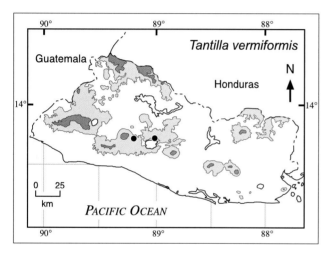

Map 117: Distribution of *Tantilla vermiformis* in El Salvador.
Closed circles represent examined-specimen locality records; open squares are published locality records. Light shading indicates 600–1200 m elevation; dark shading indicates elevations ≥ 1200 m; large bodies of freshwater are outlined in bold, black lines.

Ecological distribution: Dry forest between 400 and 700 m.
Description: A very small snake, the only specimen measured has a SVL of 69 mm (maximum recorded total length 157 mm; Wilson 1982); relative tail length 12% of SVL in single female; divided nasal; no loreal; 1 preocular; 2 postoculars; 1 anterior and 1 posterior temporal; 7 supralabials, 3rd and 4th enter orbit; 6 infralabials; dorsal scales smooth, without apical pits, in 15 rows throughout; ventrals 118; subcaudals 19; anal plate divided.

Dorsal surfaces of head, body, and tail pale brown to brown with a spotted narrow vertebral dark brown stripe which continues to tip of tail; each dorsal scale with a darker border; pale brown blotches on posterior portion of parietals; venter dirty white or cream.
Natural history: E. Greenbaum (field notes) recorded a specimen that was collected on damp mud next to a stream during the day at Lago de Ilopango, Depto. San Salvador in August. Savage (2002) noted this species eats soft-bodied insects, reproduces in the wet season (a female was noted with one egg in June), and reaches sexual maturity in one year.
Specimens examined: <u>San Salvador</u>: San Salvador: MUHNES 685; Lago de Ilopango, 13°43´N, 89°30´W, 400 m: KU 289968.

Genus *Thamnophis*

The 24 species in this genus of snakes are distributed from southern Canada to Costa Rica along both versants (Savage 2002). Two species occur in El Salvador.

Thamnophis fulvus (Bocourt 1893)
(Ranera de Montaña)
Plate 126, Map 118

1893 *Eutaenia cyrtopsis* var. *fulvus* Bocourt, Miss. Sci. Mex., Rept.: 777; type locality: Alta Verapaz, Guatemala.
Thamnophis fulvus: Hidalgo 1981a, Webb 1982, Villa et al. 1988, Rossman et al. 1996, Dueñas et al. 2001, Köhler 2001a, 2003b.
Geographic distribution: From central Chiapas, Mexico, to southwestern Honduras and northern El Salvador (Köhler 2003b).
Ecological distribution: Vicinity of freshwater habitats in pine-oak and cloud forest between 1860 and 2225 m.
Description (data also from Hidalgo 1981a): A medium-sized snake (SVL of largest specimen from El Salvador 466 mm); relative tail length 29–34% of SVL in males, 29–32% in females; divided nasal; 1 loreal; 1 preocular; 3 postoculars; 1 anterior and 2–3 posterior temporals; 8 supralabials, 4th and 5th enter orbit; 10, rarely 9 or 8, infralabials; dorsal scales keeled, without apical pits, in 19 rows at midbody, and 17 rows one head length anterior to vent; ventrals 137–147 in males, 138–146 in females; subcaudals 60–76 in males, 62–65 in fe-

Plate 126: *Thamnophis fulvus* (KU 187369) GUATE-MALA: Baja Verapaz: 3.8 km SE Purulhá (1463–1618 m). Photo: J. A. Campbell (KU CT 6853).

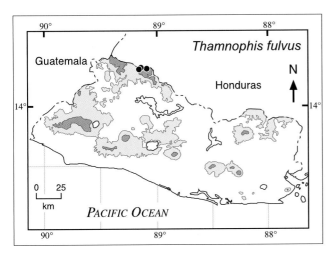

Map 118: Distribution of *Thamnophis fulvus* in El Salvador.
Closed circles represent examined-specimen locality records; open squares are published locality records. Light shading indicates 600–1200 m elevation; dark shading indicates elevations ≥ 1200 m; large bodies of freshwater are outlined in bold, black lines.

males; anal plate entire.

Head olive-brown above; supralabials grayish white with black sutures; two large black blotches on nape, separated from each other by vertebral stripe; dorsal ground color olive to olive-brown, with an incomplete vertebral and two creamish lateral (on 2nd and 3rd scale rows) stripes (dirty yellow anteriorly, pale brown posteriorly); alternating black spots above lateral stripes; ventral surfaces of head, body, and tail dirty white to greenish gray.

Natural history: O. Komar (field notes) recorded a freshly killed snake on the side of a road at Municipio de Las Pilas, Cerro El Pital, Depto. Chalatenango in May.
Specimens examined: <u>Chalatenango</u>: Cerro El Pital, Municipio de Las Pilas, 2000 m: VH 74; Las Pilas, 1860 m: KU 291240; Los Esesmiles, Cerro El Pital, 2225 m: MVZ 40431–33; 10 km NE La Palma, Municipio de Las Pilas: KU 183969–70.

***Thamnophis proximus* (Say 1823)**
(Ranera Común)
Plate 127, Map 119

1823 *Coluber proximus* Say in James, Exped. Pittsburgh to Rocky Mts. 1: 339; type locality: approximately 4.8 km ENE Fort Calhoun, Washington County, Nebraska.
Thamnophis sauritus chalceus: Mertens 1952d.
Thamnophis proximus rutiloris: Rossman 1970, Rossman et al. 1996.
Thamnophis proximus: Villa et al. 1988, Campbell 1998a, Dueñas et al. 2001, Köhler 2001a, 2003b.
Geographic distribution: From the central United States to central Costa Rica on the Atlantic versant, and disjunct populations on the Pacific versant from Guerrero to Chiapas, Mexico, El Salvador, Honduras, Nicaragua, and western Costa Rica (Savage 2002).
Ecological distribution: Vicinity of freshwater habitats in dry forest between sea level and 200 m.
Description: A medium-sized snake (SVL of largest specimen examined 506 mm); relative tail length 29–35% of SVL in males, 45–46% in females; divided nasal; 1 loreal; 1 preocular; 3–4 postoculars; 1–2 (rarely 3) anterior and 2–3 posterior temporals; 8 supralabials, 4th and 5th enter orbit; 10 infralabials; dorsal scales keeled, without apical pits, in 19 rows at midbody, and 15–17 rows one head length anterior to vent; ventrals 144–153 in males, 145–147 in females; subcaudals 74–75 in males, 92–99 in females; anal plate entire.

Dorsal ground color olive-brown with a cream vertebral stripe (one scale wide) extending from nape throughout body onto tail and bordered by narrow (half scale width) black stripes; sides of body with indistinct lighter lateral stripes on scale rows 3 and 4; head dark brown to olive-brown; a pair of fusing yellow spots on parietals and posterior portion of preocular scales; supralabials and infralabials yellow or orange, the former scales

Plate 127: *Thamnophis proximus* (KU 289903) EL SALVADOR: Usulután: Isla San Sebastián (20 m). Photo: E. Greenbaum.

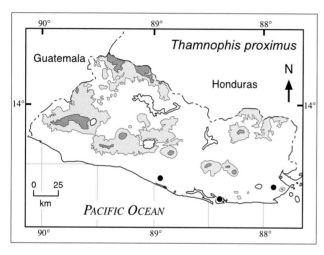

Map 119: Distribution of *Thamnophis proximus* in El Salvador.
Closed circles represent examined-specimen locality records; open squares are published locality records. Light shading indicates 600–1200 m elevation; dark shading indicates elevations ≥ 1200 m; large bodies of freshwater are outlined in bold, black lines.

edged by narrow dark brown streaks on upper margin; ventral surface cream or dirty white.
Natural history: E. Greenbaum (field notes) recorded this species from the periphery of a village during midday at Isla San Sebastián, Depto. Usulután in July. Mertens (1952d) reported a gravid female collected in shallow water of a flooded area of El Salvador in September. Campbell (1998a) noted this species may be active by day or night, and feeds upon tadpoles, small frogs, and fish; females give birth to about six young between June and July.

Specimens examined: <u>La Paz</u>: 6 km N from La Herradura: SMF 43212. <u>La Unión</u>: Laguneta de Maquique: USNM 167218, 325057–58. <u>Usulután</u>: Isla San Sebastián, 13°10.01´N, 88°24.49´W, 20 m: KU 289903, 289906, MUHNES C–30–1360.

Genus *Trimorphodon*

The two species of this genus are distributed from the western United States and Baja California along the Pacific versant to northwestern Costa Rica; a few records exist for the Atlantic versant of Guatemala, Honduras, and Nicaragua (Savage 2002). One species occurs in El Salvador.

Trimorphodon biscutatus (Duméril, Bibron & Duméril 1854)
(Zorcuata)
Plate 128, Map 120, Figure 45

1854 *Dipsas biscutata* Duméril, Bibron & Duméril, Erp. Gén. 7: 1153; type locality: "Mexico."
Trimorphodon biscutatus: K. Schmidt 1928, Villa et al. 1988, Dueñas et al. 2001, Köhler 2001a, 2003b, Leenders 2003.
Trimorphodon biscutatus quadruplex: Mertens 1952d, Gehlbach 1971, Scott & McDiarmid 1984.
Geographic distribution: Identical to genus.
Ecological distribution: Dry forest and savanna between sea level and 750 m.
Description: A large snake (SVL of largest specimen examined 960 mm); relative tail length 21–24% of SVL in males, 19–22% in females; divided nasal; 3 (rarely 1 or 2) loreals; 2–3 preoculars; 2–3 postoculars; 2–3 anterior and 3–4 posterior temporals; 8–10 supralabials, 4th and 5th enter orbit; 12–14 infralabials; dorsal scales smooth, without apical pits, in 24–26 rows at midbody, and 16–21 rows one head length anterior to vent; ventrals 254–268 in males, 250 in females; subcaudals 83–96 in males, 76–83 in females; anal plate divided.

Dorsal ground color grayish brown or pale brown with large, irregular, transverse, darkly edged, dull brown blotches, often enclosed inside smaller fields of ground coloration; top of head with dark brown transverse band on adjacent portions of frontal and prefrontals, band followed posteriorly by two lyre-shaped, darkly edged blotches; supralabials with cream spots; ventral coloration cream with a series of dark brown blotches on lateral edges of some ventral scales.

Plate 128: *Trimorphodon biscutatus* (SMF 81345) EL SALVADOR: Ahuachapán: El Refugio (225 m). Photo: G. Köhler.

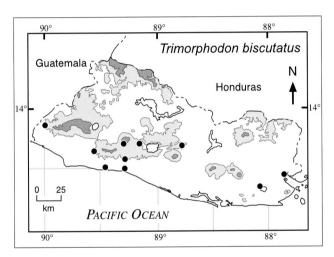

Map 120: Distribution of *Trimorphodon biscutatus* in El Salvador.
Closed circles represent examined-specimen locality records; open squares are published locality records. Light shading indicates 600–1200 m elevation; dark shading indicates elevations ≥ 1200 m; large bodies of freshwater are outlined in bold, black lines.

Natural history: M. Veselý (field notes) collected a specimen at night among flower pots at El Refugio, Depto. Ahuachapán in June. Mertens (1952d) reported a specimen collected under a rock "plate" in El Salvador. Savage (2002) noted this nocturnal, terrestrial species eats lizards as juveniles, and birds and mammals as adults. Goldberg (1995) reported clutches of 7–20 eggs in Arizona.
Specimens examined: Ahuachapán: Mariposario, El Refugio of Francisco Serrano, 13°49.4′N, 89°59.9′W, 210 m: SMF 81345. La Libertad: Nuevo San Salvador [= Santa Tecla]: SMF 42247; 15 km SE Mizata, 50 m: KU 116968; San Diego, Parque

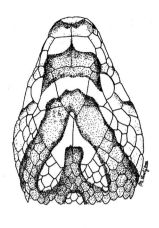

1 cm

Figure 45: *Trimorphodon biscutatus* (VH 108): Dorsal view of head.

Nacional W T Deninger: KU 183971; 2 km S Zaragoza, Cantón Guadalupe, 13°33.1′N, 89°17.3′W, 740 m: KU 291581. La Unión: 15 km N La Unión: AMNH 115667. San Miguel: Laguna de Olomega, 61 m: MVZ 40445. San Salvador: San Salvador, Soyapango, MUHNES C–30–1436. San Vicente: Barranca del Sisimico, 250 m: SMF 42946. Sonsonate: Hacienda Chilata: FMNH 11001.

Genus *Tropidodipsas*

This genus (3 species) is closely related to the genus *Sibon*. Kofron (1985) included *T. fischeri* and *T. sartorii* as species of *Sibon*. However, Wallach (1995) demonstrated that *Tropidodipsas* was distinguishable as a separate genus from *Sibon,* and we conserve this taxonomic position herein. Although Wallach (1995:478) recognized *T. fischeri*, he concluded that the identity of this species needs further study. The species of the genus *Tropidodipsas* are distributed from Nuevo León and Guerrero, Mexico to Nicaragua. Two species occur in El Salvador.

Tropidodipsas fischeri Boulenger 1894
(Tragababosa de Montaña)
Plate 129, Map 121, Figure 46

1894 *Tropidodipsas fischeri* Boulenger, Cat. Snakes Brit. Mus. 2: 296; type locality: Guatemala.
Tropidodipsas fischeri: Uzzell & Starrett 1958, Dueñas et al. 2001, Köhler 2001a, 2003b, Leenders & Watkins-Colwell 2004.
Sibon fischeri fischeri: Kofron 1985.

Plate 129: *Tropidodipsas fischeri* (YPM 14023) EL SALVADOR: Santa Ana: Cerro Montecristo (2020 m). Photo: T. Leenders.

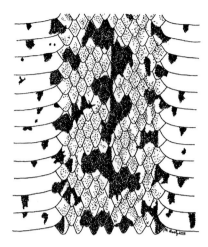

Figure 46: *Tropidodipsas fischeri* (SMF 77427): Dorsal color pattern.

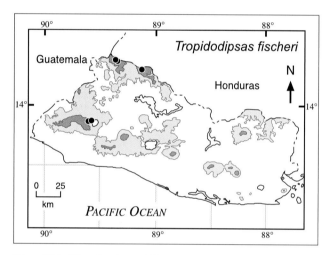

Map 121: Distribution of *Tropidodipsas fischeri* in El Salvador.
Closed circles represent examined-specimen locality records; open squares are published locality records. Light shading indicates 600–1200 m elevation; dark shading indicates elevations ≥ 1200 m; large bodies of freshwater are outlined in bold, black lines.

Sibon fischeri: Wilson & Meyer 1985, Villa et al. 1988.
Geographic distribution: From western Oaxaca, Mexico, to western El Salvador and southwestern Honduras (Köhler 2003b).
Ecological distribution: Pine-oak forest and cloud forest between 1800 and 2200 m (Leenders & Watkins-Colwell 2004).
Description: A medium-sized snake (SVL of largest specimen examined 550 mm); relative tail length 16–27% of SVL in males, 17–24% in females;

divided nasal; 1 loreal; no (rarely 1) preocular; 2 (rarely 1) postoculars; 1 anterior and 2 posterior temporals; 6 (rarely 7) supralabials, 3rd and 4th enter orbit; 7 (rarely 6 or 8) infralabials; dorsal scales smooth, without apical pits, usually in 17 rows throughout, rarely 15–16 rows one head length anterior to vent; ventrals 167–189 in males, 174–191 in females; subcaudals 51–65 in males, 51–60 in females; anal plate entire.

Dorsal ground color pale brown or orange-brown with many transverse dark brown bands, bands narrower laterally, which may or may not reach onto venter; top of the head dark brown; upper lateral part of head brown, lower portion cream; anterior infralabials with dark brown mottling; many black blotches scattered irregulary throughout the ventral area, which is otherwise cream or pale white. Iris dark brown in life.
Natural history: W. E. Duellman (field notes) encountered adults in relatively dry logs in cloud forest at Cerro Montecristo, Depto. Santa Ana in February. Uzzell & Starrett (1958) collected five snakes under logs along a road through cloud forest near Hacienda Montecristo, Depto. Santa Ana; these snakes were found "in association" with specimens of *Rhadinaea kinkelini* and *R. montecristi*. Leenders & Watkins-Colwell (2004) collected an individual under a log at Parque Nacional Montecristo, Depto. Santa Ana, and another snake was found on the crater rim of the Santa Ana volcano after being killed by a raptor.
Specimens examined: <u>Chalatenango</u>: Cerro El Pital, arriba de la Palma, Camino a Las Pilas:

TCWC 83080–81. <u>Santa Ana</u>: Montecristo, 2 km W of Hacienda, 2100 m: SMF 80721; Hacienda Los Planes de Montecristo, Metapán, 1800 m: VH 105; same locality at 2200 m: UMMZ 117288, KU 62127–33, 63898–907; same locality at unknown elevation: TCWC 83077–79; Finca Los Andes, Volcán de Santa Ana: SMF 81341, VH 68, 73; N slope Volcán de Santa Ana, 1981 m: MVZ 40428.

Published locality records: <u>Santa Ana</u>: Hacienda Montecristo, Cordillera de Metapán, 2200 m: UMMZ 117289 (Uzzell & Starrett 1958); Município Santa Ana, Cantón Los Flores, Parque Nacional Los Andes and Volcán Santa Ana (13.869°N, 89.620°W): YPM 14024 (Leenders & Watkins-Colwell 2004); Município Metapán, Cantón Metapán, Parque Nacional Montecristo (14.401°N, 89.362°W): YPM 14023 (Leenders & Watkins-Colwell 2004).

Tropidodipsas sartorii Cope 1863
(Tragababosa Anillada)
Plate 130, Map 122, Figure 47

1863 *Tropidodipsas sartorii* Cope, Proc. Acad. Nat. Sci. Philadelphia 1863: 100; type locality: Mirador, Veracruz, Mexico.
Tropidodipsas sartorii: Hidalgo 1981b, Dueñas et al. 2001, Köhler 2001a, 2003b.
Sibon sartorii: Wilson & Meyer 1985, Villa et al. 1988, Köhler 1996.
Sibon sartorii sartorii: Kofron 1988.

Geographic distribution: From San Luis Potosí, Mexico, to Honduras on the Atlantic versant and Oaxaca, Mexico, to Nicaragua on the Pacific versant (Köhler 2003b).

Ecological distribution: Dry forest and pine-oak forest between sea level and 1820 m.

Description: A medium-sized snake (SVL of largest specimen examined 490 mm); relative tail length 19–27% of SVL in males, 21–25% in females; divided nasal; 1 loreal; 1 (rarely 0 or 2) preocular; 2 postoculars; 1–2 anterior and 2 posterior temporals; 6–8 supralabials, 3rd and 4th, or 4th and 5th enter orbit; 7–9 infralabials; dorsal scales smooth, without apical pits, in 17 rows throughout; ventrals 182–188 in males, 181–187 in females; subcaudals 63–64 in males, 51–65 in females; anal plate entire. Leenders & Watkins-Colwell (2004) reported a juvenile specimen that lacks a loreal, has 181 ventrals, and 67 subcaudals.

Color pattern of body and tail consists of broad (8–14 scales long on vertebral row) black rings

Plate 130: *Tropidodipsas sartorii* (KU 289806) EL SALVADOR: La Libertad: Carretera al Puerto de La Libertad. Photo: E. Greenbaum.

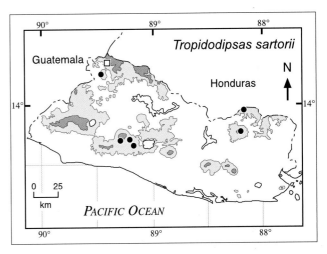

Map 122: Distribution of *Tropidodipsas sartorii* in El Salvador.
Closed circles represent examined-specimen locality records; open squares are published locality records. Light shading indicates 600–1200 m elevation; dark shading indicates elevations ≥ 1200 m; large bodies of freshwater are outlined in bold, black lines.

alternating with orange-red to cream (dirty white or cream in preservative) narrower rings (2–4 scales long on vertebral row); some dorsal and lateral scales in orange-red to cream rings with black apical margins; head mostly black; chin, posterior scales of lower and upper lips, posterior temporals, and posterior portions of parietals covered by orange-red to cream rings, including anterior 2–3 rows of nuchal scales.

Natural history: M. Veselý (field notes) collected a Salvadoran specimen in leaf litter under a coffee plant in May. Campbell (1998a) noted this noctur-

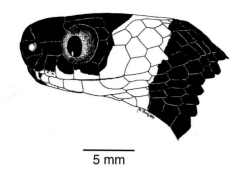

5 mm

Figure 47: *Tropidodipsas sartorii* (SMF 79239): Lateral view of head.

nal, mostly terrestrial species feeds upon slugs and snails; females lay 3–5 eggs in the early portion of the rainy season. Stafford & Meyer (2000) noted this species is occasionally found in caves; males develop tubercles on the chin and snout during the breeding season.

Specimens examined: La Libertad: Nuevo San Salvador [= Santa Tecla], Pinares de Suiza: SMF 81286; Residencial Las Piletas, Carretera al Puerto de La Libertad: KU 289806 (*). Morazán: Perquín: MUHNES 1219; Cerro Cacahuatique, 13°58.5′N, 88°12.6′W, 1500 m: MUHNES C–30–1219. San Salvador: San Salvador, 670 m: KU 183973–74, SMF 77433–34; San Marcos, 1 km S San Salvador: MUHNES C–30–1539. Santa Ana: 6 km S Metapán, Bosque San Diego, 14°17′N, 89°28′W: VH 101s.

Published locality records: Santa Ana: Município Metapán, Cantón Metapán, Parque Nacional Montecristo (14.401°N, 89.362°W), 1820 m: YPM 14022 (Leenders & Watkins-Colwell 2004).

Family Elapidae

This family includes approximately 300 species (ca. 60 genera) of snakes that are distributed on land and sea from the southern United States to southern South America, Africa (excluding Madagascar) through the Middle East and southeast Asia to southern Australia. The family includes many dangerously venomous species, including cobras, mambas, kraits, and coral snakes (Keogh 2003). One terrestrial and one marine species occur in El Salvador; both are highly venomous.

Genus *Micrurus*

This genus includes approximately 60 species of highly venomous, brightly colored snakes that are distributed from the southeastern United States south to Bolivia and southern Argentina on the Atlantic versant, and from Sonora, Mexico, south to northwestern Peru on the Pacific versant (Savage 2002). One species occurs in El Salvador.

Micrurus nigrocinctus (Girard 1854)
(Coral Común)
Plate 131, Map 123, Figure 48a–c

1854 *Elaps nigrocinctus* Girard, Proc. Acad. Nat. Sci. Philadelphia 1854: 226; type locality: Taboga Island, Bay of Panama.
Elaps nigrocinctus: Cope 1887.
Elaps fulvius: Günther 1895.
Micrurus fulvius: K. Schmidt 1928.
Micrurus nigrocinctus zunilensis: Mertens 1952d, Roze 1996.
Micrurus nigrocinctus: Villa et al. 1988, Roze 1983, Campbell & Lamar 1989, 2004, Dueñas et al. 2001, Köhler 2001a, 2003b, Leenders 2003.

Geographic distribution: From northwestern Honduras (Atlantic versant) and Oaxaca, Mexico (Pacific versant) to northern Colombia (Savage 2002).

Ecological distribution: Dry forest, premontane evergreen forest, subtropical humid forest, and pine-oak forest between sea level and 900 m.

Description: A medium-sized snake (SVL of largest specimen examined 910 mm); relative tail length 10–18% of SVL in males, 11–17% in females; divided nasal; no loreal; 1 preocular; 2 postoculars; 1 anterior and 1–2 posterior temporals; 7 (rarely 6) supralabials, 3rd and 4th enter orbit; 7 (rarely 6 or 8) infralabials; dorsal scales smooth, without apical pits, in 15 rows throughout; ventrals 195–223 in males, 204–223 in females; subcaudals 37–50 in males, 32–48 in females; anal plate divided.

The body color pattern consists of narrow black rings bordered by yellow (white in preservative) rings, and red interspaces which are usually much wider than the black rings; red scales often black tipped; tail with alternating black and yellow (white in preservative) rings; head black with yellow (white in preservative) band covering posterior tips of frontal scales, most of parietal area, temporals, posterior supralabials, infralabials, and chin; this ring followed by a black ring in nuchal region. There are 15–18 blackish body rings (not counting the nuchal ring) and 4–6 blackish tail rings. The nuchal cap extends posteriorly five dorsal scales.

Natural history: Campbell & Lamar (1989)

Plate 131: *Micrurus nigrocinctus* HONDURAS: Francisco Morazán: Tegucigalpa (930 m). Photo: J. Ferrari.

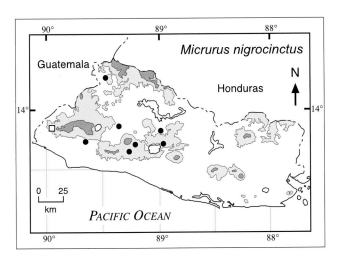

Map 123: Distribution of *Micrurus nigrocinctus* in El Salvador.

Closed circles represent examined-specimen locality records; open squares are published locality records. Light shading indicates 600–1200 m elevation; dark shading indicates elevations ≥ 1200 m; large bodies of freshwater are outlined in bold, black lines.

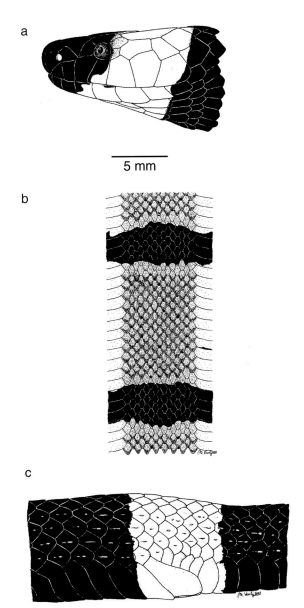

5 mm

Figure 48: *Micrurus nigrocinctus:* a. lateral view of head (SMF 79566), b. dorsal color pattern (SMF 79211), c. lateral view of cloacal region of a male (SMF 79211).

reported this species from tropical rain forest, lower montane wet forest, and dry forest. Campbell (1998a) remarked this species feeds upon small snakes and lizards; females lay eggs in the early portion of the wet season. Stafford & Meyer (2000) noted this species is primarily terrestrial but may be found in vegetation up to 3 m above the ground. Savage (2002) noted this species also eats caecilians; females lay 5–14 eggs per clutch on the Pacific versant.

Specimens examined: Ahuachapán: Cantón Los Magueyes: KU 289971 (*). Cuscatlán: Cojutepeque:

KU 183976; Tenancingo, Copalchan: KU 183977; 0.3 km E Tenancingo, 600 m: KU 183978. La Libertad: Finca El Paraíso, Nuevo San Salvador [= Santa Tecla], 900 m: SMF 42213, 45403; San Juan Opico, near Río Palio: VH 43. Santa Ana: 6 km S Metapán: KU 183979. San Salvador: San Salvador: SMF 42928, 75746; Sta. Carlota, SE San Salvador: SMF 51819 (*). Sonsonate: Izalco: USNM 192602. Depto. unknown: no specific locality: USNM 4947 (*).

Published locality records: <u>Ahuachapán</u>: Parque
Nacional El Imposible (Leenders 2003).

Genus *Pelamis*

This monotypic genus of sea snake is distributed throughout the waters of the Indo-Pacific
region from southern Siberia to Tasmania, across
the Pacific, and from southern California, United
States, to Peru (Savage 2002).

Pelamis platurus (Linnaeus 1766)
(Culebra de Mar Rayada)
Plate 132, Map 124

1766 *Anguis platurus* Linnaeus, Systema Naturae,
ed. 12: 391; type locality: unknown.
Pelamis platurus: Peters & Orejas-Miranda 1970,
Pickwell & Culotta 1980, Villa et al. 1988, Campbell
& Lamar 1989, 2004 Dueñas et al. 2001, Köhler
2001a, 2003b.
Geographic distribution: Identical to genus.
Ecological distribution: Marine waters.
Description: A medium-sized snake (SVL of
largest specimen examined 535 mm) with a compressed body and a laterally flattened tail; relative
tail length 13% of SVL; no loreal; 1 preocular; 2–3
postoculars; 8–10 supralabials, 10–11 infralabials;
dorsals smooth, juxtaposed or at best subimbricate,
without apical pits; ventrals similar in size and
shape as dorsals.

Color pattern is highly variable in respect to
abundance and configuration of yellow surfaces; the
basic pattern consists of a dark brown or black

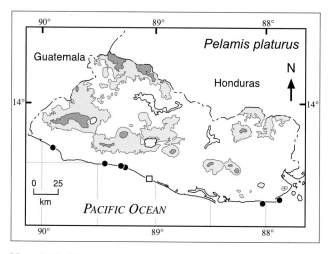

Map 124: Distribution of *Pelamis platurus* in
El Salvador.
Closed circles represent examined-specimen locality records;
open squares are published locality records. Light shading
indicates 600–1200 m elevation; dark shading indicates elevations ≥ 1200 m; large bodies of freshwater are outlined in bold,
black lines.

dorsal band, a yellow or orange-yellow lateral band
and a dark brown ventral band; the tail is yellow or
orangish yellow with black blotches.
Natural history: Campbell & Lamar (1989)
commented that this species is common at the
surface of slicks where sea currents come together
and in shallow waters exceeding 20°C. This species
is known to be especially abundant during the dry
season near Costa Rica. Savage (2002) added this
species preys upon fish. This viviparous species
gives birth to 1–6 young. The neurotoxic venom is
deadly to humans.
Specimens examined: <u>La Libertad</u>: Playa San
Blas, 13°29'05"N, 89°23'W: MUHNES 573; Playa de
San Diego: KU 183980–81. <u>La Unión</u>: El
Tamarindo: MVZ 180714; La Unión: USNM 5223.
<u>San Miguel</u>: sea coast S Laguna de Olomega: MVZ
40450. <u>Sonsonate</u>: Beach near Metalio: SMF 42047.
Published locality records: <u>La Paz</u>: Playa El
Pimental, 13°23'N, 89°06'W (Hidalgo, 1980b).

Family Leptotyphlopidae

This large family of primitive snakes (93
species; 2 genera) is distributed from the southwestern United States to central Peru, Uruguay
and Argentina in the New World (including several
Caribbean islands and the Lesser Antilles), Africa,
Turkey to northwestern India, and Socotra Island

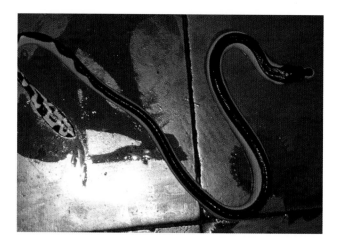

Plate 132: *Pelamis platurus* NICARAGUA: Rivas:
Reserva La Flor. Photo: G. Köhler.

(McDiarmid et al. 1999, Lehr et al. 2002, Kley 2003). One species occurs in El Salvador.

Genus *Leptotyphlops*

The 89 species of this genus have essentially the same distribution as the family Leptotyphlopidae (McDiarmid et al. 1999, Lehr et al. 2002, Dixon & Vaughan 2003).

Leptotyphlops goudotii (Duméril & Bibron 1844)
(Culebrita de Tierra Común)
Plate 133, Map 125

1844 *Stenostoma Goudotii* Duméril & Bibron, Erp. Gén. 6: 330; type locality: Valley of Río Magdalena, Colombia.
Leptotyphlops albifrons: Ahl 1940.
Leptotyphlops phenops phenops: Mertens 1952d.
Leptotyphlops goudotii: Peters & Orejas-Miranda 1970, Hahn 1980, Köhler 1996, McDiarmid et al. 1999, Dueñas et al. 2001, Köhler 2001a, 2003b, Leenders 2003.
Leptotyphlops goudotii phenops: Hahn 1980.
Leptotyphlops goudotti: Villa et al. 1988.
Geographic distribution: From Colima and Veracruz, Mexico, through Central America to Colombia and Venezuela, including numerous islands (McDiarmid et al. 1999).
Ecological distribution: Dry forest, premontane evergreen forest, pine-oak forest, and subtropical humid forest between sea level and 1050 m.
Description: A very small snake (SVL of largest specimen examined 160 mm); divided nasal; 2 supralabials; 1 supraocular; body scales smooth, in 14 rows around midbody; anal plate entire.

Body scales brown or gray becoming paler ventrally, all edged by cream (coloration of lateral borders of dorsal scales can be brighter giving a striped appearance); yellow in life (white in preservative) blotch on snout and on tip of tail.
Natural history: O. Komar (field notes) collected an adult from a cobblestone road during the day in San Francisco Gotera, Depto. Morazán in May. An adult was collected from the inside of a pine cone during the day in pine-oak forest at Perquín, Depto. Morazán in June. M. Veselý (field notes) collected a specimen on a sidewalk in the center of San Salvador, Depto. San Salvador in June. Campbell (1998a) noted that this species specializes on the eggs, larvae and adults of termites, ants, and other soft-

Plate 133: *Leptotyphlops goudotii* HONDURAS: Islas de la Bahía: Utila. Photo: G. Köhler.

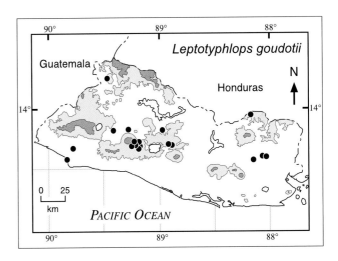

Map 125: Distribution of *Leptotyphlops goudotii* in El Salvador.
Closed circles represent examined-specimen locality records; open squares are published locality records. Light shading indicates 600–1200 m elevation; dark shading indicates elevations ≥ 1200 m; large bodies of freshwater are outlined in bold, black lines.

bodied arthropods. Females lay 8–12 eggs from June–July.
Specimens examined: <u>Cuscatlán</u>: Tenancingo, El Sitio de los Hidalgo: KU 183843. <u>La Libertad</u>: Quetzaltepeque: CAS 94257–58, 94797; San Andrés Valley, 16.1 km NW Los Chorros: CAS 147402. <u>Morazán</u>: San Francisco Gotera, 13°41.6' N, 88°6' W, 280 m: KU 291287; Montecristo Mine, 213 m: MVZ 40398; Perquín: MUHNES C–30–1536. <u>San Miguel</u>: 10 km NNE San Miguel: KU 183846. <u>San Salvador</u>: San Salvador: SMF 42801, 77236, ZMB 35702–03, 35708–09, FMNH 154796, USNM 165658–59; San Salvador, CAMRS: USNM 167214; near Hotel Pasadena II, 600 m: MUHNES (former field number fn 165); San Antonio near San Salva-

dor: SMF 42933; Instituto Tropical de
Investigaciones Científicas, San Salvador, 700 m:
SMF 43216–18, 42022–23, 42025, 75814, 77399;
Planes de Renderos, 900 m: MVZ 40397; San
Salvador, Ciudad Universitaria: KU 183844; San
Salvador, El Refugio: KU 183847; San Salvador,
Colónia Nicaragua: KU 183848; San Salvador,
Colónia 5 de Noviembre: KU 183849–50. Santa Ana:
6 km S Metapán: KU 183845. San Vicente: km 40
on the road to San Vicente: SMF 75813; 43 km
towards San Miguel: SMF 77400. Sonsonate:
Hacienda San Antonio, 13°42´N, 89°45´W: SMF
42024; Acajutla: CAS-SU 3527.

Family Loxocemidae

This family includes one genus that is distrib-
uted from southwestern Mexico to northwestern
Costa Rica (McDiarmid et al. 1999, Rodríguez-
Robles 2003).

Genus *Loxocemus*

This genus includes one species with a distribution identical to the family Loxocemidae.

Loxocemus bicolor Cope 1861
(Boa de Hule)
Plate 134, Map 126

1861 *Loxocemus bicolor* Cope, Proc. Acad. Nat. Sci.
Philadelphia 1861: 77; type locality: unknown;
restricted to La Unión, El Salvador, by Smith &
Taylor (1950: Univ. Kansas Sci. Bull 33: 316).
Loxocemus bicolor: Mertens 1952d, Nelson &
Meyer 1967, Peters & Orejas-Miranda 1970,
McDiarmid et al. 1999, Dueñas et al. 2001, Köhler
2001a, 2003b.
Geographic distribution: Identical to the family
Loxocemidae.
Ecological distribution: Dry forest and savanna
between sea level and 305 m.
Description: A large snake (SVL of largest specimen examined 1135 mm) with a prominently
upturned snout; relative tail length 12–14% of SVL
in males, 11–12% in females; a prominent upturned
rostral; 2 internasals and prefrontals; parietals
small; nasal divided; no loreal; 1 preocular; 2–3
postoculars; 9–11 supralabials, 5th and 6th enter
orbit; 12–13 infralabials; 3–4 anterior and 3–5
posterior temporals; dorsal scales smooth, without
apical pits, in 31–34 rows at midbody, and 24–40

Plate 134: *Loxocemus bicolor* COSTA RICA:
Guanacaste: Playa Bavaria (20 m). Photo: G. Köhler.

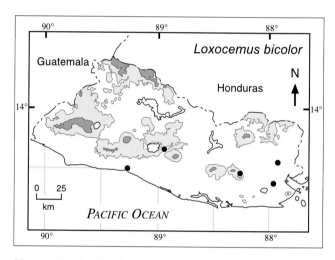

Map 126: Distribution of *Loxocemus bicolor* in El
Salvador.
Closed circles represent examined-specimen locality records;
open squares are published locality records. Light shading
indicates 600–1200 m elevation; dark shading indicates elevations ≥ 1200 m; large bodies of freshwater are outlined in bold,
black lines.

rows one head length anterior to vent; ventrals
255–260 in males, 262 in females; subcaudals 48–51
in males, 46 in females; anal plate divided.

Dorsal surfaces of head, body, and tail uniformly gray or dark brown, changing abruptly to
much paler (cream or yellow) ventral coloration;
the border between the two contrasting colors runs
from the snout through upper edges of supralabials
and 6th lateral scale row on the anterior part of
body.
Natural history: Recorded from dry forest in all
but one locality (Tala, Honduras; wet tropical
forest), this species has been collected from under
rocks, holes in the ground, under leaf litter, logs,

and bark, and while crawling on the ground (Nelson & Meyer 1967). Savage (2002) noted this semifossorial, nocturnal constrictor preys upon rodents, reptiles, and reptile eggs. Male combat is noted for this oviparous species.

Conservation status: CITES: Appendix II.

Specimens examined: <u>La Libertad</u>: S La Libertad on road to the beach: SMF 81346. <u>La Unión</u>: 25.8 km E San Miguel and 17.7 km W La Unión on Carretera Panamericana: LACM 9493; 15 km SE Jocoro: KU 102490. <u>San Miguel</u>: Volcán de San Miguel, 305 m: MVZ 40422. <u>San Vicente</u>: 23 km E San Vicente: LSUMZ 33536. <u>Sonsonate</u>: road Tonalá–Sonsonate, Camino de Algo Donares: SMF 81347 (*).

Published locality records: <u>La Unión</u>: no specific locality (*)(Smith & Taylor 1950, Nelson & Meyer 1967).

Family Typhlopidae

This widespread family contains approximately 200 species in six genera. Found in tropical America, Europe, Africa (including Madagascar), southeast Asia, Australia, and Pacific islands (McDiarmid et al. 1999). One genus has been introduced to El Salvador.

Genus *Ramphotyphlops*

Forty-eight species are distributed in Asia, New Guinea and proximate islands; one additional species *(R. braminus)* extends the range of this genus to Pakistan, India, Africa (including Madagascar), USA, Mexico, and several countries in Central America (McDiarmid et al. 1999). Only *R. braminus* is known from El Salvador.

Ramphotyphlops braminus (Daudin 1803)
(Culebrita de Tierra Introducida)
Plate 135, Map 127

1803 *Eryx braminus* Daudin 1803, Hist. Rept. VII: 279; type locality: Vizagapatam, India.
Ramphotyphlops braminus: Dueñas et al. 2001, Köhler 2001a, 2003b.

Geographic distribution: Southeast Asia, India, Pakistan, parts of Africa; introduced to many parts of the world (McDiarmid et al. 1999, Meshaka et al. 2004); in El Salvador known only from San Salvador.

Ecological distribution: Human habitations around 700 m.

Plate 135: *Ramphotyphlops braminus* (UTA R-45904) GUATEMALA: Guatemala: Guatemala City, 30 Ave. 7-54, Caminal Juyuál (1505 m). Photo: E. N. Smith.

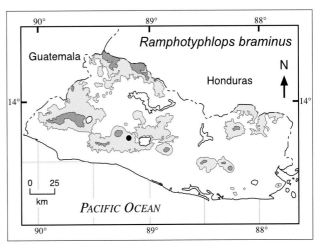

Map 127: Distribution of *Ramphotyphlops braminus* in El Salvador.
Closed circles represent examined-specimen locality records; open squares are published locality records. Light shading indicates 600–1200 m elevation; dark shading indicates elevations ≥ 1200 m; large bodies of freshwater are outlined in bold, black lines.

Description: A very small snake (up to 170 mm total length; Taylor 1965); divided nasal; prefrontal touches rostral; body scales smooth, in 20 rows around midbody. Dorsal color uniformly dark grayish brown with metallic shine, becoming paler ventrally.

Natural history: E. Greenbaum (field notes) collected an adult underneath a large pile of bricks at the only known locality. It is assumed that this small snake is transported into foreign countries along with the soil of plants. Because it is parthenogenetic, only a single female is required to establish a new population (Nussbaum 1980).

Ramphotyphlops braminus produces clutches of 2–3, possibly up to 6 eggs (Nussbaum 1980).

Specimens examined: <u>San Salvador</u>: San Salvador, Parque Zoológico Nacional: KU 289888, MUHNES 1157–59, SMF 79052.

Family Viperidae

This nearly cosmopolitan family of advanced snakes consists of 256 species in 36 genera that are distributed from southern Canada to Argentina in the New World, Africa (excluding Madagascar), Europe to Asia, and south to the Malay Archipelago (McDiarmid et al. 1999, Nilson & Gutberlet 2003). Five species in five genera occur in El Salvador.

Genus *Agkistrodon*

This genus of vipers consists of four species ranging from the northeastern United States to northwestern Costa Rica (McDiarmid et al. 1999, Parkinson et al. 2000). One species occurs in El Salvador.

***Agkistrodon bilineatus* (Günther 1863)**
(Cantil)
Plate 136, Map 128, Figure 49

1863 *Ancistrodon bilineatus* Günther, Ann. Mag. Nat. Hist. 12(3): 364; type locality: Pacific coast of Guatemala.
Agkistrodon bilineatus bilineatus: Mertens 1952d, Gloyd & Conant 1990.
Agkistrodon bilineatus: Cruz et al. 1979, Villa et al. 1988, Campbell & Lamar 1989, 2004, McDiarmid et al. 1999, Parkinson et al. 2000, Dueñas et al. 2001, Köhler 2001a, 2003b.
Geographic distribution: On the Pacific versant from southern Sonora, Mexico, to northwestern Costa Rica; also in the Grijalva Valley (Chiapas, Mexico) and on the northern portion of the Yucatán Peninsula (Parkinson et al. 2000).
Ecological distribution: Dry forest and savanna between sea level and 400 m.
Description: A medium-sized snake (SVL of largest specimen examined 404 mm); relative tail length 22% of SVL in single male (Salvadoran females unavailable); 1 loreal; 1 preocular; 3 postoculars; 8 supralabials; 11 infralabials; 1 prefrontal; 1 subfoveal; dorsal scales keeled, in 23 rows at midbody, and 19 rows one head length anterior to vent; ventrals 132; subcaudals 54; anal plate entire.

Dorsal body color consists of alternating lighter

Plate 136: *Agkistrodon bilineatus* HONDURAS: Choluteca: Choluteca (35 m). Photo: J. Ferrari.

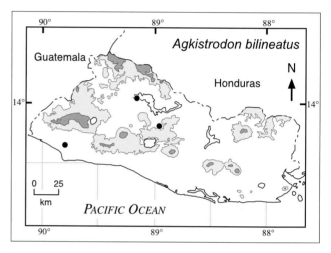

Map 128: Distribution of *Agkistrodon bilineatus* in El Salvador.
Closed circles represent examined-specimen locality records; open squares are published locality records. Light shading indicates 600–1200 m elevation; dark shading indicates elevations ≥ 1200 m; large bodies of freshwater are outlined in bold, black lines.

brown and darker brown transverse bands, which are incompletely bordered by white spots; head dark brown with distinct white or cream lines originating on rostrum and passing above eye to temporal region and downward to neck; additional lines running from rostrum around lower border of loreal pit to angle of jaws; a median vertical white line present on rostral and mental; ventral surfaces dark brown with numerous white flecks scattered over ventral scales.
Natural history: Campbell & Lamar (1989) remarked this species is very aggressive when provoked, and can cause human fatalities. Shine (1994) noted this species engages in male combat. Campbell (1998a) noted this mainly nocturnal

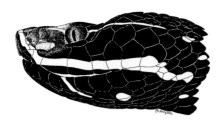

4 mm

Figure 49. *Agkistrodon bilineatus* (SMF 42218): Lateral view of head.

Plate 137: *Atropoides nummifer* EL SALVADOR: San Vicente: Finca El Carmen (1240 m). Photo: M. Veselý.

species feeds upon a wide array of vertebrate and invertebrate prey; females give birth to 5–20 young from June–July. Juveniles use their brightly colored tails to lure anuran prey.

Conservation status: CITES: Deleted 15 December 2002.

Specimens examined: <u>Cuscatlán</u>: 5.2 km ESE Tenancingo, Cantón Ajuluco: KU 183982; Municipio de Colima: KU 291394. <u>Sonsonate</u>: Hacienda San Antonio near Sonsonate, 220 m: SMF 42218.

Genus *Atropoides*

The three species of Jumping Vipers are distributed from the highlands of eastern Mexico to Panama (McDiarmid et al. 1999). Castoe et al. (2003) discussed the possible paraphyly of this genus with respect to *Cerrophidion* and *Porthidium*. These authors also recognized that the species diversity within *Atropoides* is probably underestimated at the current time, but they argued against taxonomic changes without additional morphological and molecular data.

Atropoides nummifer (Rüppell 1845)
(Timbo)
Plate 137, Map 129

1845 *Atropos nummifer* Rüppell, Verh. Mus. Senckenberg 3: 313; type locality: Mexico.
Bothrops nummifer nummifer: Mertens 1952d.
Bothrops nummifera: Wilson & Meyer 1985, Villa et al. 1988.
Porthidium nummifer: Campbell & Lamar 1989.
Atropoides nummifer: Werman 1992, Campbell 1998a, McDiarmid et al. 1999, Dueñas et al. 2001, Köhler 2001a, Castoe et al. 2003, Köhler 2003b, Leenders 2003, Leenders & Watkins-Colwell 2004.
Atropoides occiduus: Campbell & Lamar 2004.

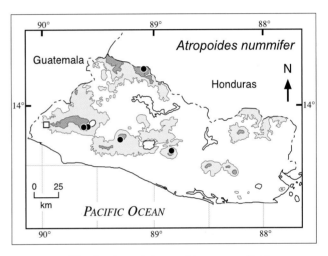

Map 129: Distribution of *Atropoides nummifer* in El Salvador.
Closed circles represent examined-specimen locality records; open squares are published locality records. Light shading indicates 600–1200 m elevation; dark shading indicates elevations ≥ 1200 m; large bodies of freshwater are outlined in bold, black lines.

Geographic distribution: San Luis Potosí and Oaxaca, Mexico, to central Panama (McDiarmid et al. 1999).

Ecological distribution: Cloud forest and pine-oak forest between 920 and 1700 m.

Description: A medium-sized snake (SVL of largest specimen 650 mm [Leenders & Watkins-Colwell 2004]); relative tail length 12–14% of SVL in males, 10–12% in females; 8–10 supralabials; 9–12 infralabials; 0–1 nasorostral; 10–12 intersupraoculars; 3 canthals; 9–10 postfoveals; 3–4 subfoveals; 5 prefoveals; 6–8 intercanthals; dorsal scales keeled, tuberculate, in 25–27 rows at midbody, and 19–21 rows one head length anterior to vent; ventrals 131–137 in males, 131–135 in females; subcaudals 24–32 in males, 26–28 in females; anal plate entire. Leenders & Watkins-Colwell (2004) reported an adult female with 130 ventrals and 23 subcaudals.

Dorsal ground color varies from pale gray, brown, reddish-brown, or yellowish brown with a series of large black or dark brown rhomboid blotches; blotches occasionally fusing at vertebral line and/or with the smaller ones in lateral series; top of the head same as body color with one or two pairs of small black dots in frontoparietal area; a distinct black postocular band extends to angle of jaw, area below this band white or same as pale dorsal color; ventral coloration dirty white, cream, or tan and usually heavily mottled with brown; subcaudals mostly dark brown.

Taxonomic comments: Campbell & Lamar (2004) recognized the three subspecies of *Atropoides nummifer* as full species, including *A. occiduus* in El Salvador. Although this action is consistent with the molecular phylogeny of Castoe et al. (2003), these authors argued against taxonomic changes within *Atropoides* without additional molecular and morphological studies.

Natural history: E. Greenbaum (field notes) encountered a beheaded individual in a recently cleared field at Bosque Las Lajas, Depto. Sonsonate in July. One adult individual was collected on a trail in a coffee plantation during the day at Finca Altamira, Depto. Sonsonate in April. M. Veselý (field notes) collected a specimen on the ground at the border of cloud forest and coffee plantation at Finca El Carmen, Depto. San Vicente in June. Mertens (1952d) found a partly digested mouse in the stomach of a specimen in El Salvador. Alvarez del Toro (1973) noted juveniles from tree holes 3 m above the ground. Campbell & Lamar (1989) reported this species from tropical rain forests. Usually nocturnal and terrestrial. Bites from this species in Guatemala and Honduras have been mild and not life-threatening. Campbell (1998a) remarked this mostly nocturnal species has been noted to eat rodents, lizards, and invertebrates; females give birth to 13–36 young from August–November. Savage (2002) added that the number of births is positively correlated with female size.

Conservation status: CITES: Deleted 15 December 2002.

Specimens examined: Chalatenango: Los Esesmiles, Cerro El Pital, 1700 m: SMF 42563.

La Libertad: Finca Los Cedros Arriba, Cumbre near Sante Tecla, ca. 1200 m: SMF 43065–66, 43176, 43211. San Vicente: Finca El Carmen, 13°36.8´N, 88°50.3´W, 1240–1320 m: SMF 51953, 81480. Sonsonate: Finca Altamira, 13°50´N, 89°42´W, 1220 m: KU 289807; Bosque Las Lajas, 13°50.04´N, 89°33.56´W, 920 m: MUHNES C–30–1344. Depto. unknown: no specific locality: USNM 86863 (*).

Published locality records: Ahuachapán: Parque Nacional El Imposible (Leenders 2003). Sonsonate: Município Izalco, Cantón Las Lajas, Bosque Las Lajas (13.829°N, 89.567°W), 970 m: YPM 12425 (Leenders & Watkins-Colwell 2004).

Genus *Cerrophidion*

This genus of moderate to high-elevation vipers includes three species that are distributed from the highlands of southern Mexico to western Panama (McDiarmid et al. 1999). One species occurs in El Salvador.

Cerrophidion godmani (Günther 1863)
(Tamagáz de Tierra Alta)
Plate 138, Map 130, Figure 50

1863 *Bothriechis godmanni* Günther, Ann. Mag. Nat. Hist. 12(3): 364; type locality: Duenas and other parts of tableland of Guatemala.
Bothrops godmani: K. Schmidt 1928, Mertens 1952d, Villa et al. 1988.
Trimeresurus godmani: Rand 1957.
Porthidium godmani: Campbell & Lamar 1989, Campbell & Solorzano 1992, Köhler 1996.
Cerrophidion godmani: Campbell & Lamar 1992, McDiarmid et al. 1999, Dueñas et al. 2001, Köhler 2001a, 2003b, Leenders 2003, Campbell & Lamar 2004, Leenders & Watkins-Colwell 2004.

Geographic distribution: From southeastern Oaxaca, and Chiapas, Mexico, to western Panama (McDiarmid et al. 1999).

Ecological distribution: Pine-oak forest and cloud forest between 1220 and 2485 m.

Description: A medium-sized snake (SVL of largest specimen examined 675 mm); relative tail length 12–14% of SVL in males, 11–19% in females; 8–10 supralabials; 8–12 infralabials; 5–7 intersupraoculars; 2–4 canthals; 4–7 postfoveals; 0–2 subfoveals; 2–3 prefoveals; 4–6 intercanthals; dorsal scales keeled (except first row), in 21 rows at midbody, and 16–19 rows one head length anterior

Plate 138: *Cerrophidion godmani* EL SALVADOR: Chalatenango: Cerro El Pital (ca. 2300 m). Photo: O. Komar.

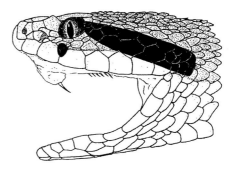

5 mm

Figure 50: *Cerrophidion godmani* (SMF 81478): Lateral view of head.

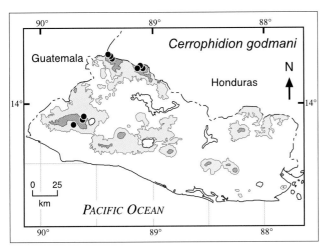

Map 130: Distribution of *Cerrophidion godmani* in El Salvador.
Closed circles represent examined-specimen locality records; open squares are published locality records. Light shading indicates 600–1200 m elevation; dark shading indicates elevations ≥ 1200 m; large bodies of freshwater are outlined in bold, black lines.

to vent; ventrals 135–147 in males, 134–144 in females; subcaudals 26–34 in males, 26–32 in females; anal plate entire.

Dorsal ground color gray or brown with a series of irregular dark brown or black blotches fusing medially, accompanied laterally by a series of smaller isolated ones; top of head dark grayish brown with diffuse black markings, sides of head paler grayish brown with distinct black postocular band reaching to angle of jaw; infralabials and gular area cream as are anterior ventrals, some anterior ventrals with a black triangular spot on the lateral edges, ventrals becoming gradually darker posteriorly; tip of subcaudal surface cream.

Natural history: E. Greenbaum (field notes) encountered a specimen sunning itself on a path in cloud forest at Cerro Montecristo, Depto. Santa Ana in July. Another individual was collected in a coffee plantation during the day at Finca Altamira, Depto. Sonsonate in April. O. Komar (field notes) encountered an adult during the day that was biting a juvenile of the same species at the edge of a trail near Cerro El Pital, Depto. Chalatenango in May; another individual was seen at this same locality in defensive posture because it was being harassed by 10 birds, including Common Bush-Tanagers (*Chlorospingus ophthalmicus*) and Rufous-browed Wrens (*Troglodytes rufociliatus*). M. Veselý (field notes) observed two specimens during the day in undergrowth (*Rubus* sp.) of pine-oak forest at Cerro Verde, Depto. Sonsonate in May. Mertens (1952d) reported a gravid specimen that contained nine embryos in El Salvador. Bites from this viperid species have resulted in relatively mild effects (e.g., fevers and swelling) according to Campbell & Lamar (1989). Campbell & Sólorzano (1992) noted this species eats a diverse array of vertebrates; juveniles eat arthropods as well. Shine (1994) reported male combat in this species. Savage (2002) noted 2–12 young are born in lower Central America; litter size was not correlated with female size. Leenders & Watkins-Colwell (2004) reported a partly digested rodent likely to be *Heteromys desmarestianus* from a snake collected at Cerro El Pital, Depto. Chalatenango.

Specimens examined: <u>Chalatenango</u>: Los
Esesmiles, Cerro El Pital, 2134 m: 40453–54; same
locality at 2225 m: MVZ 40456–71; same locality at
2438 m: MVZ 40455; same locality at 2469 m: MVZ
40651; same locality at 1829–2438 m: FMNH 11000;
10 km NE La Palma, Cantón Las Pilas: KU 183984;
12 km NE La Palma: KU 183985; Cerro El Pital,
unknown elevation: KU 291378; Cerro El Pital,
2200 m: MUHNES C–30–1531, KU 291241; Cerro
El Pital, 2280 m: MUHNES C–30–1530; Cerro El
Pital, 2440 m: YPM 12478; Cerro El Pital, 2485 m:
KU 291242. <u>Santa Ana</u>: Hacienda Montecristo,
Cordillera de Metapán, 2200 m: KU 289801, KU
62134–35, 63918, MUHNES 1220, SMF 43201–10,
77402–06, 81321–26, 81336–37, UMMZ 117285–86;
Hacienda Los Planes, Cerro Miramundo Mt., 1950
m: KU 62136; Volcán de Santa Ana, Finca Los
Andes, 13°52.1′N, 89°37.2′W, 1900 m: SMF 81478,
81481, VH 97; Volcán Santa Ana, crater rim, 2400
m: FMNH 64965. <u>Sonsonate</u>: Finca Altamira,
13°50′N, 89°42′W, 1220 m: MUHNES C–30–1353.
Published locality records: <u>Chalatenango</u>: Cerro
El Pital: YPM 12478 (Leenders & Watkins-Colwell
2004). <u>Santa Ana</u>: Município Santa Ana, Cantón Los
Flores, Parque Nacional Los Andes and Volcán
Santa Ana (13.869°N, 89.620°W): YPM 14017–20
(Leenders & Watkins-Colwell 2004); Município
Metapán, Cantón Metapán, Parque Nacional
Montecristo (14.401°N, 89.362°W): YPM 14021
(Leenders & Watkins-Colwell 2004).

Genus *Crotalus*

Commonly called rattlesnakes, this genus
(approximately 28 species) is distributed from
southern Canada to northern Argentina
(McDiarmid et al. 1999, Alvarado-Diaz & Campbell
2004). One species occurs in El Salvador.

Crotalus durissus Linnaeus 1758
(Cascabel Neotropical)
Plate 139, Map 131

1758 *Crotalus durissus* Linnaeus, Systema
Naturae, ed. 10: 214; type locality: America.
Caudisona durissa: Cope 1861.
Crotalus terrificus: Ahl 1940.
Crotalus durissus durissus: Gloyd 1940, Mertens
1952d, Klauber 1956, Peters & Orejas-Miranda
1970, McCranie 1993, Domínguez 1996, Klauber
1972.
Crotalus durissus: Villa et al. 1988, Campbell &

Plate 139: *Crotalus durissus* (KU 289815) EL SALVA-
DOR: La Libertad: Zaragoza. Photo: E. Greenbaum.

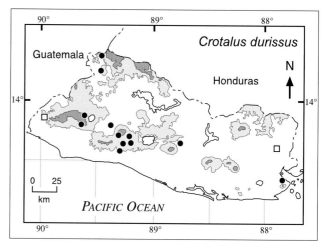

Map 131: Distribution of *Crotalus durissus* in El
Salvador.
Closed circles represent examined-specimen locality records;
open squares are published locality records. Light shading
indicates 600–1200 m elevation; dark shading indicates elevations ≥ 1200 m; large bodies of freshwater are outlined in bold,
black lines.

Lamar 1989, McDiarmid et al. 1999, Dueñas et
al. 2001, Köhler 2001a, 2003b, Leenders 2003.
Crotalus simus: Campbell & Lamar 2004.
Geographic distribution: Discontinuous from
southern Tamaulipas and Michoacan, Mexico, to
Brazil and northern Argentina (McDiarmid et al.
1999).
Ecological distribution: Dry forest, savanna,
premontane evergreen forest, and subtropical
humid forest between sea level and 1870 m. Al-

though the highest elevation from the examined specimens is 900 m, J. P. Domínguez (pers. comm.) noted a Salvadoran specimen at 1870 m.

Description: A large snake (SVL of largest specimen examined 1060+ mm [head missing]); relative tail length 10–14% of SVL in males, 14% in single female; 13–16 supralabials; 15–18 infralabials; 3 scales between supralabials and orbit; 2–3 intersupraoculars; 1 canthal; 7–9 postfoveals; 1–4 subfoveals; 5–8 prefoveals; no intercanthals; interpreocular present; 1–3 postsupraloreals; dorsal scales keeled (except lower two rows), tuberculate and strongly ridged vertebrally, in 27–29 rows at midbody, and 19–21 rows one head length anterior to vent; ventrals 172–178 in males, 172 in single female; subcaudals 21–32 in males, 31 in single female; anal plate entire.

Dorsal ground color grayish or yellowish brown; a pair of black longitudinal stripes on head and neck replaced posteriorly by series of dark or reddish brown and black edged rhomboidal blotches, accompanied laterally by smaller ones; head sometimes with dark brown crossbands bordering frontal area anteriorly and posteriorly, and with obscure postocular stripe running to angle of jaw; infralabials and ventral surfaces cream or whitish.

Taxonomic comments: Presumably based upon morphological differences, Campbell & Lamar (2004) recognized *Crotalus simus* for Mexican and Central American populations of *C. durissus*. Although this taxonomic change might eventually prove to be correct, we believe this change is premature until an extensive study on the molecular systematics of this group is published.

Natural history: Campbell & Lamar (1989) reported that bites from this species are potentially fatal, with effects ranging from swelling to renal failure. Shine (1994) reported that male combat occurs in this species. Campbell (1998a) noted this terrestrial species can be active during the day or night. Prey items include mammals, birds, and lizards; females give birth to 15–47 young during the mid- or late rainy season. Savage (2002) added that litter size is positively correlated with female size. Costa Rican bites rarely resulted in permanent damage or death, possibly because of low venom yields.

Specimens examined: La Libertad: no specific locality: SMF 42259 (*); Sitio del Niño, Río Sucio: SMF 42254, 42866–67; Finca Los Cedros: SMF 42844, 43197; Finca El Paraíso, Santa Tecla: MVZ

40451; Zoragoza at enrada de San José Villanueva: KU 289815. La Unión: La Unión: USNM 4945. San Salvador: San Salvador: ZMB 35711; San Marcos: E. Greenbaum tissue sample. Santa Ana: Finca Los Andes, Volcán de Santa Ana: VH 69; 16 km N Metapán, San Geronimo: KU 183986; 6 km S Metapán: KU 183987; "El Salvador, Departamento Santa Ana?": SMF 81343 (*). San Vicente: 4.8 km E San Vicente, Interamerican Hwy: LACM 28267. Sonsonate: Volcán Izalco: SMF 42063.

Published locality records: Ahuachapán: Parque Nacional El Imposible (Domínguez 1996). Cuscatlán: no specific locality (*)(Domínguez 1996). La Unión: vicinity of Santa Rosa de Lima (Domínguez 1996).

Genus *Porthidium*

This genus includes seven species of vipers ranging from Colima and Chiapas, Mexico, to Ecuador and Venezuela (McDiarmid et al. 1999, Savage 2002). One species occurs in El Salvador.

Porthidium ophryomegas (Bocourt 1868)
(Toboba)
Plate 140, Map 132

1868 *Bothrops ophryomegas* Bocourt, Ann. Sci. Nat. Paris 10(5): 201; type locality: warm regions on western [actually southern] slope of mountains at Escuintla, Guatemala.
Bothriechis brachystoma (part): Cope 1861.
Bothrops lansbergi: Amaral 1927.
Bothrops ophryomegas: Amaral 1929, Dunn 1928, Mertens 1952d, Villa et al. 1988.
Porthidium ophryomegas: Campbell & Lamar 1989, 2004, McDiarmid et al. 1999, Dueñas et al. 2001, Köhler 2001a, 2003b.

Geographic distribution: Pacific versant from Guatemala to Costa Rica (possibly southwestern Panama); also on the Atlantic versant in Guatemala and Honduras (McDiarmid et al. 1999).

Ecological distribution: Dry forest and savanna between sea level and 400 m.

Description: A medium-sized snake (SVL of largest specimen examined 315 mm); relative tail length 14–21% of SVL in males (Salvadoran females unavailable); 1 loreal; 3 preoculars; 3 postoculars; 9–10 supralabials; 11–12 infralabials; 4–6 intersupraoculars; 2 canthals; 2–3 postfoveals; 0–1 subfoveal; 3 prefoveals; 4–5 intercanthals; 3 lacunals; dorsal scales keeled, in 25–27 dorsal scale rows at midbody, and 19 rows one head length

Plate 140: *Porthidium ophryomegas* HONDURAS: El Paraíso: Danlí (780 m). Photo: J. Ferrari.

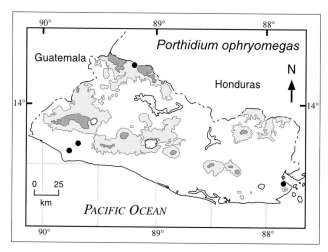

Map 132: Distribution of *Porthidium ophryomegas* in El Salvador.

Closed circles represent examined-specimen locality records; open squares are published locality records. Light shading indicates 600–1200 m elevation; dark shading indicates elevations ≥ 1200 m; large bodies of freshwater are outlined in bold, black lines.

anterior to vent; ventrals 161–163 in males; subcaudals 36–43 in males; anal plate entire.

Dorsal ground color gray or grayish brown with a series of irregular, broad, dark brown blotches edged by black; a narrow pink or orange vertebral stripe from nuchal region through length of dorsum to base of tail, creamish stripe dividing dark brown blotches; head gray or grayish brown with dark brown markings; infralabials and ventral surface cream or white with numerous small dark brown blotches.

Natural history: Campbell & Lamar (1989) reported that this species is most active during the wet season, will readily bite when molested, but no fatalities have been reported from envenomations. Savage (2002) added this species injects a small amount of venom in bites, which makes the effects to humans "innocuous, although unpleasant."

Conservation status: CITES: Deleted 15 December 2002.

Specimens examined: <u>Chalatenango</u>: El Poy, 14°22'N, 89°12'W: MUHNES C–30–1539. <u>La Unión</u>: La Unión: USNM 4950. <u>Sonsonate</u>: 7.6 km NW CA Hwy 12 (Acajutla-Sonsonate Jct) on CAZ: LACM 114155; 1.1 km SW CA Hwy 12 (Acajutla Sonsonate Jct) on CAZ: LACM 114156.

Literature Cited

Ahl, E. (1940): Über eine Sammlung von Reptilien aus El Salvador. – SB. Ges. naturf. Freunde Berlin **1940:** 245–248.

Altig, R. (1987): Key to the anuran tadpoles of Mexico. – Southwest. Nat. **32:** 75–84.

Alvarado-Diaz, J. & Campbell, J. A. (2004): A new montane rattlesnake (Viperidae) from Michoacán, Mexico. – Herpetologica **60:** 281–286.

Alvarez del Toro, M. (1973): Los Reptiles de Chiapas (2nd ed.). – Tuxtla Gutiérrez (Gobierno del Estado de Chiapas): 178 pp.

Amaral, A. do (1927): Studies of neotropical ophidea. V. Notes on *Bothrops lansbergii* and *B. brachystoma*. – Bull. Antivenin Inst. Amer. **1:** 22.

Amaral, A. do (1929): Studies of neotropical ophidea. XII. On ths *Bothrops lansbergii* group. – Bull. Antivenin Inst. Amer. **3:** 19–27.

AmphibiaWeb: Information on amphibian biology and conservation. [web application]. (2005): Berkeley, California: AmphibiaWeb. Available: http://amphibiaweb.org/. (Accessed: April 2005).

Baker, P. J. (2003a): Testudines (Turtles and tortoises). pp. 65–73 – In: Hutchins, M., Murphy, J. B. & Schlager, N. (eds.): Grzimek's Animal Life Encyclopedia (2nd ed.). Vol. 7, Reptiles. Farmington Hills (Gale Group): 593 pp.

Baker, P. J. (2003b): New World pond turtles (Emydidae). pp. 105–113 – In: Hutchins, M., Murphy, J. B. & Schlager, N. (eds.): Grzimek's Animal Life Encyclopedia (2nd ed.). Vol. 7, Reptiles. Farmington Hills (Gale Group): 593 pp.

Barker, D. G. & Barker, T. M. (2003): Boas (Boidae). pp. 409–417 – In: Hutchins, M., Murphy, J. B. & Schlager, N. (eds.): Grzimek's Animal Life Encyclopedia (2nd ed.). Vol. 7, Reptiles. Farmington Hills (Gale Group): 593 pp.

Barrio-Amorós, C. L., Orellana, A. & Chacón, A. (2004): A new species of *Scinax* (Anura: Hylidae) from the Andes of Venezuela. – J. Herpetol. **38:** 105–112.

Bauer, A. M. (2003): Geckos and pygopods (Gekkonidae). pp. 259–269 – In: Hutchins, M., Murphy, J. B. & Schlager, N. (eds.): Grzimek's Animal Life Encyclopedia (2nd ed.). Vol. 7, Reptiles. Farmington Hills (Gale Group): 593 pp.

Benitez, M. (1985): Informe Nacional de El Salvador. Primer simposio sobre tortugas marinas del Pacifico Americano. – San Jose (Universidad de Costa Rica): 7 pp.

Berry, J. F. & Iverson, J. B. (2001): *Kinosternon scorpioides* (Linnaeus), Scorpion Mud Turtle. – Cat. Amer. Amph. Rept. **725:** 1–11.

Bezy, R. L. (1989): Morphological differentiation in unisexual and bisexual xantusiid lizards of the Genus *Lepidophyma* in Central America. – Herpetol. Monogr. **3:** 61–80.

Bezy, R. L. & Grismer, L. L. (2003): Night lizards (Xantusiidae). pp. 291–296 – In: Hutchins, M., Murphy, J. B. & Schlager, N. (eds.): Grzimek's Animal Life Encyclopedia (2nd ed.). Vol. 7, Reptiles. Farmington Hills (Gale Group): 593 pp.

Biju, S. D. & Bossuyt, R. (2003): New frog family from India reveals an ancient biogeographical link with the Seychelles. – Nature **425:** 711–714.

Bocourt, M. F. (1873–1879): Etudes sur les reptiles. pp. 9–1012 – In: Duméril, A., Bocourt, M. -F. & Mocquard, F. (eds.): Recherches Zoologiques pour Sevir a l´histoire de la Faune de l´Amérique Centrale et du Mexique. Mission Scientifique au Mexique et dans l´Amérique Centrale, recherches Zool., part 3, sect. 1. Paris (Imprimerie au Nat.) : i-xiv + 1012 pp.

Böhme, W. (1990): Book review. – Zschr. zool. Syst. Evol. forsch. **28:** 315–316.

Bowen, B. W. & Karl, S. A. (1999): In war, truth is the first casualty. – Cons. Biol. **13:** 1013–1016.

Brame, A. H. (1968): Systematics and evolution of the Mesoamerican salamander genus *Oedipina*. – J. Herpetol. **2:** 1–64.

Britton, A. R. C. (2003): Crocodilians (Crocodiles, alligators, caimans, and gharials). pp. 157–165 – In: Hutchins, M., Murphy, J. B. & Schlager, N. (eds.): Grzimek's Animal Life Encyclopedia (2nd ed.). Vol. 7, Reptiles. Farmington Hills (Gale Group): 593 pp.

Brongersma, L. D. (1954a): On some snakes from the republic of El Salvador. – Proc. Acad. Sci. Amst. **57**: 159–164.

Brongersma, L. D. (1954b): On some lizards from the republic of El Salvador. – Proc. Acad. Sci. Amst. **57**: 165–174.

Burt, C. E. (1931): A study of the teiid lizards genus *Cnemidophorus* with special reference to their phylogenetic relationships. – Smithsonian Inst. U.S. Natl. Mus. Bull. **154**: 1–286.

Campbell, J. A. (1998a): Amphibians and Reptiles of Northern Guatemala, the Yucatán, and Belize. – Norman (University of Oklahoma Press): 380 pp.

Campbell, J. A. (1998b): Comments on the identities of certain *Tantilla* (Squamata: Colubridae) from Guatemala, with the description of two new species. – Sci. Pap. Nat. Hist. Mus. Univ. Kansas **7**: 1–14.

Campbell, J. A. (1999): Distribution patterns of amphibians in Middle America. pp. 111–210 – In: Duellman, W. E. (ed.): Patterns of Distribution of Amphibians: A Global Perspective. Baltimore (The Johns Hopkins University Press): 633 pp.

Campbell, J. A. & Camarillo, J. L. (1994): A new lizard of the genus *Diploglossus* (Anguidae: Diploglossinae) from Mexico, with a review of the Mexican and northern Central American species. – Herpetologica **50**: 193–209.

Campbell, J. A., Ford, L. S. & Karges, J. P. (1983): Resurrection of *Geophis anocularis* Dunn with comments on its relationships and natural history. – Trans. Kansas Acad. Sci. **86**: 38–47.

Campbell, J. A. & Frost, D. R. (1993): Anguid lizards of the genus *Abronia*: revisionary notes, descriptions of four new species, a phylogenetic analysis, and key. – Bull. Am. Mus. Nat. Hist. **216**: 1–121.

Campbell, J. A. & Lamar, W. W. (1989): The Venomous Reptiles of Latin America. – Ithaca (Cornell Univ. Press): 425 pp.

Campbell, J. A. & Lamar, W. W. (1992): Taxonomic status of miscellaneous neotropical viperids, with description of a new genus. – Occ. Pap. Mus. Texas Tech Univ. **153**: 1–31.

Campbell, J. A. & Lamar, W. W. (2004): The Venomous Reptiles of the Western Hemisphere. 2 volumes. – Ithaca (Cornell Univ. Press): 898 pp.

Campbell, J. A. & Savage, J. M. (2000): Taxonomic reconsideration of Middle American frogs of the *Eleutherodactylus rugulosus* group (Anura: Leptodactylidae): A reconnaissance of subtle nuances among frogs. – Herpetol. Monogr. **14**: 186–292.

Campbell, J. A. & Smith, E. N. (1992): A new frog of the genus *Ptychohyla* (Hylidae) from the Sierra de Santa Cruz, Guatemala, and description of a new genus of Middle American stream-breeding hylid frogs. – Herpetologica **48**: 153–167.

Campbell, J. A. & Solórzano, A. (1992): Biology of the montane pitviper, *Porthidium godmani*. pp. 223–250 – In: Campbell, J. A. & Brodie, E. D. (eds.): Biology of the Pitvipers. Tyler (Selva): 467 pp.

Cannatella, D. (2003): True toads, harlequin frogs, and relatives (Bufonidae). pp. 183–195 – In: Hutchins, M., Duellman, W. E. & Schlager, N. (eds.): Grzimek's Animal Life Encyclopedia (2nd ed.). Vol. 6, Amphibians. Farmington Hills (Gale Group): 507 pp.

Cannatella, D. C. & De Queiroz, K. (1989): Phylogenetic systematics of the anoles: Is a new taxonomy warranted? – Syst. Zool. **38**: 57–69.

Cánseco-Marquez, L., Mendelson, J. R., III & Gutiérrez-Mayén, G. (2002): A new species of large *Tantilla* (Squamata: Colubridae) from the Sierra Madre Oriental of Puebla, Mexico. – Herpetologica **58**: 492–497.

Caramaschi, U., Feio, R. N. & Guimarães-Neto, A. S. (2003): A new, brightly colored species of *Physalaemus* (Anura: Leptodactylidae) from Minas Gerais, southeastern Brazil. – Herpetologica **59**: 519–524.

Castoe, T. A., Chippindale, P. T., Campbell, J. A., Ammerman, L. K. & Parkinson, C. L. (2003): Molecular systematics of the Middle American jumping pitvipers (Genus *Atropoides)* and phylogeography of the *Atropoides nummifer* complex. – Herpetologica **59**: 420–431.

Channing, A. & Stanley, W. T. (2002): A new tree toad from the Ukaguru Mountains, Tanzania. – African J. Herpetol. **51**: 121–128.

Chiszar, D. & Smith, H. M. (2003): What is a reptile? pp. 3–11 – In: Hutchins, M., Murphy, J. B. & Schlager, N. (eds.): Grzimek's Animal Life Encyclopedia (2nd ed.). Vol. 7, Reptiles. Farmington Hills (Gale Group): 593 pp.

Christensen, C. M. (1975): Breeding Central American wood turtles. Chelonia 2: 8–10.

CITES. (2003): CITES-listed Species Data base. <http://www.cites.org/eng/resources/species. html> Downloaded 18 November 2003.

Collins, J. T. (1991): Viewpoint: A new taxonomic arrangement for some North American amphibians and reptiles. – Herpetol. Rev. 22: 42–43.

Cope, E. D. (1860): Catalogue of the Colubridae in the museum of the Academy of Natural Sciences of Philadelphia with notes and descriptions of new species. Part 2, 3. – Proc. Acad. Nat. Sci. Philadelphia 1860: 241–266, 553–566.

Cope, E. D. (1861): Contributions to the ophiology of Lower California, Mexico and Central America. – Proc. Acad. Nat. Sci. Philadelphia 1861: 292–306.

Cope, E. D. (1879): Eleventh contribution to the herpetology of tropical America. – Proc. Amer. Philos. Soc. 17: 85–98.

Cope, E. D. (1887): Catalogue of batrachians and reptiles of Central America and Mexico. – Bull. U.S. Natl. Mus. 32: 1–98.

Cornelius, S. E. (1995): Status of sea turtles along the Pacific coast of Middle America. – pp. 211–219 – In: Bjorndal, K. A. (ed.): Biology and Conservation of Sea Turtles. Washington, D.C. (Smithsonian Inst. Press): 615 pp.

Cruz, G. A., Wilson, L. D. & Espinosa, J. (1979): Two additions to the reptile fauna of Honduras, Eumeces managuae Dunn and Agkistrodon bilineatus (Günther), with comments on Pelamis platurus (Linnaeus). – Herpetol. Rev. 10: 26–27.

Dean, R. H. & Bickham, J. W. (1983): Staurotypus salvini Gray, Central American Musk Turtle. – Cat. Amer. Amph. Rept. 327: 1–2.

Dixon, J. R. (1964): The systematics and distribution of lizards of the Genus Phyllodactylus in North and Central America. – New Mexico State Univ. Sci. Bull. 64: 1–139.

Dixon, J. R. & Tipton, B. L. (2004): Dryadophis versus Mastigodryas (Ophidia: Colubridae): a proposed solution. – Herpetol. Rev. 35: 347–349.

Dixon, J. R. & Vaughan, R. K. (2003): The status of Mexican and southwestern United States blind snakes allied with Leptotyphlops dulcis (Serpentes: Leptotyphlopidae). – Texas J. Sci. 55: 3–24.

Dixon, J. R., Wiest, J. A. & Cei, J. M. (1993): Revision of the neotropical snake genus Chironius Fitzinger (Serpentes, Colubridae). – Museo Reg. Sci. Nat. Torino Monogr. 8: 1–279.

Doan, T. M. & Schargel, W. E. (2003): Bridging the gap in Proctoporus distribution: a new species (Squamata: Gymnophthalmidae) from the Andes of Venezuela. – Herpetologica 59: 68–75.

Domínguez, J. P. (1996): Caracterización del veneno de Crotalus durissus durissus (Serpiente de Cascabel Centroamericana) en El Salvador. – Thesis de Licenciatura, Universidad de El Salvador, San Salvador: 92 pp.

Downs, F. L. (1967): Intrageneric relationships among colubrid snakes of the genus Geophis Wagler. – Misc. Publ. Mus. Zool. Univ. Michigan 131: 1–193.

Dubois, A. (2003): True frogs (Ranidae). pp. 245–264 – In: Hutchins, M., Duellman, W. E. & Schlager, N. (eds.): Grzimek's Animal Life Encyclopedia (2nd ed.). Vol. 6, Amphibians. Farmington Hills (Gale Group): 507 pp.

Dubois, A. & Heyer, W. R. (1992): Leptodactylus labialis, the valid name for the American white-lipped frog (Amphibia: Leptodactylidae). – Copeia 1992: 584–585.

Duellman, W. E. (1958): A monographic study of the colubrid snake genus Leptodeira. – Bull. Am. Mus. Nat. Hist. 114: 1–152.

Duellman, W. E. (1960): A distributional study of the amphibians of the Isthmus of Tehuantepec, Mexico. – Univ. Kansas Pub. Mus. Nat. Hist. 13: 19–72.

Duellman, W. E. (1963): A review of the Middle American tree frogs of the genus Ptychohyla. – Univ. Kansas Publ. Mus. Nat. Hist. 15: 297–349.

Duellman, W. E. (1968): Smilisca baudinii (Duméril & Bibron), Mexican smilisca. – Cat. Amer. Amph. Rept. 59: 1–2.

Duellman, W. E. (1970): The hylid frogs of Middle America. – Monogr. Mus. Nat. Hist. Kansas 1: 1–753.

Duellman, W. E. (1971): The burrowing toad, Rhinophrynus dorsalis, on the Caribbean lowlands of Central America. – Herpetologica 27: 55–56.

Duellman, W. E. (2001): The Hylid Frogs of Middle America, 2nd ed. 2 volumes – Ithaca (Society for the Study of Amphibians and Reptiles): 1170 pp.

Duellman, W. E. (2003a): What is an amphibian? pp. 3–6 – In: Hutchins, M., Duellman, W. E. & Schlager, N. (eds.): Grzimek's Animal Life Encyclopedia (2nd ed.). Vol. 6, Amphibians. Farmington Hills (Gale Group): 507 pp.

Duellman, W. E. (2003b): Anura (Frogs and toads). pp. 61–68 – In: Hutchins, M., Duellman, W. E. & Schlager, N. (eds.): Grzimek's Animal Life Encyclopedia (2nd ed.). Vol. 6, Amphibians. Farmington Hills (Gale Group): 507 pp.

Duellman, W. E. (2003c): Amero-Australian treefrogs (Hylidae). pp. 225–243 – In: Hutchins, M., Duellman, W. E. & Schlager, N. (eds.): Grzimek's Animal Life Encyclopedia (2nd ed.). Vol. 6, Amphibians. Farmington Hills (Gale Group): 507 pp.

Duellman, W. E. (2003d): Leptodactylid frogs (Leptodactylidae). pp. 155–171 – In: Hutchins, M., Duellman, W. E. & Schlager, N. (eds.): Grzimek's Animal Life Encyclopedia (2nd ed.). Vol. 6, Amphibians. Farmington Hills (Gale Group): 507 pp.

Duellman, W. E. & Campbell, J. A. (1992): Hylid frogs of the genus *Plectrohyla*: Systematics and phylogenetic relationships. – Misc. Publ. Mus. Zool. Univ. Michigan **181**: 1–32.

Duellman, W. E. & Trueb, L. (1986): Biology of Amphibians. – New York (McGraw-Hill Book Company): 670 pp.

Dueñas, C., Wilson, L. D. & McCranie, J. R. (2001): A list of the amphibians and reptiles of El Salvador, with notes on additions and deletions. pp. 93–99 – In: Johnson, J. D., Webb, R. G. & Flores-Villela, O. A. (eds.): Mesoamerican Herpetology: Systematics, Zoogeography, and Conservation. Special Publication 1. El Paso (Centennial Mus., Univ. Texas): 200 pp.

Dunn, E. R. (1926): The Salamanders of the Family Plethodontidae. – Northampton (Smith College): 441 pp.

Dunn, E. R. (1928): Notes on *Bothrops lansbergii* and *Bothrops ophryomegas*. – Bull. Antivenin Inst. Amer. **2**: 29–30.

Dunn, E. R. (1942): The American caecilians. – Bull. Mus. Comp. Zool. **91**: 439–540.

Dunn, E. R. & Stuart, L. C. (1951): Comments on some recent restrictions of type localities of certain South and Central American amphibians and reptiles. – Copeia **1951**: 55–61.

Easteal, S. (1986): *Bufo marinus* (Linnaeus), Giant toad. – Cat. Amer. Amph. Rept. **395**: 1–4.

Ernst, C. H. (1978): A revision of the Neotropical turtle genus *Callopsis* (Testudines: Emydidae: Batagurinae). – Herpetologica **34**: 116–134.

Ernst, C. H. (1981): *Rhinoclemmys pulcherrima*. – Cat. Am. Amph. Rept. **275**: 1–2.

Ernst, C. H. & Barbour, R. W. (1989): Turtles of the World. – Washington, D.C. (Smithonian Inst. Press): 313 pp.

Ernst, C. H., Ross, F. D. & Ross, C. A. (1999): *Crocodylus acutus* (Cuvier), American Crocodile. – Cat. Amer. Amph. Rept. **700**: 1–17.

Etheridge, R. (1959): The relationships of the anoles (Reptilia: Sauria: Iguanidae) – an interpretation based on skeletal morphology. – Unpubl. Ph.D. Dissert., Univ. Michigan, Ann Arbor: 236 pp.

Etheridge, R. (1967): Lizard caudal vertebrae. – Copeia **1967**: 699–721.

Etheridge, R. E. & de Queiroz, K. (1988): A phylogeny of Iguanidae. pp. 283–367 – In: Estes, R. & Pregill, G. (eds.): Phylogenetic Relationships of the Lizard Families. Stanford (Stanford Univ. Press): 631 pp.

Faivovich, J. (2002): A cladistic analysis of *Scinax* (Anura: Hylidae). – Cladistics **18**: 367–393.

Fitch, H. S. (1970): Reproductive cycles in lizards and snakes. – Misc. Pub. Mus. Nat. Hist. Univ. Kansas **52**: 1–247.

Fitch, H. S., Echelle, A. A. & Echelle, A. F. (1972): Variation in the Central American iguanid lizard, *Anolis cupreus*, with the description of a new subspecies. – Occ. Pap. Nat. Hist. Mus., Univ. Kansas **8**: 1–20.

Fitzgerald, L. A. (2003a): Microteiids (Gymnophthalmidae). pp. 303–308 – In: Hutchins, M., Murphy, J. B. & Schlager, N. (eds.): Grzimek's Animal Life Encyclopedia (2nd ed.). Vol. 7, Reptiles. Farmington Hills (Gale Group): 593 pp.

Fitzgerald, L. A. (2003b): Whiptail lizards, tegus, and relatives (Teiidae). pp. 309–317 – In: Hutchins, M., Murphy, J. B. & Schlager, N. (eds.): Grzimek's Animal Life Encyclopedia (2nd ed.). Vol. 7, Reptiles. Farmington Hills (Gale Group): 593 pp.

Flores-Villela, O. & Sánchez-H., O. (2003): A new species of *Abronia* (Squamata: Anguidae) from the Sierra Madre del Sur of Guerrero, Mexico with comments on *Abronia deppii*. – Herpetologica **59**: 524–531.

Foster, M. S. & McDiarmid, R. W. (1983): *Rhinophrynus dorsalis* (Alma de Vaca, Sapo Borracho, Mexican Burrowing Toad). pp. 419–421 – In: Janzen, D. H. (ed.): Costa Rican Natural History. – Chicago (Univ. Chicago Press): 816 pp.

Fouquette, M. J., Jr. (1969): *Rhinophrynus dorsalis* Duméril & Bibron, Mexican burrowing toad. – Cat. Amer. Amph. Rept. **78:** 1–2.

Frazier, J. (1985): Misidentifications of sea turtles in the East Pacific: *Caretta caretta* and *Lepidochelys olivacea*. – J. Herpetol. **19:** 1–11.

Fritts, T. H., Almendariz, A. A. & Samec, S. (2002): A new species of *Echinosaura* (Gymnophthalmidae) from Ecuador and Colombia with comments on other members of the genus and *Teuchocercus keyi*.– J. Herpetol. **36:** 349–355.

Frost, D. R. (2002): Amphibian Species of the World. Version 2.21. <http://research.amnh.org/herpetology/amphibia/> – Updated 15 July 2002.

Frost, D. R. (2004): Amphibian Species of the World: an Online Reference. Version 3.0 (22 August, 2004). – Electronic Database accessible at http://research.amnh.org/herpetology/amphibia/index.html. American Museum of Natural History, New York, USA.

Frost, D. R. & Etheridge, R. (1989): A phylogenetic analysis and taxonomy of iguanian lizards (Reptilia: Squamata). – Misc. Publ. Mus. Nat. Hist. Univ. Kansas **81:** 1–65.

Frost, D. R., Etheridge, R., Janies, D. & Titus, T. (2001): Total evidence, sequence alignment, evolution of polychrotid lizards, and a reclassification of the Iguania (Squamata: Iguania). – Amer. Mus. Novit. **3343:** 1–38.

Frost, J. S. (1982): Functional genetic similarity between geographically separated populations of Mexican leopard frogs (*Rana pipiens* complex). – Syst. Zool. **31:** 57–67.

Gehlbach, F. R. (1971): Lyre snakes of the *Trimorphodon biscutatus* complex: a taxonomic résumé. – Herpetologica **27:** 200–211.

Gicca, D. F. (1983): *Enyaliosaurus quinquecarinatus* (Gray), Central American Armored Lizard. – Cat. Amer. Amph. Rept. **329:** 1–2.

Gierloff-Emden, H. G. (1976): La Costa de El Salvador: Monografía Morfológica-Oceonográfica. – San Salvador (Ministerio de Educación, Dirección de Publicaciones): 275 pp.

Glaw, F. (2003): Madagascan toadlets (Scaphiophrynidae). pp. 317–321 – In: Hutchins, M., Duellman, W. E. & Schlager, N. (eds.): Grzimek's Animal Life Encyclopedia (2nd ed.). Vol. 6, Amphibians. Farmington Hills (Gale Group): 507 pp.

Gloyd, H. K. (1940): The rattlesnakes, genera *Sistrurus* and *Crotalus*: a study in zoogeography and evolution. – Chicago Acad. Sci. Spec. Publ. **4:** 1–270.

Gloyd, H. K. & Conant, R. (1990): Snakes of the *Agkistrodon* Complex. – Athens (SSAR Contrib. Herpetol. Vol. 6): 614 pp.

Goldberg, S. R. (1995): Reproduction in the lyre snake, *Trimorphodon biscutatus* (Colubridae) from Arizona. – Southwest. Nat. **40:** 334–335.

Greding, E. J. & Hellebuyck, V. J. (1980): Ecological separation by prey selection among five species of Central American anuran amphibians. – Carib. J. Sci. **16:** 23–31.

Greenbaum, E. (2002): Geographic distribution. *Hemidactylus frenatus* (Common house gecko). – Herpetol. Rev. **33:** 65–66.

Greenbaum, E. (2004): A new species of *Bolitoglossa* (Amphibia: Caudata: Plethodontidae) from montane forests in Guatemala and El Salvador. – J. Herpetol. **38:** 411–421.

Greenbaum, E., Herrera, N., Portillo, R. I., Komar, O. & Rivera, R. (2002a): Geographic distribution. *Mesoscincus managuae* (Managua skink). – Herpetol. Rev. **33:** 322.

Greenbaum, E., Komar, O. & Bolaños, R. (2002b): Geographic distribution. *Ninia espinali* (Espinal's coffee snake). – Herpetol. Rev. **33:** 325.

Greenbaum, E., Carr, J. L. & Almendáriz, A. (2004): Taxonomic status of *Tantilla equatoriana* Wilson and Mena 1980 (Serpentes: Colubridae). – Southwest. Nat. **49:** 457–464.

Greenbaum, E. & Komar, O. (in press): Threat assessment and conservation prioritization of the herpetofauna of El Salvador. – Biodiv. Cons.

Grenard, S. (1991): Handbook of Alligators and Crocodiles. – Malabar (Krieger): 210 pp.

Griffith, H., Ngo, A. & Murphy, R. W. (2000): A cladistic evaluation of the cosmopolitan genus *Eumeces* Wiegmann (Reptilia, Squamata, Scincidae). – Russian J. Herpetol. **7:** 1–16.

Grismer, L. L., Das, I. & Leong, T. M. (2003): A new species of *Gongylosoma* (Squamata: Colubridae) from Pulau Tioman, West Malaysia. – Herpetologica **59:** 565–572.

Günther, A. C. L. G. (1885–1902): Biologia Centrali-Americana. Reptila and Batrachia. – London (Porter): 326 pp.

Gutberlet, R. L., Jr. (2003): Alligator lizards, galliwasps, glass lizards, and relatives (Anguidae). pp. 339–345 – In: Hutchins, M., Murphy, J. B. & Schlager, N. (eds.): Grzimek's Animal Life Encyclopedia (2nd ed.). Vol. 7, Reptiles. Farmington Hills (Gale Group): 593 pp.

Guyer, C. & Savage, J. M. (1987): Cladistic relationships among anoles (Sauria: Iguanidae). – Syst. Zool. **35:** 509–531.

Guyer, C. & Savage, J. M. (1992): Anole systematics revisited. – Syst. Biol. **41:** 89–110.

Guzmán López, G. T. (1995): Clima y recursos atmosfericos. pp. 169–208 – In: Serrano, F. (ed.): Historia Natural y Ecológica de El Salvador. Tome I. – San Salvador (Ministerio de Educación): 397 pp.

Haas, W. & Köhler, G. (1997): Freilandbeobachtungen, Pflege und Zucht von *Bufo luetkenii* Boulenger (1891). – Herpetofauna **19:** 5–9.

Hahn, D. E. (1980): Liste der rezenten Amphibien und Reptilien. Anomalepidae, Leptotyphlopidae, Typhlopidae. – Das Tiereich **101:** 1–93.

Haines, T. P. (1940): Delayed fertilization in *Leptodeira annulata polysticta.* – Copeia **1940:** 116–118.

Harris, D. M. (1985): Infralingual plicae: support for Boulenger´s Teiidae (Sauria). – Copeia **1985:** 560–565.

Hasbún, C. R. (2001): Herpetofaunal biodiveristy of the endangered spiny-tailed lizards of the *Ctenosaura quinquecarinata/flavidorsalis* complex: geographic variation, mtDNA phylogeography and systematics. – Unpubl. Ph.D. Diss., University of Hull, England: 403 pp.

Hasbún, C. R. (2002): Observations on the first day of dispersal of neonatal hawks bill turtles (*Eretmochelys imbricata*). – Marine Turtle Newsletter **96:** 7–10.

Hasbún, C. R., Köhler, G., McCranie, J. R. & Lawrence, A. (2001): Additions to the description of *Ctenosaura flavidorsalis* Köhler & Klemmer, 1994 and its occurrence in southwestern Honduras, El Salvador, and Guatemala (Squamata: Sauria: Iguanidae). – Herpetozoa **14:** 55–63.

Hasbún, C. R. & Melara, M. V. (1994): Sea turtle conservation program at Barra de Santiago, El Salvador. – NOAA Technical Memorandum NMFS SEFSC **341:** 235–237.

Hasbún, C. R. & Ramos, L. A. (1999): Phytobezoar in a captive olive ridley sea turtle (*Lepidochelys olivacea*). – J. Wild. Rehab. **22:** 9–12.

Hasbún, C. R. & Vásquez, M. (1991): Proyecto de conservación de la tortuga marina en Barra de Santiago, El Salvador, Agosto-Diciembre 1990. – Presentado a US Fish and Wildlife Service y World Wildlife Fund. AMAR, El Salvador: 45 pp.

Hasbún, C. R., & Vásquez, M. (1999): Sea Turtles of El Salvador. – Marine Turtle Newsletter **85:** 7–9.

Hasbún, C. R., Vásquez, M. & León, E. (1999): Unusual record of a juvenile hawksbill sea turtle in a mangrove estuary, El Salvador. – Marine Turtle Newsletter **81:** 10.

Hedges, S. B. & Thomas, R. (2001): At the lower size limit in amniote vertebrates: a new diminutive lizard from the West Indies. – Carib. J. Sci. **37:** 168–173.

Heyer, W. R. (1970a): Studies on the frogs of the genus *Leptodactylus* (Amphibia, Leptodactylidae). II. Diagnosis and distribution of the *Leptodactylus* of Costa Rica. – Rev. Biol. Trop. **16:** 171–205.

Heyer, W. R. (1970b): Studies on the frogs of the genus *Leptodactylus* (Amphibia, Leptodactylidae). VI. Biosystematics of the *melanonotus* group. – Los Angeles Co. Mus. Nat. Hist., Contrib. Sci. **191:** 1–48.

Heyer, W. R. (1971): *Leptodactylus labialis* (Cope), White-lipped frog. – Cat. Amer. Amph. Rept. **104:** 1–3.

Heyer, W. R. (1978): Systematics of the *fuscus* group of the frog genus *Leptodactylus* (Amphibia, Leptodactylidae). – Nat. Hist. Mus. Los Angeles Sci. Bull. **29:** 1–85.

Heyer, W. R. (2002): *Leptodactylus fragilis,* the valid name for the Middle American and northern South American white- lipped frog (Amphibia: Leptodactylidae). – Proc. Biol. Soc. Wash. **115:** 321–322.

Hidalgo, H. (1979): Range extension of the snake *Sibon anthracops* (Cope), in El Salvador. – Herpetol. Rev. **10:** 103.

Hidalgo, H. (1980a): *Enyaliosaurus quinquecarinatus* (Gray) and *Leptodeira nigrofasciata* Günther in El Salvador. – Herpetol. Rev. **11**: 42–43.

Hidalgo, H. (1980b): Occurrence of *Pelamis platurus* (Linnaeus) in El Salvador. – Herpetol. Rev. **11**: 117.

Hidalgo, H. (1981a): Additions to the snake fauna of El Salvador. – Herpetol. Rev. **12**: 67–68.

Hidalgo, H. (1981b): Additions to the reptile fauna of El Salvador. – Trans. Kansas Acad. Sci. **84**: 55–58.

Hidalgo, H. (1982a): *Centrolenella fleischmanni* (Boettger): new to the anuran fauna of El Salvador. – Herpetol. Rev. **13**: 54–55.

Hidalgo, H. (1982b): Rediscovery of the anguid lizard *Diploglossus atitlanensis* (Smith). – Trans. Kansas Acad. Sci. **85**: 34–38.

Hidalgo, H. (1982c): Courtship and mating behavior in *Rhinoclemmys pulcherrima incisa* (Testudines: Emydidae: Batagurinae). – Trans. Kansas Acad. Sci. **85**: 82–95.

Hidalgo, H. (1983): Two new species of *Abronia* (Sauria: Anguidae) from the cloud forests of El Salvador. – Occ. Pap. Mus. Nat. Hist. Univ. Kansas. **105**: 1–11.

Hillis, D. M. & de Sá, R. (1988): Phylogeny and taxonomy of the *Rana palmipes* group. – Herpetol. Monogr. **2**: 1–26.

Hirth, H. F. (1980): *Chelonia mydas* (Linnaeus), Green Turtle. – Cat. Amer. Amph. Rept. **249**: 1–4.

Holm, P. (1995): *Leptophis modestus* (NCN) Morphology. – Herpetol. Rev. **26**: 39.

Honda, M., Ota, H., Köhler, G., Ineich, I., Chirio, L., Chen, S. L. & Hikida, T. (2003): Phylogeny of the subfamily Lygosominae (Reptilia: Scincidae), with special reference to the origin of New World taxa. – Gen. Genetic Syst. **78**: 71–80.

Hoyt, D. L. (1964): The rediscovery of the snake *Leptophis modestus*. – Copeia **1964**: 214–215.

IUCN. (2001): IUCN Red List Categories, Version 3.1. <http://www.redlist.org/info/categories_criteria2001.html> – Prepared by the IUCN Species Survival Commission. IUCN, Gland, Switzerland and Cambridge, UK. Downloaded 18 November 2003.

IUCN. (2003): 2003 IUCN Red List of Threatened Species. <www.redlist.org> – Downloaded 18 November 2003.

IUCN, Conservation International & NatureServe. (2004): Global Amphibian Assessment. <www.globalamphibians.org>. Accessed 11 December 2004.

Iverson, J. B. (1992): A Revised Checklist with Distribution Maps of the Turtles of the World. – Richmond (privately printed): 363 pp.

Iverson, J. B. (2003a): Sea turtles (Cheloniidae). pp. 85–92 – In: Hutchins, M., Murphy, J. B. & Schlager, N. (eds.): Grzimek's Animal Life Encyclopedia (2nd ed.). Vol. 7, Reptiles. Farmington Hills (Gale Group): 593 pp.

Iverson, J. B. (2003b): Leatherback seaturtles (Dermochelyidae). pp. 101–103 – In: Hutchins, M., Murphy, J. B. & Schlager, N. (eds.): Grzimek's Animal Life Encyclopedia (2nd ed.). Vol. 7, Reptiles. Farmington Hills (Gale Group): 593 pp.

Iverson, J. B. (2003c): Eurasian pond and river turtles, and Neotropical wood turtles (Geoemydidae). pp. 115–120 – In: Hutchins, M., Murphy, J. B. & Schlager, N. (eds.): Grzimek's Animal Life Encyclopedia (2nd ed.). Vol. 7, Reptiles. Farmington Hills (Gale Group): 593 pp.

Iverson, J. B. (2003d): American mud and musk turtles (Kinosternidae). pp. 121–127 – In: Hutchins, M., Murphy, J. B. & Schlager, N. (eds.): Grzimek's Animal Life Encyclopedia (2nd ed.). Vol. 7, Reptiles. Farmington Hills (Gale Group): 593 pp.

Johnson, J. D. (1977): The taxonomy and distribution of the Neotropical whipsnake *Masticophis mentovarius* (Reptilia, Serpentes, Colubridae). – J. Herpetol. **11**: 287–309.

Johnson, J. D. (1982): *Masticophis mentovarius* (Duméril, Bibron & Duméril). – Cat. Amer. Amph. Rept. **295**: 1–4.

Kamezaki, N. & Matsui, M. (1995): Geographic variation in skull morphology of the green turtle, *Chelonia mydas,* with a taxonomic decision. – J. Herpetol. **29**: 51–60.

Karl, S. A. & Bowen, B. W. (1999): Evolutionary significant units versus geopolitical taxonomy: molecular systematics of an endangered sea turtle (genus *Chelonia*). – Cons. Biol. **13**: 990–999.

Keiser, E. D., Jr. (1982): *Oxybelis aeneus* (Wagler), Neotropical vine snake. – Cat. Amer. Amph. Rept. **305**: 1–4.

Keogh, J. S. (2003): Cobras, kraits, seasnakes, death adders, and relatives (Elapidae). pp. 483–499 – In: Hutchins, M., Murphy, J. B. & Schlager, N. (eds.): Grzimek's Animal Life Encyclopedia (2nd ed.). Vol. 7, Reptiles. Farmington Hills (Gale Group): 593 pp.

King, F. W. & Burke, R. L. (eds.). (1989): Crocodilian, Tuatara, and Turtle Species of the World: A Taxonomic and Geographic Reference. – Washington, D.C. (Association of Systematics Collections): 216 pp.

Klauber, L. M. (1945): The geckos of the genus *Coleonyx* with descriptions of new subspecies. – Trans. San Diego Soc. Nat. Hist. **10**: 133–216.

Klauber, L. M. (1956): Rattlesnakes: Their Habits, Life Histories, and Influence on Mankind. 2 volumes. – Berkeley (University of California Press): 1476 pp.

Klauber, L. M. (1972): Rattlesnakes: Their Habits, Life Histories, and Influence on Mankind. 2nd edition. 2 volumes. – Berkeley (University of California Press): 1533 pp.

Kley, N. J. (2003): Slender blindsnakes (Leptotyphlopidae). pp. 373–377 – In: Hutchins, M., Murphy, J. B. & Schlager, N. (eds.): Grzimek's Animal Life Encyclopedia (2nd ed.). Vol. 7, Reptiles. Farmington Hills (Gale Group): 593 pp.

Köhler, G. (1996): Notes on a collection of reptiles from El Salvador collected between 1951 and 1956. – Senckenbergiana biol. **76**: 29–38.

Köhler, G. (1999): Eine neue Saumfingerart der Gattung *Norops* von der Pazifikseite des nördlichen Mittelamerika. – Salamandra **35**: 37–52.

Köhler, G. (2000): Reptilien und Amphibien Mittelamerikas. Band 1: Krokodile, Schildkröten, Echsen. – Offenbach (Herpeton Verlag): 158 pp.

Köhler, G. (2001a): Reptilien und Amphibien Mittelamerikas. Band 2: Schlangen. – Offenbach (Herpeton Verlag): 174 pp.

Köhler, G. (2001b): Anfibios y Reptiles de Nicaragua. – Offenbach (Herpeton Verlag): 208 pp.

Köhler, G. (2003a): Geographic distribution: *Bufo valliceps*. – Herpetol. Rev. **34**: 161.

Köhler, G. (2003b): Reptiles of Central America. – Offenbach (Herpeton Verlag): 368 pp.

Köhler, G. (2003c): Two new species of *Euspondylus* (Squamata: Gymnophthalmidae) from Peru. – Salamandra **39**: 5–20.

Köhler, G. & Heimes, P. (2002): Stachelleguane – Lebensweise, Pflege, Zucht. – Offenbach (Herpeton): 174 pp.

Köhler, G. & Klemmer, K. (1994): Eine neue Schwarzleguanart der Gattung *Ctenosaura* aus La Paz, Honduras. – Salamandra **30**: 197–208.

Köhler, G. & Kreutz, J. (1999): *Norops macrophallus* (Werner, 1917), a valid species of anole from Guatemala and El Salvador (Squamata: Sauria: Iguanidae). – Herpetozoa **12**: 57–65.

Köhler, G., Lehr, E. & McCranie, J. R. (2000): The tadpole of the Central American toad *Bufo luetkenii* Boulenger. – J. Herpetol. **34**: 303–306.

Köhler, G. & McCranie, J. R. (1998): Zur Kenntnis von *Norops heteropholidotus* (Mertens, 1952). – Herpetofauna **20**: 12–13.

Köhler, G. & McCranie, J. R. (1999): Taxonomic status of *Rhadinaea pinicola* Mertens (Serpentes: Colubridae). – Copeia **1999**: 529–530.

Köhler, G., Schmidt, F. & Eusemann, P. (1998): Morphologie, Verbreitung und Fortpflanzung der Stachelschuppenleguane in El Salvador: 1. *Sceloporus squamosus* Bocourt, 1874. – Salamandra **34**: 301–308.

Kofron, C. P. (1985): Review of the Central American colubrid snakes, *Sibon fischeri* and *S. carri*. – Copeia **1985**: 164–174.

Kofron, C. P. (1987): Systematics of Neotropical gastropod-eating snakes: The *fasciata* group of the genus *Sibon*. – J. Herpetol. **21**: 210–225.

Kofron, C. P. (1988): Systematics of Neotropical gastropod-eating snakes: The *sartorii* group of the genus *Sibon*. – Amphibia-Reptilia **9**: 145–168.

Kofron, C. P. (1990): Systematics of the Neotropical gastropod-eating snakes: The *dimidiata* group of the genus *Sibon*, with comments on the *nebulata* group. – Amphibia-Reptilia **11**: 207–223.

Kraus, F. & Allison, A. (2002): A new species of *Xenobatrachus* (Anura: Microhylidae) from northern Papua New Guinea. – Herpetologica **58**: 56–66.

Landy, M. J., Langerbartel, S. A., Moll, E. O. & Smith, H. M. (1966): A collection of snakes from Volcán Tacana, Chiapas, Mexico. – J. Ohio Herp. Soc. **5**: 93–101.

Lazell, J. D. (1992): The family Iguanidae: Disagreement with Frost and Etheridge (1989). – Herpetol. Rev. **23**: 109–112.

Lee, J. C. (1980): Variation and systematics of the *Anolis sericeus* complex (Sauria: Iguanidae). – Copeia **1980**: 310–320.

Lee, J. C. (1983): *Anolis sericeus* Hallowell, Silky Anole. – Cat. Amer. Amph. Rept. **340**: 1–2.

Lee, J. C. (1996): The Amphibians and Reptiles of the Yucatán Peninsula. – Ithaca (Cornell Univ. Press): 500 pp.

Leenders, T. (2003): Amphibians and reptiles. pp. 158–161 – In: Alvarez, J. M. & Komar, O. (eds.): El Imposible National Park and its Wildlife. Biodiversity Series No. 2. – San Salvador (SalvaNATURA): 227 pp.

Leenders, T. A. A. M. & Watkins-Colwell, G. J. (2003a): *Boa constrictor* (Boa Constrictor). Diet. – Herpetol. Rev. **34**: 146–147.

Leenders, T. A. A. M. & Watkins-Colwell, G. J. (2003b): *Oxybelis fulgidus* (Green Vine Snake). Prey. – Herpetol. Rev. **34**: 152.

Leenders, T. A. A. M. & Watkins-Colwell, G. J. (2003c): *Norops heteropholidotus* (NCN). Dewlap coloration. – Herpetol. Rev. **34**: 369–370.

Leenders, T. A. A. M. & Watkins-Colwell, G. J. (2004): Notes on a collection of amphibians and reptiles from El Salvador. – Postilla (231): 1–31.

Legler, J. M. (1964): A narrow mouthed toad (*Gastrophryne usta*) in El Salvador. – Herpetologica **19**: 286–287.

Legler, J. M. (1990): The genus *Pseudemys* in Mesoamerica: taxonomy, distribution and origins. pp. 82–105 – In: Gibbons, J. W. (ed.): Life History and Ecology of the Slider Turtle. – Washington, D.C. (Smithsonian Inst. Press): 368 pp.

Lehr, E., Wallach, V., Köhler, G. & Aguilar, C. (2002): New species of tricolor *Leptotyphlops* (Reptilia: Squamata: Leptotyphlopidae) from Central Peru. – Copeia **2002**: 131–136.

Leviton, A. E., Gibbs, R. H., Jr., Heal, E. & Dawson, C. E. (1985): Standards in herpetology and ichthyology: Part I. Standard symbolic codes for institutional resource collections in herpetology and ichthyology. – Copeia **1985**: 802–832.

Limbaugh, B. A. & Volpe, E. P. (1957): Early development of the Gulf Coast toad *Bufo valliceps* Wiegmann. Amer. Mus. Novitates **1842**: 1–32.

Lips, K. R. & Savage, J. M. (1996): Key to the known tadpoles (Amphibia: Anura) of Costa Rica. – Stud. Neotrop. Fauna & Environm. **31**: 17–26.

Lynch, J. D. (1965): A review of the *rugulosus* group of *Eleutherodactylus* in northern Central America. – Herpetologica **21**: 102–113.

Lynch, J. D. (2000): The relationships of an ensemble of Guatemalan and Mexican frogs (*Eleutherodactylus*: Leptodactylidae: Amphibia). – Rev. Acad. Colomb. Cienc. **24**: 67–94.

Lynch, J. D. & Duellman, W. E. (1973): A review of the centrolenid frogs of Ecuador, with descriptions of new species. – Occ. Pap. Mus. Nat. Hist. Univ. Kansas **16**: 1–66.

Macedonia, J. M. (2001): Habitat light, colour variation, and ultraviolet reflectance in the Grand Cayman anole, *Anolis conspersus*. – Biol. J. Linn. Soc. **73**: 299–320.

Macey, J. R., Larson, A., Ananjeva, N. B. & Papenfuss, T. J. (1997): Evolutionary shifts in three major structural features of the mitochondrial genome among Iguanian lizards. – J. Mol. Evol. **44**: 660–674.

Marquez, R. (1990): Sea Turtles of the World. FAO Fisheries Synopsis Vol. 11, No. 125. Rome (FAO): 81 pp.

Mather, C. M. & Sites, J. W., Jr. (1985): *Sceloporus variabilis* Wiegmann, Rose-bellied lizard. – Cat. Amer. Amph. Rept. **373**: 1–3.

McCranie, J. R. (1980): *Drymarchon* Fitzinger. *Drymarchon corais* (Boie). – Cat. Amer. Amph. Rept. **267**: 1–4.

McCranie, J. R. (1993): *Crotalus durissus* Linnaeus. – Cat. Amer. Amph. Rept. **577**: 1–11.

McCranie, J. R. & Köhler, G. (1999): A new species of salamander of the *Bolitoglossa dunni* group from Cerro El Pital, Honduras and El Salvador (Amphibia, Caudata: Plethodontidae). – Senckenbergiana biol. **78**: 225–229.

McCranie, J. R. & Wilson, L. D. (1991a): *Rhadinaea kinkelini* Boettger. – Cat. Amer. Amph. Rept. **523**: 1–2.

McCranie, J. R. & Wilson, L. D. (1991b): *Rhadinaea montecristi* Mertens. – Cat. Amer. Amph. Rept. **524**: 1–2.

McCranie, J. R. & Wilson, L. D. (1992): *Rhadinaea godmani* (Günther). – Cat. Amer. Amph. Rept. **546**: 1–3.

McCranie, J. R. & Wilson, L. D. (1993a): A review of the *Bolitoglossa dunni* group (Amphibia: Caudata) from Honduras with the description of three new species. – Herpetologica **49**: 1–15.

McCranie, J. R. & Wilson, L. D. (1993b): *Leptophis modestus* (Günther). – Cat. Amer. Amph. Rept. **578**: 1–2.

McCranie, J. R. & Wilson, L. D. (1999): Description of a new species of *Plectrohyla* from Cerro Celaque, Honduras, formerly referred to *Plectrohyla glandulosa* (Amphibia, Anura, Hylidae). – Senckenbergiana biol. **78**: 231–236.

McCranie, J. R. & Wilson, L. D. (2002): The Amphibians of Honduras. – Ithaca (Society for the Study of Amphibians and Reptiles): 625 pp.

McCranie, J. R., Wilson, L. D. & Williams, K. L. (1987): *Plectrohyla guatemalensis*. Reproduction. – Herpetol. Rev. **18**: 72.

McDiarmid, R. W. & Altig, R. (1999): Tadpoles: The Biology of Anuran Larvae. – Chicago (The University of Chicago Press): 444 pp.

McDiarmid, R. W., Campbell, J. A. & Touré, T. A. (eds.). (1999): Snake Species of the World: A Taxonomic and Geographic Reference. Vol. 1. – Washington (The Herpetologists' League): 511 pp.

McDiarmid, R. W. & Foster, M. S. (1981): Breeding habits of the toad *Bufo coccifer* in Costa Rica, with a description of the tadpole. – Southwest. Nat. **26**: 353–363.

McLain, R. B. (1899): Contributions to Neotropical Herpetology. – Wheeling (privately printed): 13 pp.

Mendelson, J. R., III. (1998): Geographic variation in *Bufo valliceps* (Anura: Bufonidae), a widespread toad in the United States and Middle America. – Sci. Pap. Nat. Hist. Mus. Univ. Kansas **8**: 1–12.

Mendelson, J. R., III., Williams, B. L., Sheil, C. A. & Mulcahy, D. G. (2005): Systematics of the *Bufo coccifer* Complex (Anura: Bufonidae) of Mesoamerica. – Sci. Pap. Nat. Hist. Mus. Univ. Kansas **38**: 1–27.

Mertens, R. (1952a): Neues über die Reptilienfauna von El Salvador. – Zool. Anz. **148**: 87–93.

Mertens, R. (1952b): Weitere neue Reptilien aus El Salvador. – Zool. Anz. **149**: 133–138.

Mertens, R. (1952c): Zur Kenntnis der Amphibienfauna von El Salvador. – Senckenbergiana **33**: 169–171.

Mertens, R. (1952d): Die Amphibien und Reptilien von El Salvador. – Abh. Senckenb. Naturf. Ges. **487**: 1–120.

Mertens, R. (1952e): El Salvador. Biologische Reisen im Lande der Vulkane. – Frankfurt (Verlag Waldemar Kramer): 116 pp.

Mertens, R. (1973): Bemerkenswerte Schlanknattern der neotropischen Gattung *Leptophis*. – Stud. Neotrop. Fauna **8**: 141–154.

Mertz, L. A. (2003a): Alligators and caimans (Alligatoridae). pp. 171–178 – In: Hutchins, M., Murphy, J. B. & Schlager, N. (eds.): Grzimek's Animal Life Encyclopedia (2nd ed.). Vol. 7, Reptiles. Farmington Hills (Gale Group): 593 pp.

Mertz, L. A. (2003b): Anoles, iguanas, and relatives (Iguanidae). pp. 243–257 – In: Hutchins, M., Murphy, J. B. & Schlager, N. (eds.): Grzimek's Animal Life Encyclopedia (2nd ed.). Vol. 7, Reptiles. Farmington Hills (Gale Group): 593 pp.

Meshaka, W. E., Jr., Butterfield, B. P. & Hauge, J. B. (2004): The Exotic Amphibians and Reptiles of Florida. – Malabar (Krieger Publishing Company): 155 pp.

Mitchell, M. A. & Tully, T. N. (1998): Captive propagation of the green iguana, *Iguana iguana,* in Costa del Sol, El Salvador. – Proceedings of the Annual Conference of the Association of Reptilian and Amphibian Veterinarians **5**: 139–140.

Mittermeier, R. A. (1970): Turtles in Central American markets. – Int. Turtle Tortoise Soc. Journ. **4**: 20–26.

Molina, C., Senaris, J. C. & Ayarzaguena, J. (2002): Contribution to the knowledge of the taxonomy, distribution, and natural history of *Leposoma hexalepis* (Reptilia: Gymnophthalmidae) in Venezuela. – Herpetologica **58**: 485–491.

Mulcahy, D. G. & Mendelson, J. R., III. (2000): Phylogeography and speciation of the morphologically variable, widespread species *Bufo valliceps,* based on molecular evidence from mtDNA. – Molec. Phylog. Evol. **17**: 173–189.

Myers, C. W. (1974): The systematics of *Rhadinaea* (Colubridae), a genus of New World snakes. – Bull. Am. Mus. Nat. Hist. **153**: 1–261.

Myers, C. W. & Donnelly, M. A. (1996): A new herpetofauna from Cerro Yaví, Venezuela: First results of the Robert G. Goelet American Museum-Terramar expedition to the northwestern Tepuis. – Amer. Mus. Novit. **3172**: 1–56.

Nelson, C. E. (1966a): Notes on some Mexican and Central American amphibians and reptiles. – Southwest. Nat. **11**: 128–131.

Nelson, C. E. (1966b): The evolution of frogs of the family Microhylidae in North America. – Unpubl. Ph.D. Diss., Univ. Texas, Austin: 293 pp.

Nelson, C. E. (1972a): Systematic studies on the North American microhylid genus *Gastrophryne*. – J. Herpetol. **6**: 111–137.

Nelson, C. E. (1972b): *Gastrophryne usta* (Cope), Two-spaded narrow-mouthed toad. – Cat. Amer. Amph. Rept. **123**: 1–2.

Nelson, C. E. (1973a): Systematics of the Middle American upland populations of *Hypopachus* (Anura: Microhylidae). – Herpetologica **29**: 6–17.

Nelson, C. E. (1973b): Mating calls of the Microhylinae: Descriptions and phylogenetic and ecological considerations. – Herpetologica **29**: 163–176.

Nelson, C. E. & Altig, R. (1972): Tadpoles of the microhylids *Gastrophryne elegans* and *G. usta*. – Herpetologica **28**: 381–383.

Nelson, C. E. & Cuellar, H. S. (1968): Anatomical comparison of tadpoles of the genera *Hypopachus* and *Gastrophryne* (Microhylidae). – Copeia **1968**: 423–424.

Nelson, C. E. & Hoyt, D. L. (1961): New Central American records for *Rhinophrynus dorsalis*. – Herpetologica **17**: 216.

Nelson, C. E. & Meyer, J. R. (1967): Variation and distribution of the Middle American snake genus *Loxocemus* Cope (Boidae?). – Southwest. Nat. **12**: 439–453.

Nevarez, J. G., Mitchell, M. A., Le Blanc, C. & Graham, P. (2002): Determination of plasma biochemistries, ionized calcium, vitamin D3, and hematocrit values in captive green iguanas (*Iguana iguana*) from El Salvador. – Proceedings of the Annual Conference of the Association of Reptilian and Amphibian Veterinarians **9**: 87–91.

Nieto-Montes de Oca, A. (2003): A new species of the *Geophis dubius* group (Squamata: Colubridae) from the Sierra de Juárez of Oaxaca, Mexico. – Herpetologica **59**: 572–585.

Nilson, G. & Gutberlet, R. L., Jr. (2003): Vipers and pitvipers (Viperidae). pp. 445–460 – In: Hutchins, M., Murphy, J. B. & Schlager, N. (eds.): Grzimek's Animal Life Encyclopedia (2nd ed.). Vol. 7, Reptiles. Farmington Hills (Gale Group): 593 pp.

Nussbaum, R. A. (1980): The Brahminy blind snake (*Ramphotyphlops braminus*) in the Seychelles Archipelago: distribution, variation, and further evidence for parthenogenesis. Herpetologica **36**: 215–221.

Oeser, R. (1933): Meine Centralamerika-Reise. – Blätter Aquar. Terrar. Knde. **44**: 75–78, 99–102, 219–224, 256–261.

Parkinson, C. L., Zamudio, K. R. & Greene, H. W. (2000): Phylogeography of the pitviper clade *Agkistrodon*: historical ecology, species status, and conservation of cantils. – Mol. Ecol. **9**: 411–420.

Parra-Olea, G., García-París, M. & Wake, D. B. (2004): Molecular diversification of salamanders of the tropical American genus *Bolitoglossa* (Caudata: Plethodontidae) and its evolutionary and biogeographic implications. – Biol. J. Linn. Soc. **81**: 325–346.

Pellegrino, K. C. M., Rodrigues, M. T., Yonenaga, Y. Y. & Sites, J. W., Jr. (2001): A molecular perspective on the evolution of microteiid lizards (Squamata, Gymnophthalmidae), and a new classification for the family. – Biol. J. Linn. Soc. **74**: 315–338.

Peters, J. A. (1960): The snakes of the subfamily Dipsadinae. – Misc. Publ. Mus. Zool. Univ. Michigan **114**: 1–224.

Peters, J. A. & Donoso-Barros, R. (1970): Catalogue of the Neotropical Squamata. Part II. Lizards and amphisbaenians. – Smith. Inst. U.S. Natl. Mus. Bull. **297**: 1–293.

Peters, J. A. & Orejas-Miranda, B. (1970): Catalogue of the Neotropical Squamata. Part I. Snakes. – Smith. Inst. U.S. Natl. Mus. Bull. **297**: 1–347.

Pianka, E. R. (2003a): Squamata (Lizards and snakes). pp. 195–208 – In: Hutchins, M., Murphy, J. B. & Schlager, N. (eds.): Grzimek's Animal Life Encyclopedia (2nd ed.). Vol. 7, Reptiles. Farmington Hills (Gale Group): 593 pp.

Pianka, E. R. (2003b): Skinks (Scincidae). pp. 327–
    338 – In: Hutchins, M., Murphy, J. B. &
    Schlager, N. (eds.): Grzimek's Animal Life
    Encyclopedia (2nd ed.). Vol. 7, Reptiles.
    Farmington Hills (Gale Group): 593 pp.

Pickwell, G. V. & Culotta, W. A. (1980): *Pelamis*
    Daudin, Pelagic or yellow-bellied sea snake. –
    Cat. Amer. Amph. Rept. **255**: 1–4.

Poe. S. (2004): Phylogeny of anoles. – Herpetol.
    Monogr. **18**: 37–89

Porter, K. R. (1962): Mating calls and note worthy
    collections of some Mexican amphibians.
    Herpetologica **18**: 165–171.

Porter, K. R. (1964a): Distribution and taxonomic
    status of seven species of Mexican *Bufo*. –
    Herpetologica **19**: 229–247.

Porter, K. R. (1964b): Morphological and mating call
    comparisons in the *Bufo valliceps* complex. –
    Amer. Midland Nat. **71**: 232–245.

Porter, K. R. (1965): Intraspecific variation in
    mating call of *Bufo coccifer* Cope. – Amer.
    Midland Nat. **74**: 350–356.

Porter, K. R. (1966): Mating calls of six Mexican and
    Central American toads (Genus *Bufo*). –
    Herpetologica **22**: 60–67.

Porter, K. R. (1970): *Bufo valliceps* Wiegmann. –
    Cat. Amer. Amph. Rept. **94**: 1–4.

Presch, W. (1983): The lizard family Teiidae: is it a
    monophyletic group? – Zool. J. Linn. Soc. **77**:
    189–197.

Price, R. M. (1991): *Senticolis* Dowling and Fries. –
    Cat. Amer. Amph. Rept. **525**: 1–4.

Pritchard, P. C. H. (1980): *Dermochelys coriacea*
    Leatherback turtle. – Cat. Amer. Amph. Rept.
    238: 1–4.

Pritchard, P. C. H. (1999): Status of the black
    turtle. – Cons. Biol. **13**: 1000–1003.

Rainer, G. (2003): Three new species of the genus
    Oreophryne from western Papua, Indonesia. –
    Spixiana **26**: 175–191.

Rand, A. S. (1952): A new salamander of the genus
    Oedipina from El Salvador. – Chicago Acad. Sci.
    Nat. Hist. Misc. **98**: 1–3.

Rand, A. S. (1957): Notes on amphibians and
    reptiles from El Salvador. – Fieldiana,
    Zool. **34**: 505–534.

Rand, A. S. (1968): A nesting aggregation of iguanas.
    Copeia **1968**: 552–561.

Reeder, T. W. (1990): *Eumeces managuae* Dunn. –
    Cat. Amer. Amph. Rept. **467**: 1–2.

Reeder, T. W., Cole, C. J. & Dessauer, H. C. (2002):
    Phylogenetic relationships of whiptail lizards of
    the genus *Cnemidophorus* (Squamata: Teiidae):
    A test of monophyly, reevaluation of karyo-
    typic evolution, and a review of hybrid origins.
    – Amer. Mus. Novit. **3365**: 1–61.

Rest, J. S., Ast, J. C., Austin, C. C., Waddell, P. J.,
    Tibbetts, E. A., Hay, J. M. & Mindell, D. P.
    (2003): Molecular systematics of primary
    reptilian lineages and the tuatara mitochon-
    drial genome. Mol. Phylog. Evol. **29**: 289–297.

Rodríguez-Robles, J. A. (2003): Neotropical
    sunbeam snakes (Loxocemidae). pp. 405–407 –
    In: Hutchins, M., Murphy, J. B. & Schlager, N.
    (eds.): Grzimek's Animal Life Encyclopedia (2nd
    ed.). Vol. 7, Reptiles. Farmington Hills (Gale
    Group): 593 pp.

Ron, S. R., Cannatella, D. C. & Coloma, L. A.
    (2004): Two new species of *Physalaemus*
    (Anura: Leptodactylidae) from western
    Ecuador. – Herpetologica **60**: 261–275.

Rossman, D. A. (1970): *Thamnophis proximus* (Say),
    Western ribbon Snake. – Cat. Amer. Amph.
    Rept. **98**: 1–3.

Rossman, D. A., Ford, N. B. & Seigel, R. A. (1996):
    The Garter Snakes – Evolution and Ecology. –
    Norman (Univ. Oklahoma Press): 332 pp.

Roze, J. A. (1983): New World coral snakes (Elapi-
    dae): a taxonomic and biological summary. –
    Mem. Inst. Butantan **46**: 305–338.

Roze, J. A. (1996): Coral Snakes of the Americas:
    Biology, Identification, and Venoms. – Malabar
    (Krieger Publishing Company): 328 pp.

Savage, J. M. (1960): Geographic variation in the
    tadpole of the toad, *Bufo marinus*. – Copeia
    1960: 233–235.

Savage, J. M. (1974): Type localities for species of
    amphibians and reptiles described from Costa
    Rica. – Rev. Biol. Trop. **22**: 71–122.

Savage, J. M. (1975): Systematics and distribution
    of the Mexican and Central American stream
    frogs related to *Eleutherodactylus rugulosus*.
    Copeia **1975**: 254–306.

Savage, J. M. (2002): The Amphibians and Reptiles
    of Costa Rica: A Herpetofauna Between Two
    Continents, Between Two Seas. – Chicago
    (University of Chicago Press): 934 pp.

Savage, J. M. & Guyer, C. (1989): Infrageneric
    classification and species composition of the
    anole genera, *Anolis, Ctenonotus, Dactyloa,
    Norops* and *Semiurus* (Sauria: Iguanidae). –
    Amphibia-Reptilia **10**: 105–116.

Savage, J. M. & Slowinski, J. B. (1996): Evolution of coloration, urotomy and coral snake mimicry in the snake genus *Scaphiodontophis* (Serpentes: Colubridae). – Biol. J. Linnean Soc. **57**: 129–194.

Savage, J. M. & Wake, M. H. (1972): Geographic variation and systematics of the Middle American caecilians, genera *Dermophis* and *Gymnopis*. – Copeia **1972**: 680–695.

Savage, J. M. & Wake, M. H. (2001): Reevaluation of the status of taxa of Central American caecilians (Amphibia: Gymnophiona), with comments on their origin and evolution. – Copeia **2001**: 52–64.

Savitzky, A. H. (2003): Colubrids (Colubridae). pp. 465–482 – In: Hutchins, M., Murphy, J. B. & Schlager, N. (eds.): Grzimek's Animal Life Encyclopedia (2nd ed.). Vol. 7, Reptiles. Farmington Hills (Gale Group): 593 pp.

Sawaya, R. J. & Sazima, I. (2003): A new species of *Tantilla* (Serpentes: Colubridae) from southeastern Brazil. – Herpetologica **59**: 119–126.

Schmidt, F., Köhler, G. & Kreutz, J. (1999): Morphologie, Verbreitung und Fortpflanzung der Stachelschuppenleguane in El Salvador: 2. *Sceloporus malachiticus* Cope, 1864. – Salamandra **35**: 279–288.

Schmidt, K. P. (1928): Reptiles collected in Salvador for the California Institute of Technology. – Field Mus. Nat. Hist. Zool. Ser. **12**: 193–201.

Schmidt, K. P. & Rand, A. S. (1957): Geographic variation in the Central American colubrine snake, *Ninia sebae*. – Fieldiana, Zool. **39**: 73–84.

Schmidt, K. P. & Stuart, L. C. (1941): The herpetological fauna of the Salama Basin, Baja Verapaz, Guatemala. – Field Mus. Nat. Hist., Zool. Ser. **24**: 233–247.

Schulte, J. A., II, Macey, J. R., Larson, A. & Papenfuss, T. (1998): Molecular tests of phylogenetic taxonomies: a general procedure and example using four subfamilies of the lizard family Iguanidae. – Mol. Phylog. Evol. **10**: 367–376.

Scott, N. J. & McDiarmid, R. W. (1984): *Trimorphodon biscutatus*. – Cat. Amer. Amph. Rept. **353**: 1–4.

Seidel, M. E. (2002): Taxonomic observations on extant species and subspecies of slider turtles, genus *Trachemys*. – J. Herpetol. **36**: 285–292.

Serrano, F. (1995): Àreas naturales de El Salvador: Ecología y conservación. pp. 237–281 – In: Serrano, F. (ed.): Historia Natural y Ecológica de El Salvador. Tomo II. – San Salvador (Ministerio de Educación): 365 pp.

Shine, R. (1994): Sexual dimorphism in snakes revisited. – Copeia **1994**: 326–346.

Smith, H. M. (1937): A synopsis of the *variabilis* group of the lizard genus *Sceloporus*, with descriptions of new subspecies. - Occ. Papers Mus. Zool. Univ. Michigan **358**: 1–14.

Smith, H. M. (1939): The Mexican and Central American lizards of the genus *Sceloporus*. – Zool. Ser. Field Mus. Nat. Hist. **26**: 1–397.

Smith, H. M. (1946): Notes on Central American *Leiolopisma*. – Herpetologica **3**: 110–111.

Smith, H. M. & Chizar, D. (1996): Speciesgroup Taxa of the False Coral Snake Genus *Pliocercus*. – Pottsville (Ramus Publ.): 112 pp.

Smith, H. M. & Chiszar, D. (2001): *Pliocercus elapoides* Cope, Variegated False Coral Snake. – Cat. Amer. Amph. Rept. **739**: 1–11.

Smith, H. M., Chiszar, D. & Humphrey, R. (2001): The distribution of *Sceloporus acanthinus* (Reptilia: Sauria) and its relationships. – Bull. Maryland Herpetol. Soc. **37**: 3–9.

Smith, H. M. & Larsen, K. R. (1974): The nominal snake genera *Mastigodryas* Amaral, 1934, and *Dryadophis* Stuart, 1939. Gt. Basin Nat. **33**: 276.

Smith, H. M., Pérez–Higareda, G. & Chizar, D. (1993): A review of the members of the *Sceloporus variabilis* complex. – Bull. Maryland Herpetol. Soc. **29**: 85–125.

Smith, H. M. & Taylor, E. H. (1950): An annotated checklist and key to the reptiles of Mexico exclusive of the snakes. – Bull. U.S. Natl. Mus. **199**: 1–253.

Sokol, O. M. (1949): Range extension of *Eupemphix pustulosus* in El Salvador. – Herpetologica **5**: 48.

Stafford, P. J. (2004): A new species of *Tantilla* (Serpentes; Colubridae) of the *Taeniata* Group from southern Belize. – J. Herpetol. **38**: 43–52.

Stafford, P. J. & Meyer, J. R. (2000): A Guide to the Reptiles of Belize. – San Diego, (Academic Press): 356 pp.

Starrett, P. (1960): Descriptions of tadpoles of Middle American frogs. – Misc. Publ. Mus. Zool. Univ. Michigan **110**: 1–37.

Starrett, P. H. & Savage, J. M. (1973): The systematic status and distribution of Costa Rican glass-frogs, genus *Centrolenella* (family Centrolenidae), with description of a new species. – Bull. Southern Calif. Acad. Sci. **72**: 57–78.

Stephens, P. R. & Wiens, J. J. (2003): Ecological diversification and phylogeny of emydid turtles. Biol. J. Linn. Soc. **79**: 577–610.

Straughan, I. R. & Heyer, W. R. (1976): A functional analysis of the mating calls of the Neotropical frog genera of the *Leptodactylus* complex (Amphibia, Leptodactylidae). Pap. Avul. Zool. **29**: 221–245.

Stuart, L. C. (1940): Notes on the "*Lampropholis*" group of Middle American *Lygosoma* (Scincidae) with descriptions of two new forms. – Occ. Pap. Mus. Zool. Univ. Michigan **421**: 1–16.

Stuart, L. C. (1941): Studies of Neotropical Colubrinae. VIII. A revision of the genus *Dryadophis* Stuart, 1939. – Misc. Publ. Mus. Zool. Univ. Michigan **49**: 1–106.

Stuart, L. C. (1971): Comments on the malachite *Sceloporus* (Reptilia: Sauria: Iguanidae) of southern Mexico and Guatemala. – Herpetologica **27**: 235–259.

Taylor, E. H. (1956): A review of the lizards of Costa Rica. – Univ. Kansas Sci. Bull. **38**: 3–322.

Taylor, E. H. (1965): The serpents of Thailand and adjacent waters. – Univ. Kansas Sci. Bull. **45**: 609–1096.

Taylor, E. H. (1968): The Caecilians of the World. A Taxonomic Review. – Lawrence (University of Kansas Press): 848 pp.

Taylor, E. H. & Smith, H. M. (1943): A review of American sibynophine snakes, with a proposal of a new genus. – Univ. Kansas Sci. Bull. **29**: 301–337.

Taylor, E. H. & Smith, H. M. (1945): Summary of the collections of amphibians made in Mexico under the Walter Rathbone Bacon traveling scholarship. – Proc. U.S. Natl. Mus. **95**: 521–613.

Tihen, J. A. (1949): A review of the lizard genus *Barisia*. – Univ. Kansas Sci. Bull. **33**: 217–256.

Towns, D. R. (2003): Sphenodontia Tuatara (Sphenodontidae). pp. 189–193 – In: Hutchins, M., Murphy, J. B. & Schlager, N. (eds.): Grzimek's Animal Life Encyclopedia (2nd ed.). Vol. 7, Reptiles. Farmington Hills (Gale Group): 593 pp.

Uzzell, T. M., Jr. & Starrett, P. (1958): Snakes from El Salvador. – Copeia **1958**: 339–342.

Vences, M., Raxworthy, C. J., Nussbaum, R. A. & Glaw, F. (2003): A revision of the *Scaphiophryne marmorata* complex of marbled toads from Madagascar, including the description of a new species. Herpetol. J. **13**: 69–79.

Ventura Montenegro, C. (1995): Hidrología: El Recurso Agua. pp. 133–168 – In: Serrano, F. (ed.): Historia Natural y Ecológica de El Salvador. Tomo I. – San Salvador (Ministerio de Educación): 397 pp.

Verdade, V. K. & Rodrigues, M. T. (2003): A new species of *Cycloramphus* (Anura, Leptodactylidae) from the Atlantic Forest, Brazil. – Herpetologica **59**: 513–518.

Veselý, M. & Köhler, G. (2001): Zur Kenntnis von *Mesaspis moreletii* (Bocourt, 1871) in El Salvador. – Salamandra **37**: 185–192.

Villa, J. D. (1979): Synopsis of the biology of the Middle American highland frog *Rana maculata* Brocchi. – Milwaukee Publ. Mus. Contrib. Biol. Geol. **21**: 1–17.

Villa, J. (1988): *Crisantophis* Villa. – Cat. Amer. Amph. Rept. **429**: 1–2.

Villa, J., Wilson, L. D. & Johnson, J. D. (1988): Middle American Herpetology: A Bibliographic Checklist. – Columbia (Univ. Miss. Press): 131 pp.

Villa, J. D. & Wilson, L. D. (1988): *Celestus bivittatus* (Boulenger). – Cat. Amer. Amph. Rept. **423**: 1–2.

Wake, D. B. & Lynch, J. F. (1976): The distribution, ecology, and evolutionary history of plethodontid salamanders in tropical America. – Bull. Nat. Hist. Mus. Los Angeles Co. **25**: 1–65.

Wake, D. B. (2003a): Caudata (Salamanders and newts). pp. 323–326 – In: Hutchins, M., Duellman, W. E. & Schlager, N. (eds.): Grzimek's Animal Life Encyclopedia (2nd ed.). Vol. 6, Amphibians. Farmington Hills (Gale Group): 507 pp.

Wake, D. B. (2003b): Lungless salamanders (Plethodontidae). pp. 389–404 – In: Hutchins, M., Duellman, W. E. & Schlager, N. (eds.): Grzimek's Animal Life Encyclopedia (2nd ed.). Vol. 6, Amphibians. Farmington Hills (Gale Group): 507 pp.

Wake, M. H. (1980): Reproduction, growth, and population structure of the Central American caecilian *Dermophis mexicanus*. – Herpetologica **36**: 244–256.

Wake, M. H. (2003a): Gymnophiona (Caecilians). pp. 411–413 – In: Hutchins, M., Duellman, W. E. & Schlager, N. (eds.): Grzimek's Animal Life Encyclopedia (2nd ed.). Vol. 6, Amphibians. Farmington Hills (Gale Group): 507 pp.

Wake, M. H. (2003b): Tailless caecilians (Caeciliidae). pp. 435–441 – In: Hutchins, M., Duellman, W. E. & Schlager, N. (eds.): Grzimek's Animal Life Encyclopedia (2nd ed.). Vol. 6, Amphibians. Farmington Hills (Gale Group): 507 pp.

Wallach, V. (1995): Revalidation of the genus Tropidodipsas Günther, with notes on the Dipsadini and Nothopsini (Serpentes: Colubridae). – J. Herpetol. 29: 476–81.

Webb, R. G. (1982): Taxonomic status of some Neotropical garter snakes (genus Thamnophis). – Bull. So. California Acad. Sci. 81: 26–40.

Wellman, J. (1963): A revision of snakes of the genus Conophis (Family Colubridae, from Middle America). – Univ. Kansas Publ. Mus. Nat. Hist. 15: 251–295.

Werman, S. D. (1992): Phylogenetic relationships of Central and South American pit vipers of the genus Bothrops (sensu lato): cladistic analyses of biochemical and anatomical characters. – pp. 21–40 In: Campbell, J. A. & Brodie, E. D. (eds.): Biology of the Pitvipers. Tyler (Selva): 467 pp.

Whitaker, L. E., Jr. & Whitaker, N. (2003): Crocodiles and false gharials (Crocodylidae). pp. 179–188 – In: Hutchins, M., Murphy, J. B. & Schlager, N. (eds.): Grzimek's Animal Life Encyclopedia (2nd ed.). Vol. 7, Reptiles. Farmington Hills (Gale Group): 593 pp.

Wild, E. R. (2003): Glass frogs (Centrolenidae). pp. 215–223 – In: Hutchins, M., Duellman, W. E. & Schlager, N. (eds.): Grzimek's Animal Life Encyclopedia (2nd ed.). Vol. 6, Amphibians. Farmington Hills (Gale Group): 507 pp.

Wilkinson, M. (1996): Resolution of the taxonomic status of Nectocaecilia haydee (Roze) and a revised key to the genera of Typhlonectidae (Amphibia: Gymnophiona). – J. Herpetol. 30: 413–415.

Williams, E. E. (1989): A critique of Guyer & Savage (1987): Cladistic relationships among anoles (Sauria: Iguanidae): Are the data available to reclassify the anoles? pp. 433–478 – In: Woods, C. A. (ed.): Biogeography of the West Indies. Gainesville (Sandhill Crane Press): 878 pp.

Williams, K. L. (1978): Systematics and natural history of the American milk snake, Lampropeltis triangulum. – Publ. Biol. Geol. Milwaukee Publ. Mus. 2: 1–258.

Williams, K. L. (1994): Lampropeltis triangulum (Lacepéde). – Cat. Amer. Amph. Rept. 594: 1–10.

Wilson, L. D. (1970): A review of the chloroticus group of the colubrid snake genus Drymobius, with notes on a twin-striped form of D. chloroticus (Cope) from southern Mexico. – J. Herpetol. 4: 155–163.

Wilson, L. D. (1974a): Drymobius margaritiferus (Cope). – Cat. Amer. Amph. Rept. 172: 1–2.

Wilson, L. D. (1974b): Tantilla taeniata (Bocourt): an addition to the snake fauna of El Salvador. – Bull. South. Calif. Acad. Sci. 73: 53–54.

Wilson, L. D. (1975): Drymobius chloroticus (Cope). – Cat. Amer. Amph. Rept. 171: 1.

Wilson, L. D. (1982): A review of the colubrid snakes of the genus Tantilla from Central America. – Publ. Biol. Geol. Milwaukee Publ. Mus. 52: 1–77.

Wilson, L. D. (1983): Tantilla taeniata (Bocourt). – Cat. Amer. Amph. Rept. 344: 1–2.

Wilson, L. D. (1987): Tantilla vermiformis (Hallowell). – Cat. Amer. Amph. Rept. 410: 1.

Wilson, L. D. (1988): Tantilla brevicauda Mertens. – Cat. Amer. Amph. Rept. 432: 1.

Wilson, L. D. (1992): Tantilla melanocephala (Linnaeus). – Cat. Amer. Amph. Rept. 547: 1–3.

Wilson, L. D. (1999): Checklist and key to the species of the genus Tantilla (Serpentes: Colubridae), with some comments on distribution. – Smithson. H. I. S. 122: 1–36.

Wilson, L. D. & Campbell, J. A. (2001): A new species of the calamarina group of the colubrid snake genus Tantilla (Reptilia: Squamata) from Guerrero, Mexico, with a review of and key to members of the group. – Proc. Biol. Soc. Wash. 113: 820–827.

Wilson, L. D. & McCranie, J. R. (1993): Preliminary key to the known tadpoles of anurans from Honduras. – Royal Ontario Mus. Life Sci. Occ. Pap. 40: 1–12.

Wilson, L. D. & McCranie, J. R. (1999): The systematic status of Honduran populations of the Tantilla taeniata group (Serpentes: Colubridae), with notes on other populations. – Amphibia-Reptilia 20: 326–329.

Wilson, L. D. & Mena, C. E. (1980): Systematics of the *melanocephala* group of the colubrid snake genus *Tantilla*. – Mem. San Diego Soc. Nat. Hist. **11**: 1–58.

Wilson, L. D. & Meyer, J. R. (1985): The Snakes of Honduras, 2nd edition. – Milwaukee (Milwaukee Public Museum): 150 pp.

Wüster, W., Yrausquin, J. L. & Mijares-Urrutia, A. (2001): A new species of indigo snake from north-western Venezuela (Serpentes: Colubridae: *Drymarchon*). – Herpetol. J. **11**: 157–165.

Yasukawa, Y., Hirayama, R. & Hikida, T. (2001): Phylogenetic relationships of geoemydine turtles (Reptilia: Bataguridae). – Current Herpetol. **20**: 105–133.

Ziehr, W. (1974): Die Große Enzyklopädie der Erde. Band 13. – Munich (Novaria Verlag): 435 pp.

Zug, G. R., Ernst, C. H. & Wilson, R. V. (1998): *Lepidochelys olivacea* (Eschscholtz), Olive Ridley Seaturtle, Tortuga Golfina, Lora. – Cat. Amer. Amph. Rept. **653**: 1–13.

Zug, G. R., Vitt, L. J. & Caldwell, J. P. (2001): Herpetology: An Introductory Biology of Amphibians and Reptiles, 2nd edition. – San Diego (Academic Press): 630 pp.

Zweifel, R. G. (2003): Narrow-mouthed frogs (Microhylidae). pp. 301–316 – In: Hutchins, M., Duellman, W. E. & Schlager, N. (eds.): Grzimek's Animal Life Encyclopedia (2nd ed.). Vol. 6, Amphibians. Farmington Hills (Gale Group): 507 pp.

Index